MOLECULAR PHOTOCHEMISTRY

FRONTIERS IN CHEMISTRY

Ronald Breslow and Martin Karplus, Editors
Columbia University

CONTRIBUTIONS TO THE THEORY
OF CHEMICAL KINETICS

T. A. Bak
Københavns Universitet

MOLECULAR ORBITAL THEORY

C. J. Ballhausen
Københavns Universitet

H. B. Gray
Columbia University

NONCLASSICAL IONS: Reprints and Commentary

P. D. Bartlett
Harvard University

OPTICAL PUMPING: An Introduction

R. A. Bernheim
The Pennsylvania State University

ELECTRON PARAMAGNETIC RESONANCE

M. Bersohn
University of Toronto

J. Baird
Brown University

TOPICS IN BIOORGANIC MECHANISMS

T. C. Bruice
University of California, Santa Barbara

S. J. Benkovic
The Pennsylvania State University

THERMODYNAMICS OF SMALL SYSTEMS: Parts 1 and 2

T. L. Hill
University of Oregon

LECTURES ON QUANTUM THEORY OF MOLECULAR
ELECTRONIC STRUCTURE

R. G. Parr
Johns Hopkins University

THE BIOSYNTHESIS OF STEROIDS, TERPENES,
AND ACETOGENINS

J. H. Richards
California Institute of Technology

J. B. Hendrickson
Brandeis University

OXIDATION MECHANISMS: Applications to Organic Chemistry

R. Stewart
University of British Columbia

MOLECULAR PHOTOCHEMISTRY

N. J. Turro
Columbia University

COMPUTER PROGRAMMING FOR CHEMISTS

K. B. Wiberg
Yale University

MOLECULAR
PHOTOCHEMISTRY

NICHOLAS J. TURRO
Columbia University

W. A. BENJAMIN, Inc.   1967

New York   Amsterdam

547.135
T 961

MOLECULAR PHOTOCHEMISTRY

The final manuscript was put into production on January 13, 1965; this volume was published on November 15, 1965; second printing with corrections February 1967.

W. A. BENJAMIN, INC.
New York, New York 10016

TO **Sandy, Cindy, and Claire**

Preface

The need for an introductory book on the mechanisms and applications of organic photochemical reactions has become pronounced over the last few years as a result of the tremendous surge of interest and activity in photochemistry which has occurred during the last decade. The reasons for this activity are several, but two of the most important contributing factors are (a) the development of new analytical techniques, which have enormously simplified the unravelling of complex problems of structure and purification associated with many photochemical programs and (b) the advent of a somewhat belated appreciation by the organic photochemist of the theoretical concepts and methods of electronic spectroscopy and quantum mechanics.

The purpose of this book is to familiarize chemists with the important concepts involved in organic photochemistry and to present a number of representative examples of organic photochemical reactions which can be understood and interpreted in terms of previously developed principles. It is hoped that, after studying the text, the reader will be better able to rationalize known photochemical reactions and furthermore will be able to control and predict new photochemical reactions.

Although a number of descriptive reviews of organic photochemistry have appeared, there has been no recent introductory book available which extensively covers the theoretical foundations of photoreactions and then applies these theoretical concepts toward the interpretation of organic photochemistry. As a result the organic chemist who is interested in initiating a photochemical study may tend to proceed with a lack of appreciation of the elementary theory of photochemistry because of the dearth of suitable introductory material. This text is intended to bridge this gap.

The level of this text is such that it may be used for an introductory course on photochemistry for advanced undergraduates or first-year graduate students. The first half of the text should be useful in introductory physical chemistry courses in which photochemistry is discussed as a special topic. It is also desired that this work shall serve as a reference book for those who are doing or who anticipate doing work in the field of organic photochemistry. The numerous references to the original literature hopefully will stimulate deeper literature surveys on the part of the reader. The treatment of the subject matter is such that a background which includes an elementary course in organic chemistry and physical chemistry and an introductory course on quantum mechanics should suffice for an understanding of the material presented. The level of presentation is intended to neither offend the physical chemist nor confound the organic chemist; however, treatment of quantum mechanical applications are nonrigorous, because the author feels it is better to present material in a useful and functional form than to have the naked truth in an unscrutable mathematical framework.

The concepts of modern day photochemistry are the outgrowth of quantum theory and electronic spectroscopy. A firm grasp of these concepts, therefore, demands a certain familiarity with the results and methods of these two disciplines. It is for this reason that such topics as molecular orbitals, the Franck-Condon principle, radiationless transitions, and energy transfer are treated in great detail in this text. The author feels that with the presentation of these subject materials, reinforced by a large amount of pertinent data, examples, and references, the reader can best equip himself for an understanding of organic photochemistry.

The first three chapters review and explain the important principles and concepts of quantum mechanics and spectroscopy which are required to discuss and interpret the properties of electronically excited states. Chapter 4 is a detailed presentation of the nature of electronically excited states as derived from absorption and emission spectra. Radiationless processes, the rates of interconversion of electronically excited states, and the chemical properties of excited states are also discussed. In Chapter 5 the methods and results of energy transfer experiments in solid and fluid solution are discussed in detail. Chapters 6–9 provide numerous examples of important photochemical reactions which are discussed and developed in terms of the principles and concepts given in Chapters 1–5. Chapter 10 discusses several miscellaneous topics, including lasers, actinometry, and the technique of photochemistry.

The choice of material in a text of this sort must of necessity be quite limited. The subject matter presented reflects the interests of the author, whereas the material omitted probably reflects his failings. However, thorough documentation of the subject matter is presented throughout in order to compensate for the latter shortcoming.

This text is an outgrowth of courses and lectures on photochemistry given at Columbia University and at the Organic Chemicals Division (1964) and Photoproducts Divisions (1965) of the DuPont Company. It is a pleasure to acknowledge the criticism concerning the text which the members of these courses provided. I would like to thank W. B. Hammond, M. Tobin, and R. Engel for reading and correcting page proof. Professor Peter A. Leermakers deserves special thanks for a detailed reading and criticism of the manuscript.   To my wife Sandra goes a particular thanks for typing the first draft of this manuscript and for her encouragement and patient understanding, without which this work would not have been possible.   Finally, the author finds it impossible to express his gratitude to Professor George S. Hammond, whose inspiration, ideas, and pioneering research thoroughly pervade this book.

NICHOLAS J. TURRO

New York, New York
August, 1965

Contents

chapter
one

Introduction

When approaching a new subject, one should start at the beginning. In the case of photochemistry, the beginning was probably with the origin of the sun. Indeed, photochemical reactions, such as photosynthesis, have played a crucial role in the development of life as we know it. An enormous amount of energy from the sun bombards the earth. For example, an average of nearly 100 $kcal/cm^2/day$ is being continuously provided to the earth by the sun's radiant energy.

1-1. BRIEF HISTORY OF PHOTOCHEMISTRY

Reports of organic photochemical reactions can be found in the earliest chemical literature.[1] However, discovery and study of photochemical reactions were often the result of an accident or last-gap attempt to effect a reaction which could not be achieved by conventional synthetic methods. Until the advent of quantum mechanics, the effect of light on matter was not properly understood. As a result, during the primeval age of photochemistry (from about 1850 to 1920) numerous and wondrous photochemical reactions were discovered, but both useful application of these results and emanation of a unifying theory were lacking. The results [2, 3] obtained by the early pioneers of photochemistry—Ciamician, Silber, and Paterno—were both exciting and discouraging. The products of some of the early reactions studied were not available from other methods of synthesis, but, unfortunately, the photochemical reaction mixtures were often hopelessly complex, and no method for control of the reaction was apparent. Failure to appreciate (1) the importance of trace impurities, (2) the need for control experiments, and (3) the effect of secondary

1

reactions of the initially formed products makes the early photochemical literature difficult to interpret.

From 1920 to 1950, photochemistry was perhaps considered the realm of the physical chemist who studied the details of photoreactions in the gas phase.[4] The availability of new spectroscopic and analytical techniques during the 1950's to the present date and the concomitant development of important theories concerning electronically excited states (1) reduced the difficulty in characterizing the complex products of photoreactions and (2) gave promise of control of photochemistry (as a result of a more fundamental understanding of the nature of excited states).

It soon became increasingly clear that selectivity can be achieved in photochemical reactions.[5-15] In fact, the promise of the method is due in part to the highly selective nature of light absorption which allows injection of energy into particular bonds or particular molecules (i.e., an absorbing solute in a transparent solvent). Under proper conditions, photochemistry may provide a short route for the syntheses of systems which are essentially unavailable by alternate synthetic methods. This aspect, coupled with the development of *spectroscopic techniques* (such as flash photolysis—see Section 4-5) for the direct study of transient intermediates and excited state theory of photochemical reactions, fired the imagination of a number of workers. Recently, the phenomenon of electronic energy transfer has been shown to be of great generality and importance in photochemical systems and has provided a range of new and unique photochemical techniques and applications.[10, 11, 15]

1-2. PHOTOCHEMICAL REACTIONS

The essence of an organic photochemical reaction is that *activation* is provided by absorption of a photon of light by the system. The interaction of photons with molecules and the physical and chemical processes which follow absorption of light are of greatest interest to the organic photochemist. The chronology of a photochemical sequence can be divided conveniently into three stages:

1. *the absorptive act* which produces an electronically excited state
2. *the primary photochemical processes* which involve electronically excited states
3. *the secondary or "dark"* (thermal) *reactions* of the various chemical species produced by the primary processes.

Each of the stages listed above should be treated in some detail if complete comprehension of a photochemical reaction is desired. Although many of the concepts to be dealt with in this work require rather elaborate mathematical treatment for detailed understanding, an attempt will be made to elicit as much basic information as possible from models which *result* from approximate mathematical treatment.   Our guide shall be the premise that it is far better to have useful and functional knowledge which suits our purposes than to have the naked truth in an inscrutable mathematical form.   However, references will be supplied throughout, in order to provide the interested reader with a means of probing deeper into advanced material.   Pictorial terms will be used to supplement the essential mathematics.   It shall be assumed that the reader has been exposed, at least, to the postulates of quantum mechanics and is aware of the basic results of this elegant theory—i.e., to the extent that such material is presented in an undergraduate course in physical chemistry.

In this work we are mainly concerned with organic photochemistry in solution.   We shall seek to answer a number of questions concerning photochemistry in general:

1. What is the detailed fate of excitation pumped into a molecule by ultraviolet or visible light?

2. What is the chemical nature of the various electronically excited states?

3. From knowledge of answers to questions 1 and 2 how can we deduce the scope and limitations of photoreactions—i.e., how can we predict and exploit photochemistry?

In order to fix the energy and time scale of photochemical reactions, we shall first present generalizations concerning the energetics and rates of some important photochemical processes.   Next, we shall develop the theoretical background necessary for a proper understanding of the nature of photochemical reactions.   Finally, a number of selected examples of photoreactions shall be discussed with emphasis on the application of mechanistic theory developed earlier in the book.   No need or desire to provide a comprehensive survey of organic photochemistry is made since a number of excellent recent review articles are available which provide this descriptive material.[5-14]

1-3. PHOTOCHEMICAL ACTIVATION

The selective nature of photochemical activation differentiates it from thermal activation.   Absorption of a photon (quantum) of light can specifically excite (activate) a particular bond or group in a given molecule.   Use of the proper frequency of exciting light allows activation of a solute molecule in the presence of a large excess of a transparent solvent.   Thermal activation of the same molecule or a particular bond can only be achieved by an increase in the over-all molecular energy of the environment.

Energies

The *primary processes* of a photochemical sequence include the initial act of absorption and all of the processes which involve an electronically excited state of the absorbing molecule. The energy required to produce an excited state is obtained by inspection of the absorption or emission spectrum of the molecule in question (see Chapter 4) together with the application of the equation

$$E_2 - E_1 = h\nu \tag{1-1}$$

where h is Planck's constant, ν is the frequency (sec^{-1}) at which absorption occurs, and E_2 and E_1 are the energies of a single molecule in the final and initial states.

The position of an absorption band is often expressed by its wavelength (λ) in angstroms or its wave number ($\bar{\nu} = 1/\lambda$) in reciprocal centimeters. For example, 3,000 Å is equivalent in wave numbers to

$$\bar{\nu} = \frac{1}{3,000 \text{ Å}} = \frac{1}{3 \times 10^{-5} \text{ cm}} = 3.33 \times 10^4 \text{ cm}^{-1}$$

or in frequency to

$$\nu = \frac{c}{\lambda} = \frac{3 \times 10^{10} \text{ cm/sec}}{3 \times 10^{-5} \text{ cm}} = 10^{15} \text{ sec}^{-1}$$

Equation 1-1 may be rewritten as

$$E_2 - E_1 = h\bar{\nu}c = 2.86 \times 10^{-3}\bar{\nu} \tag{1-2}$$

or

$$E_2 - E_1 = \frac{2.86 \times 10^5}{\lambda}$$

where $E_2 - E_1$ is the energy difference between the initial and final states in kcal/mole, and $\bar{\nu}$ and λ are the position of absorption expressed in wave numbers (reciprocal centimeters) and angstroms, respectively.

The amount of energy produced through the absorption of one mole of photons by a compound at a given wavelength is equivalent to the energy of 6.02×10^{23} photons. This energy is called an *einstein*. Thus an einstein of 7,000 Å (14,300 cm^{-1}) light is equal to

$$E_2 - E_1 = \frac{2.86 \times 10^5}{7,000 \text{ Å}} = 40.8 \text{ kcal}$$

while an einstein of 2,000 Å light is

$$E_2 - E_1 = \frac{2.86 \times 10^5}{2,000 \text{ Å}} = 143 \text{ kcal}$$

Table 1-1 summarizes the energies corresponding to absorption in the region of interest to the organic photochemist. The 2,000 Å short

Table 1-1   *Energy conversion table*

λ Å	$\bar{\nu}$ cm^{-1}	$(E_2 - E_1)$	
		kcal/mole	*eV*
2,000	50,000	143.0	6.20
2,500	40,000	114.4	4.96
3,000	33,333	95.3	4.13
3,500	28,571	81.7	3.54
4,000	25,000	71.5	3.10
4,500	22,222	63.5	2.76
5,000	20,000	57.2	2.48
5,500	18,182	52.0	2.25
6,000	16,666	47.7	2.07
6,500	15,385	44.0	1.91
7,000	14,286	40.8	1.77

wavelength limit is arbitrarily set by the transparency of quartz equipment, and the 7,000 Å long wavelength limit corresponds to the beginning of the infra-red region.

Photochemical Laws

Four important photochemical rules or laws have evolved over the years that apply quite generally for organic photochemistry. These may be stated as follows:

1. Only the light absorbed by a system is effective in producing a photochemical change.

2. Each photon or quantum absorbed activates one molecule in the primary excitation step of a photochemical sequence.

3. Each photon or quantum absorbed by a molecule has a certain probability of populating either the lowest excited singlet state S_1, or lowest triplet state T_1.

4. The lowest excited singlet and triplet states are the starting points (in solution) of most organic photochemical processes.

Quantum Yield

A photochemical reaction requires activation by light. The quantitative relationship between the number of molecules which react or are formed and the number of photons absorbed in a unit time is given by the *quantum yield* Φ, which may be defined for a given system as

$$\Phi = \frac{\text{number of molecules undergoing a particular process}}{\text{number of quanta absorbed by the system}} \quad (1\text{-}3)$$

The number of molecules reacting or formed per unit time is measured by any convenient analytical kinetic technique, and the number of photons absorbed per unit time is measured by an *actinometer* (a chemical or physical device capable of "counting" photons). Thus, if for every photon absorbed a molecule undergoes a certain photochemical process, the quantum yield for the process is unity. If other processes compete with the one under consideration, the quantum yield will be less than unity.

The quantum yields of photochemical reactions are important because they inform us of the paths by which the electronically excited molecule disposes of its energy.

The *primary quantum yield* Φ of a photochemical process may be different from the over-all or measured quantum yield ϕ. For example, if a molecule undergoes a particular photochemical cleavage which is then reversed, the primary quantum yield may be high for dissociation even though the over-all quantum yield for measured net reaction is nearly zero. A classic example is the dissociation of ketones which proceeds with a high primary and over-all quantum yield in the vapor phase where recombination of the initially formed radicals is negligible. In solution at room temperature, photolysis of the same ketones is inhibited because of "cage" recombination, so that the over-all quantum yield is zero for dissociation.

Finally, one must be careful to differentiate between the organic chemist's "yield" and the quantum yield. The former merely indicates the extent of side reactions and the ultimate efficiency of conversion of starting material into product, irrespective of the number of quanta absorbed. There are many examples of organic photosyntheses which proceed with a high over-all "yield" but with relatively low absolute quantum yields.

1-4. PHOTOCHEMICAL PROCESSES

All photochemical reactions involve electronically excited states at some point. Each excited state has a definite energy, lifetime, and structure. These properties may all be somewhat different as we go from one state to another. In addition, the excited states are different chemical entities than the ground state and are expected to behave differently. In order to understand photochemical processes we must seek information concerning the energies, lifetimes, and structures of the electronically excited states.

Electronically Excited States

The excitation energy, which a molecule A acquires upon absorption of a photon, may be dissipated by any one of the three general processes given in Eqs. 1-4, 1-5, and 1-6:

$$\xrightarrow{\text{emission}} A_0 + h\nu \tag{1-4}$$

$$A^*(\text{excited}) \xrightarrow[\text{conversion}]{\text{radiationless}} A_0 + \text{heat} \tag{1-5}$$

$$\xrightarrow[\text{reaction}]{\text{chemical}} \text{products} \tag{1-6}$$

Energy diagrams such as Fig. 2-10 (see Chapter 2) illustrate the important processes involving electronically excited states. The figure indicates the lowest singlet (spins paired) S_1 and the lowest triplet (spins unpaired) T_1 excited states. The horizontal lines indicate the electronic excitation energy (relative to the ground state) of the various states in their lowest vibrational level. Radiative processes are indicated by a solid arrow and radiationless processes are indicated by a wavy arrow.

Emission

The radiative lifetime of an excited state may be often defined in terms of a first-order decay process. It is important to differentiate the "true" or inherent radiative lifetime τ^0 of a state—i.e., the reciprocal of the rate constant for the disappearance of this state if emission were the only path of energy dissipation—and the "actual" or measured lifetime τ, which is the reciprocal of the sum of the rate constants of a number of competing first-order (or pseudo-first-order) processes.

The time scale of a photochemical sequence is set by the rate of spontaneous radiative emission to the ground state S_0, from S_1 and/or T_1— i.e., no reaction which competes for deactivation of these states can require much longer time than τ^0 for emission, or the latter process will dominate. *Fluorescence* is the phenomenon of emission from S_1 to the ground state. The inherent fluorescent lifetime of S_1 varies from 10^{-9} to 10^{-6} sec for most organic molecules. *Phosphorescence* is the emission from T_1 to ground state. The inherent phosphorescent lifetime of T_1 varies from 10^{-3} to 10 sec for most commonly encountered organic molecules.

Radiationless Processes

A *radiationless process* converts one electronic state to another without involving the absorption or emission of radiation. Excesses of vibrational energy which result from a radiationless process are carried away rapidly as heat by collisions with surrounding molecules. Two extremely important types of radiationless processes are:

1. *internal conversion*, the intramolecular radiationless interconversion between different electronic states of like multiplicity—i.e., singlet-singlet or triplet-triplet processes ($S_1 \rightsquigarrow S_0$, $T_2 \rightsquigarrow T_1$)

2. *intersystem crossing*, the intramolecular radiationless interconversion between singlet and triplet states ($S_1 \rightsquigarrow T_1$, $T_1 \rightsquigarrow S_0$)

All radiationless transitions involve some type of *energy transfer*—i.e., transfer of energy from the excited molecule to its environment. This energy may be transferred in large portions (electronic-energy transfer) or in relatively small packets (vibrational-, rotational-, and translational-energy transfer).

Mechanisms of Organic Photochemical Reactions

The organic chemist may treat photochemistry as a special case of unstable intermediates—i.e., electronically excited states. A mechanistic investigation of an organic photoreaction should indicate whether the reactive state is S_1 or T_1 or whether deactivation of these states produces "hot" ground states (molecules produced in upper vibrational levels of S_0), unstable zwitterions, tautomers, etc., which ultimately lead to the final products. Although quantum mechanics is a most helpful and elegant aid for the interpretation of photochemical reactions, we shall attempt to achieve an appreciation of fundamental principles involved without use of a detailed knowledge of the mathematical methods of quantum mechanics.

REFERENCES

1. For an exhaustive review of organic photochemistry up to 1940 see C. Ellis and A. A. Wells, *The Chemical Action of Ultraviolet Rays* (New York: Reinhold, 1941).
2. For an interesting review of the state of photochemistry before the advent of quantum theory see G. Ciamician, *Science*, **36**, 385 (1912).
3. For example, see G. Ciamician and P. Silber, *Ber.*, **44**, 1280 (1911), and E. Paterno, *Gazz. chim. ital.*, **44**, 151 (1914), and earlier papers by these workers.
4. P. Borrell, *Ann. Reports Chem. Soc.* (London), **60**, 62 (1963).
5. For recent reviews of photochemistry, see the following references: P. de Mayo, *Adv. in Organic Chem.*, **2**, 367 (1960).
6. P. de Mayo and S. T. Reid, *Quart. Revs.*, **15**, 393 (1961).
7. C. R. Masson, V. Boekelheide, and W. A. Noyes, Jr., in *Technique of Organic Chemistry*, ed. A. Weissberger (vol. 2, New York: Interscience, 1956), p. 257.

8. A. Schonberg, *Praeparative Organische Photochemie* (Berlin: Springer-Verlag, 1958).
9. G. O. Schenck and R. Steinmetz, *Bull. Soc. chim. belges*, **71,** 781 (1962).
10. G. S. Hammond and N. J. Turro, *Science*, **142,** 1541 (1964).
11. P. A. Leermakers and G. F. Vesley, *J. Chem. Ed.*, **41,** 535 (1964).
12. See the series *Advances in Photochemistry*, ed. W. A. Noyes, Jr., G. S. Hammond, and J. N. Pitts, Jr. (New York: Interscience).
13. K. Schaffner, *Fortschr. Chem. Org. Naturstoffe*, **22,** 1 (1964).
14. J. Saltiel in *Survey of Progress in Chemistry*, ed. A. F. Scott (vol. 2, New York: Academic Press, 1964), p. 239.
15. F. Wilkinson in *Advances in Photochemistry*, ed. W. A. Noyes, Jr., G. S. Hammond, and J. N. Pitts, Jr. (vol. 3, New York: Interscience, 1964), p. 241.

Electronic Excitation

chapter two

2-1. ELECTRONIC TRANSITIONS AND QUANTUM THEORY

A molecule can exist only in discrete energy states. In order to explain phenomena such as electronic transitions between states (which occur on a molecular level) the language of the elegant theory of quantum mechanics must be employed.

Molecular Wave Functions

The discrete energy states that a molecule may assume are characterized by molecular wave functions Ψ_n which are solutions of the Schrodinger equation

$$\mathcal{H}\Psi_n = E_n\Psi_n \tag{2-1}$$

where $\mathcal{H}$ is the complete quantum mechanical Hamiltonian—i.e., the operator whose eigenvalues E_n are the possible energy levels of the molecule. The molecular wave functions determine the value of any physically observable property of a molecule. The *mean value* of the observable in the state Ψ_n is given by the integral

$$\bar{P} = \int \Psi_n{}^* \mathcal{P}\Psi_n \, d\tau \equiv \langle \Psi_n | \mathcal{P} | \Psi_n \rangle \tag{2-2}$$

where $\Psi_n{}^*$ is the complex conjugate of Ψ_n, $\mathcal{P}$ is the operator corresponding to the observable property P, and the integration is over the spin and space co-ordinates of all of the electrons in the molecule.

The form of the quantum mechanical operator which corresponds to a particular observable is usually obtained from the corresponding classical expression. The final test of the correctness of an operator is whether it gives answers in agreement with experiment.

Electronic Orbitals and Electronic Spin

The molecular wave function Ψ defines the orbits and properties of electrons in molecules. An imprecise but pictorially useful interpretation of the orbit of an electron is that of an electron "cloud" whose probability density in a region of space depends on the value of Ψ^2. A boundary surface which confines most of the electronic charge (e.g., greater than 95 %) can be defined for each electron. This boundary surface is the pictorial representation of an *electronic orbital*. A complex molecule possesses a large number of such orbitals which may be described by a subfunction ψ such that the molecular wave function is expressed as a product function

$$\Psi \sim \psi_1 \psi_2 \psi_3 \cdots \qquad (2\text{-}3)$$

The orbitals ψ may be essentially localized on one nucleus (an unperturbed atomic orbital) or delocalized over two or more nuclei (a molecular orbital or MO).

Each ψ in turn may be approximated as the product of a space part ϕ and a spin part α or β. Each orbital may accommodate no more than two electrons, and these must have opposite spin functions—i.e., the spins must be paired as in

$$\psi_1 = \phi_1(\alpha)\ \phi_1(\beta) \quad V.\,B.\cdot Theory \qquad (2\text{-}4)$$

where α represents an electron in ψ_1, with spin $+\frac{1}{2}$, and β represents a second electron in ψ_1, with spin $-\frac{1}{2}$ (Pauli principle).

The orbitals ϕ are generally approximated by "one-electron" orbitals (Hückel theory [8, 9]) which have the form of the solutions of Eq. 2-1 for the hydrogen atom (which can be handled precisely by quantum mechanics). In order to solve Eq. 2-1 even approximately,

1. a "one-electron" Hamiltonian H (which ignores electrostatic interactions between electrons) is usually used

2. the nuclei are assumed to be in their equilibrium positions

3. the spin functions are factored out, and the molecular wave function Ψ is given by

$$\Psi \sim \phi(\text{orbit})\chi(\text{vibration})\mathcal{S}(\text{spin}) \qquad (2\text{-}5)$$

where ϕ is the electronic part of the complete wave function, χ is the nuclear (vibration) wave function and $\mathcal{S}$ is the spin wave function.

An *electronic wave function* ψ_e may now be defined as

$$\psi_e = \phi_1 \phi_2 \phi_3 \cdots \qquad (2\text{-}6)$$

where the eigenfunctions (orbitals) $\phi_n (n = 1, 2, 3 \cdots)$ are the "one-electron" molecular eigenfunctions of the molecule. These orbitals are filled with a maximum of two electrons in accordance with the Aufbau (lowest energy orbitals filled first) and Pauli principles.   Each ψ_e then corresponds to an *electronic configuration*.

Molecular Orbitals

Five types of molecular orbitals are of interest to the organic photochemist.   These are pi-bonding (π), pi-antibonding (π^*), nonbonding (n), sigma-bonding (σ) and sigma-antibonding (σ^*) orbitals.   Single bonds between two atoms involve σ orbitals and the electrons located in such orbitals are called σ electrons.   These electrons are strongly bonding and essentially localized.   Consequently, σ electrons require greater excitation energy than π electrons which occupy the π or multiple-bond orbitals. For each σ and π orbital there corresponds a σ^*- and π^*-antibonding orbital, respectively.   Certain heteroatoms (e.g., oxygen, nitrogen) introduce the possibility of n orbitals which are essentially localized on one particular atom and have no antibonding counterpart.

Typical n Orbitals

The n orbital is often involved in the lowest energy electronic transitions possible for molecules containing heteroatoms.   The form of such orbitals is shown for a carbonyl group and for pyridine in Fig. 2-1.   These orbitals are called "nonbonding" because they take little part in the actual bonding and concentrate very little density between nuclei.   In the case of the carbonyl group, the n orbital is assumed to be an essentially pure p orbital localized on the oxygen atom, while for pyridine the n orbital is a sp^2 hybrid.   For both molecules the n orbital is located in the plane of the molecule and is perpendicular to the π orbitals of the molecule.   The "lone-pair" electrons of aniline and furan are not nonbonding because they are conjugated with the π-orbital system, as shown in Fig. 2-2.   The n orbital is found to be more delocalized than indicated by this simple picture when more refined calculations are made (see Section 7-1).

Electrons in n orbitals are characterized by

1. a low ionization potential required to remove them from the molecular system

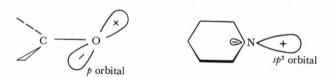

Fig. 2-1   *Form of the n orbital of a carbonyl group (left) and pyridine (right).*

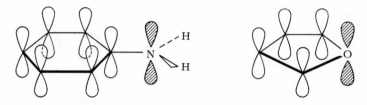

Fig. 2-2   *Form of the lone-pair (shaded) orbitals of aniline (left) and furan (right).*

2. a relative insensitivity of the (spectroscopic) vibrational constants of the molecule from which this electron is removed—i.e., since *n* electrons contribute little to the bonding between atoms, removal of the *n* electron has little effect on the vibrations between atoms.

π *and* π^* *Orbitals*

π and π^* orbitals are delocalized over two or more nuclei. The π orbitals of interest to the organic photochemist are usually pictured as some combination of p orbitals as, for example, the carbonyl group shown in Fig. 2-3. Corresponding to each π orbital there is a π^* orbital which has a node between the carbon and oxygen atoms, as shown in Fig. 2-3.

The relatively greater electronegativity of oxygen versus carbon causes the mobile π electrons to undergo a considerable displacement from carbon to oxygen. In contrast, the π^* orbital has charge displacement from oxygen to carbon. Both the π and π^* orbitals possess a plane of antisymmetry which coincides with the molecular plane. Virtually all electronic transitions of interest to the organic photochemist involve a π or π^* orbital.

The molecular orbitals of benzene are more complicated than the simple double bonds described earlier and are shown (ignoring the σ-bond skeleton) in Fig. 2-4. The lowest molecular orbital π_1 is nondegenerate (of unique energy), but the next two bonding orbitals π_2 and π_3 are degenerate (of equal energy) as are the two lowest antibonding orbitals π_4^* and π_5^*. The highest energy antibonding orbital π_6^* is nondegenerate.

Fig. 2-3   *Form of a π orbital (left) and a π^* orbital (right) of a carbonyl compound.*

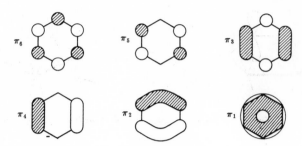

Fig. 2-4   *Form of the π orbitals of benzene.   The figures represent electron density of an electron in a given orbital.   Shaded areas represent a positive wave function, open areas a negative wave function (as the molecule is viewed from above).*

σ and σ* Orbitals

Since the σ-bonding orbitals σ are usually of low energy with respect to π and n orbitals and the σ-antibonding orbitals σ* are of relatively high energy, compared to π* orbitals, neither of these σ orbitals will be encountered very often.   Both the σ and σ* orbitals are cylindrically symmetrical about the nuclear axis of the atoms forming the σ bond (see Fig. 2-5).   The σ* orbital has a node between the atoms forming the σ bond, which causes the bond to break when an electron is promoted to a σ* orbital.

Fig. 2-5   *Form of a σ orbital (right) and a σ* orbital (left) of a carbonyl group.*

2-2. ELECTRONIC CONFIGURATIONS AND ELECTRONIC STATES

An electronic *configuration* is constructed by adding the electrons to the orbitals available to the system.   In the ground or lowest energy state, the electrons will occupy the orbitals of lowest energy.   Excitation by absorption of a photon of appropriate energy will promote an electron from one of the low energy occupied MO's to one of the high energy (previously unoccupied) antibonding orbitals.

The Ground State Configuration

As an example, consider the formaldehyde molecule.   The energies of the MO's for this molecule probably increase in the order $1s_O < 1s_C <$

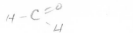

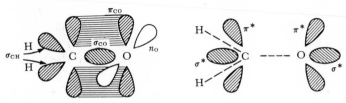

Fig. 2-6 *Form of the bonding orbitals (left) and antibonding orbitals (right) of formaldehyde.*

$2s_O < \sigma_{CH} < \sigma_{CO} < \pi_{CO} < n_O$ where $1s_O$, $2s_O$ and $1s_C$ refer to the essentially atomic MO's localized on oxygen and carbon and the other MO's refer to Fig. 2-6.

In the *ground state* each of the orbitals in this configuration contains two electrons. The configuration of the ground state is represented below (the superscripts designate the number of electrons in each orbital)

$$(1s_O)^2(1s_C)^2(2s_O)^2(\sigma_{CH})^2(\sigma'_{CH})^2(\sigma_{CO})^2(\pi_{CO})^2(n_O)^2(\pi_{CO}^*)^0(\sigma_{CO}^*)^0$$

In general, the energetic order of the molecular orbitals, the number of available electrons and the Pauli and Aufbau principles are employed to designate the *ground-electronic configuration* of a molecule. Physically, the *total* electronic distribution of a configuration may be approximated as a superposition of each of the one-electron MO's which make up the configuration.

Excited State Configurations and Transitions Between States

If we ignore the σ and lower-energy molecular orbitals, which are not expected to be involved in electronic transitions of interest to the photochemist, we may write the ground state (S_0) electronic configuration of formaldehyde as

$$S_0 = (\pi_{CO})^2(n_O)^2(\pi_{CO}^*)^0(\sigma_{CO}^*)^0$$

where the MO's are placed in order of increasing energy, going from left to right. We may approximate the transition from the ground state S_0 to an excited state by the excitation of one electron from the π_{CO} or n_O orbital into either the π_{CO}^* or σ_{CO}^* orbital which will lead to one of the four excited state configurations given in Figs. 2-7 and 2-8.

The excitation of an n electron into a π^* orbital is called an n-π^* transition, and the resulting excited state is called an n,π^* state. Similarly, excitation of a π_{CO} electron into a π_{CO}^* state is called a π-π^* transition and leads to a π,π^* state. The excited state designation and type of transition are listed along with the excited state configuration in Fig. 2-7.

The Pauli principle demands that any ground state configuration,

Designation

Excited State	Transition	Configuration
n,π^*	$n \rightarrow \pi^*$	$(\pi_{CO})^2(n_O)^1(\pi_{CO}{}^*)^1(\sigma_{CO}{}^*)^0$
π,π^*	$\pi \rightarrow \pi^*$	$(\pi_{CO})^1(n_O)^2(\pi_{CO}{}^*)^1(\sigma_{CO}{}^*)^0$
n,σ^*	$n \rightarrow \sigma^*$	$(\pi_{CO})^2(n_O)^1(\pi_{CO}{}^*)^0(\sigma_{CO}{}^*)^1$
π,σ^*	$\pi \rightarrow \sigma^*$	$(\pi_{CO})^1(n_O)^2(\pi_{CO}{}^*)^0(\sigma_{CO}{}^*)^1$

Fig. 2-7   *Excited state configurations of formaldehyde.*

such as that for formaldehyde, in which the electrons are paired in orbitals must be a *ground-state singlet*—i.e., the spins of the two electrons in each orbital are paired. In the excited state two electrons are *orbitally unpaired* —i.e., each is in a different orbital. As a result, the Pauli principle makes no prohibition with regard to the spin of these two electrons and a singlet excited state in which there is no net spin (i.e., electron spins are paired as in the ground state) or a triplet excited state (the two electrons which are orbitally unpaired now possess parallel spins) may result from the same electronic configuration of orbitals. This means that each of the excited states given on the left of Fig. 2-7 may be either a singlet or a triplet. This situation is depicted in Fig. 2-8 for the n,π^* and π,π^* case in which the arrows represent the spins of electrons in various orbitals.

It appears from the discussion above that even a simple molecule such as formaldehyde possesses a large number of excited states. Fortunately, most of organic photochemistry is concerned with only the lowest of these excited states, which represents an enormous simplification. Indeed, *four* types of excited states account for much of the known organic photochemistry. These are the singlet and triplet n,π^* states and the singlet and triplet π,π^* states. Each excited state has a particular energy, lifetime and electronic distribution. In a real sense, a molecule in an excited state is a different chemical species from that of the ground-state molecule. The excited state is expected to be considerably more reactive because of its high energy content and peculiar electronic distribution—i.e., a "hole" exists in an orbital where there was an electron. The essence of photochemistry is that activation to produce such an excited state is supplied by absorption of light.

State	Configuration
$^3(n,\pi^*)$	$(\pi_{CO}\,\uparrow\downarrow\,)^2(n_O\,\uparrow\,)^1(\pi_{CO}{}^*\,\uparrow\,)^1$
$^1(n,\pi^*)$	$(\pi_{CO}\,\uparrow\downarrow\,)^2(n_O\,\uparrow\,)^1(\pi_{CO}{}^*\,\downarrow\,)^1$
$^3(\pi,\pi^*)$	$(\pi_{CO}\,\uparrow\,)^1(n_O\,\uparrow\downarrow\,)^2(\pi_{CO}{}^*\,\uparrow\,)^1$
$^1(\pi,\pi^*)$	$(\pi_{CO}\,\uparrow\,)^1(n_O\,\uparrow\downarrow\,)^2(\pi_{CO}{}^*\,\downarrow\,)^1$

Fig. 2-8   *Configurations of singlet and triplet states.*

Energy Level Diagrams

The use of one-electron orbital "jumps" to describe electronic transitions (Fig. 2-9) has several major disadvantages. First, it does not indicate that in general the energies of the molecular orbitals are different in the ground and excited states. For instance, the energy of the n electron which is left behind in the n,π^* state will probably be lower than it was prior to excitation, whereas the π electrons may move toward the slightly positive "hole" on the carbonyl oxygen atom because of the latter's attraction, and the repulsion set up by the relative preponderance of electronic (negative) charge on carbon due to an electron in the π^* orbital. Second, it is difficult to visualize transitions between excited levels other than radiative ones. Third, only pure electronic transitions are considered. Finally, no indication is given of the difference in energy of various spin states which may result for the same excited configuration.

State or energy level diagrams are more satisfactory for the description of electronic transitions which occur upon absorption of a photon. In such diagrams the energy of the lowest vibrational level of each state is shown (other vibration levels being ignored for the present) relative to the energy of the lowest vibrational level of the ground state. The energy levels (Fig. 2-10) are represented by horizontal lines such that the vertical distance between any two of these lines corresponds to the energy difference between the states. The units of energy are given on a scale at the left, and the ground state is arbitrarily assigned a relative energy of zero. The singlet and triplet states are separated on the left- and right-hand sides of the diagrams, respectively, but the abscissa has no physical meaning in these diagrams.

A typical state diagram is given in Fig. 2-10, which represents a molecule which possesses n and π^* electrons and for which the $^1(n,\pi^*)$ and $^3(n,\pi^*)$ states (the superscripts refer to singlet and triplet states, respectively) are of lowest energy among the excited states of their respective multiplicities. Such a situation applies to many ketones, nitro compounds and pyridines. Diagrams similar to Fig. 2-10 are also representative of

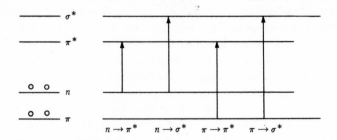

Fig. 2-9   *One electronic orbital "jumps."*

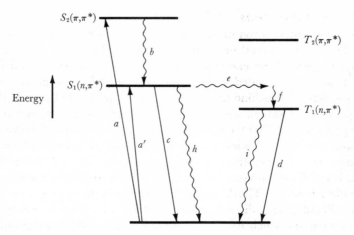

Fig. 2-10   *Typical energy level diagram for an unsaturated compound possessing hetero-atoms. An aromatic hydrocarbon would possess a similar diagram except that all of the states would be π, π^*.*

aromatic hydrocarbons except, of course, for the absence of n electrons. Electronic transitions accompanied by absorption or emission of a photon are represented in such diagrams by a solid line; radiationless transitions are represented by a wiggly line.

The triplet state is invariably of lower energy than the corresponding singlet which is derived from the same transition. The lower energy of the triplet results from operation of the Pauli principle which demands that if the orbitally unpaired electrons have parallel spin, they cannot occupy the same space simultaneously (electron-electron repulsion is therefore reduced). This is not so for the corresponding singlet, and greater electron repulsion results, so that this state has a higher energy than the corresponding triplet.

Paths of Molecular Excitation

An energy diagram such as Fig. 2-10 can be used to describe the fate of electronic excitation. Consider absorption of a photon which excites the molecule to the second excited state $S_2(\pi,\pi^*)$. This process is indicated by the solid arrow a. The absorption of a photon to excite the $S_1(n,\pi^*)$ state is indicated by the arrow, a'. Emission from $S_1(n,\pi^*)$ and $T_1(n,\pi^*)$ is similarly depicted by the arrow c, fluorescence, and d, phosphorescence, respectively. Absorption to excite the molecule from the ground state S_0 to $T_2(\pi,\pi^*)$ or $T_1(n,\pi^*)$ is strongly forbidden and is not observed to occur to a significant extent (see Section 3-3 for a discussion of forbiddenness). This does not mean that triplet states are unpopulated, however, since an alternate *nonradiative* path to populate triplets via S_2 or S_1 exists (wavy line e).

In condensed phases a radiationless conversion of $S_2(\pi,\pi^*)$ to $S_1(n,\pi^*)$ is extremely rapid (wavy line b). Once the molecule is in the lowest vibrational level of S_1, however, the excited system pauses momentarily. If a radiationless conversion from S_1 to T_1 (line e) can occur during this "hesitation" period, we will have a path for the production of triplets by an *indirect* excitation process. The occurrence of such a process could be detected by observation of the phosphorescence emission depicted by the arrow d.

Radiationless transitions from one state to another occur *isoenergetically* (line e) so that $S_1(n,\pi^*)$ in its *lowest* vibrational level will pass to $T_1(n,\pi^*)$, which will be produced in some upper vibrational level. The radiationless conversions of both S_1 and T_1 to S_0 also occur isoenergetically, but, for the sake of simplicity, the stepwise deactivation is not shown. The $T_1(n,\pi^*)$ state thereby produced is rapidly relaxed to its lowest vibrational level (in condensed phases) by collisions with the environment (wavy line f). The rapid vibrational cascade from higher levels of a state to the lowest level of the same state may be called *intrastate* conversion to distinguish it from *internal conversion* (radiationless transitions between states whose wave functions possess different electronic parts; see Section 3-3).

We shall see (Section 4-4) that the combination of dense distribution of excited states and the high collision frequency among molecules in liquids and solids causes relaxation of vibrational (and rotational) modes to occur so rapidly (with rare exceptions) that *only molecules in the lowest vibrational levels of the lowest excited states persist long enough to be important photochemically.* On the other hand, radiationless deactivations from S_1 or T_1 to S_0 (wavy lines h and i) are relatively slow, compared to the rate of radiationless processes among excited states.

Note that the triplet state has lower energy than the corresponding singlet state derived from the same configuration (see Section 4-6).

REFERENCES

1. C. A. Coulson, *Valence* (London: Oxford University Press, 1961).
2. G. Herzberg, *Spectra of Diatomic Molecules* (Princeton, N.J.: Van Nostrand, 1950).
3. H. H. Jaffe and M. Orchin, *Theory and Applications of Ultraviolet Spectroscopy* (New York: Wiley, 1962).
4. M. Kasha, in *Comparative Effects of Radiation*, ed. M. Burton, J. S. Kirby Smith, and J. L. Magee (New York: Wiley, 1960), p. 72.

5. M. Kasha, *Light and Life* ed. W. D. McElroy and B. Glass (Baltimore, Md.: Johns Hopkins Press, 1961), p. 31.
6. M. Kasha, *Radiation Research*, Supplement 2, 243 (1960).
7. J. N. Murrell, *The Theory of the Electronic Spectra of Organic Molecules* (New York: Wiley, 1963).
8. J. D. Roberts, "Molecular Orbital Calculations" (New York: Benjamin, 1961).
9. A. Streitwieser, Jr., "Molecular Orbital Theory for Organic Chemists (New York: Wiley, 1961).

Electronic Spectra and Electronically Excited States

chapter three

3-1. THEORY OF ELECTRONIC SPECTRA

Since light possesses the dualistic properties of both waves and particles, it can both eject electrons from a metal (particle behavior) and be diffracted at a grating (wave behavior). In order to investigate the problems of absorption and emission of light, we must concentrate on the wave properties of light.

Transition Moments

A light wave is characterized by an electric vector $\mathbf{E}$ and a magnetic vector $\mathbf{M}$, which form a mutually perpendicular set of axes with a propagation vector $\mathbf{c}$. The absorption of light arises mainly from the interaction of the *electric vector* with the electrons of a molecule. The classical electric force exerted by an electric field on an electron is equal to $e\mathbf{E}$, whereas the magnetic force exerted on the same electron is $ev\mathbf{H}/c$ (where $\mathbf{H}$ is the magnetic field strength, v is the velocity of the electron and c is the velocity of light). The magnetic term is small because $v \ll c$.

To a first approximation, the nature of the perturbation that the electric field of light exerts on electrons is similar to the interaction of $\mathbf{E}$ with the *electric dipole moment* of the molecule. The dipole moment R is given by the average distance between the centers of gravity of positive and negative charge multiplied by the magnitude of these charges. The value of R may be calculated by averaging the electrons' distance and direction (given by the vector $\mathbf{r}$) from the center of positive charge (the nuclei). Accordingly, the quantum mechanical operator which corre-

21

sponds to the observable property of light absorption has the form

$$\mathbf{R} = e \sum_i \mathbf{r}_i \qquad (3\text{-}1)$$

where $\mathbf{r}_i$ is the vector which corresponds to the dipole moment operator for electron i.

Two conditions must be fulfilled if a molecule initially in state Ψ_m is to absorb light of a given frequency ν:

1. There must exist a state Ψ_n of greater energy such that

$$E_n - E_m = h\nu \qquad (3\text{-}2)$$

2. The transition-moment integral

$$R_{mn} = \langle \Psi_m | \mathbf{R} | \Psi_n \rangle \neq 0 \qquad (3\text{-}3)$$

which represents the charge displacement (dipole-moment change) during transition, must not equal zero. The probability of absorption (if the two conditions above are met) is then proportional to the magnitude of $|R_{mn}|^2$.

Three important *electric-dipole transitions* of interest to the spectroscopist and photochemist are:

1. spontaneous emission
2. stimulated emission
3. stimulated absorption

The latter two processes are dependent on the presence of a radiation field, but spontaneous emission is not. (Spontaneous absorption, which corresponds to excitation from a lower energy state to a higher energy state in the absence of a radiation field, is statistically improbable.)

Stimulated Absorption

The intensity of absorption I_a of radiation of frequency ν by a molecule is the energy absorbed from an incident beam across a unit area in a unit time, so that

$$I_a = \rho(N_1 - N_2)B_{12}h\nu \qquad (3\text{-}4)$$

where, for a unit volume, ρ is the density of radiation of frequency ν impinging on the absorbing material, $(N_1 - N_2)$ is the difference between the number of molecules in the initial state Ψ_1 and the number in the final state Ψ_2, and B_{12} is the probability coefficient of absorption from Ψ_1 to Ψ_2. For electronic transitions, under normal conditions $N_2 \ll N_1$, so that the number of molecules in Ψ_2 may be neglected in calculating absorption intensities.

Experimentally, the intensity of absorption takes the more familiar form (for a unit volume)

$$I_a = I_0[1 - \exp(-\epsilon c_1 \ell)] \tag{3-5}$$

where I_0 is the intensity of the radiation field, ϵ is the extinction coefficient of the molecule at frequency ν, ℓ is the length of absorbing material, and c_1 is the concentration of molecules in state Ψ_1.

Spontaneous and Stimulated Emission

If a molecule is in an excited state Ψ_2, it may undergo a transition to Ψ_1 by either spontaneous or stimulated emission, the latter requiring the presence of an electromagnetic field external to the excited molecule. The intensity of emission from Ψ_2 to Ψ_1 is given by

$$I_e = N_2 h\nu[A_{21} + \rho B_{21}] \tag{3-6}$$

where N_2 is the number of excited molecules in a radiation field of density equal to ρ, A_{21} is the probability coefficient for spontaneous emission (A_{21} has the physical significance of a transition probability—i.e., the number of transitions per unit time from Ψ_2 to Ψ_1), and B_{21} is the probability coefficient for stimulated emission (assumed to be equal to the induced absorption coefficient B_{12}).

Under normal conditions, spontaneous emission completely dominates stimulated emission,[9, 10, 11] so that

$$I_e = N_2 h\nu A_{21} \tag{3-7}$$

For pure electronic transitions between Ψ_1 and Ψ_2 the probability coefficients A_{21} and B_{21} (which is equal to B_{12}) are related to each other and to the transition moment R by the equations [9, 11]

$$B_{21} = B_{12} = \left(\frac{8\pi^3}{3h^2c}\right)|R_{12}|^2 \tag{3-8}$$

and

$$A_{21} = \left(\frac{64\pi^4}{3hc^3}\right)\nu^3|R_{21}|^2 \tag{3-9}$$

Equations 3-8 and 3-9 show that the differences in the probability of radiative electronic transitions between two states will *depend mainly on the magnitudes of the transition moment connecting these states*. In addition, the probability of spontaneous emission is seen to depend strongly on the frequency ν at which the transition occurs.

Oscillator Strength

A quantity often used in relation to intensities is the oscillator strength f. Classically, the oscillator strength measures the effective number of electrons whose oscillations give rise to a particular absorption or emission band. The quantum mechanical counterpart of the oscillator strength for the transition from Ψ_1 to Ψ_2 is given by

$$f_{12} = \left(\frac{8\pi^2 cvm}{3he^2}\right)|R_{12}|^2 \tag{3-10}$$

where m is the mass of the electron, v is the frequency at which absorption occurs, and the other constants have their usual meanings. The oscillator strength is considered here because *it may be related to the experimental absorption coefficient* as follows:

$$f_{12} = 4.32 \times 10^{-9} \int \epsilon \, d\bar{v} \tag{3-11}$$

where $\int \epsilon \, d\bar{v}$ is the integrated absorption band (on a wave-number scale) for the transition from Ψ_1 to Ψ_2. Equations 3-10 and 3-11 make it possible to relate theoretical transition moments with experimental extinction coefficients or oscillator strengths.

Radiative Lifetimes

If a molecule is in an excited state and no radiationless paths exist for its deactivation, then the rate of its spontaneous emission is given by A_{21}. This means that, on the average, after the time τ (in seconds) where

$$\tau = \frac{1}{A_{21}} \tag{3-12}$$

the excited molecule will emit a photon of frequency v. A_{21} is related to f_{12} by the expression

$$f_{12} = 1.5\left(\frac{A_{21}G_2}{v_{21}^2 G_1}\right) \tag{3-13}$$

where G_2/G_1 is a statistical factor which is equal to one for singlet-singlet transitions and three for singlet-triplet transitions.[4]

From manipulation of Eqs. 3-8 through 3-13 we may relate the inherent radiative lifetime and experimental extinction coefficient by the equation

$$\tau^0 = \frac{3.5 \times 10^8 G_2}{G_1 \bar{v}^2 \int \epsilon \, d\bar{v}} \tag{3-14}$$

where $\bar{v}$ (in reciprocal centimeters) is equal to v/c. Equation 3-14 indicates that the mean emission lifetime of a state is relatively short when the corresponding absorption to that state is intense and that the mean emission lifetime of a state is relatively long if the corresponding absorption to that state is weak. An experimental test of a modified form of Eq. 3-14 is given in Section 4-1.

3-2. INTENSITIES OF ELECTRONIC TRANSITIONS

Equations 3-8 and 3-9 show that the probability of absorption and emission depends strongly on the magnitude of the transition-moment integral R. Sometimes it is possible to estimate the magnitude of R without explicit calculation. In particular, the transition-moment integral is frequently equal to zero because of the form of the wave functions corresponding to the states involved in the transition. Such transitions are "forbidden" (according to the approximate theory) and should not occur with high probability, or at least they should occur with reduced probability (compared to an equivalent transition which is not "forbidden").

Selection Rules [10]

Selection rules tell us the conditions under which the transition-moment integral R given by Eq. 3-3 is equal to zero. If $R = 0$, the corresponding transition is said to be "forbidden" by one or more selection rules. If $R \neq 0$, then the corresponding transition is "allowed" by selection rules. In practice, incomplete molecular wave functions are used to calculate R so that the selection rules which are generated from such calculations are only approximate. The transition moment R given in Eq. 3-3 could be calculated exactly if the exact eigenfunctions Ψ_1 and Ψ_2 were known.

The complete molecular wave function Ψ is first approximated as a product of one-electron orbitals ϕ, such that only one electron is excited in the transition, and that the energies of the orbitals ϕ are the same in the excited and ground states. Next, it is assumed that the vibrational (χ) and spin $(\S)$ portions of Ψ can be factored out, so that the molecular wave function is approximated by the product function

$$\Psi_i \cong \phi_i \chi_i \S_i \qquad (3\text{-}15)$$

The transition moment for the orbitals involved in the transition from Ψ_1 to Ψ_2 will thus be approximated by

$$R_{12} \sim e \int \phi_2 \chi_2 \S_2 \sum_i \mathbf{r}_i \phi_1 \chi_1 \S_1 \, d\tau \qquad (3\text{-}16)$$

The operator $\mathbf{r}$ only interacts with electrons and not nuclei or electron spins, so that Eq. 3-16 may be rewritten as

$$R_{12} \sim e \int \phi_2 \sum_i \mathbf{r}_i \phi_1 \, d\tau_e \int \chi_2 \chi_1 \, d\tau_v \int \S_2 \S_1 \, d\tau_s \qquad (3\text{-}17)$$

where $d\tau_e$, $d\tau_v$, and $d\tau_s$ refer to integrations over the electronic, vibrational (nuclear), and spin coordinates, each of which has been assumed to be independent of the others. The first integral on the left is called the *electronic transition moment*, R_e. This integral applies to pure electronic transitions between two states. The second integral depends on the overlap of molecular vibrational eigenfunctions, and the third is dependent on the relative spins of the electrons in orbitals ϕ_1 and ϕ_2.

Symmetry Requirements

The integral R_e may vanish if ϕ_1 and ϕ_2, the electronic wave functions of the initial and final states, are of appropriate symmetry. The state symmetry is a composite symmetry which in turn is a product of the one-electron orbital symmetries, the latter being taken in the product as many times as there are electrons in the orbital. All of the filled one-electron orbitals are therefore symmetric as far as state symmetry is concerned, in the sense that they are multiplied by themselves, and the square of either a symmetrical or an antisymmetrical function is always symmetrical. The operator **R** is a vector, and like all vectors may be analyzed into three components such that

$$\mathbf{R} = \mathbf{R}_x + \mathbf{R}_y + \mathbf{R}_z \qquad (3\text{-}18)$$

These three components $\mathbf{R}_x$, $\mathbf{R}_y$, and $\mathbf{R}_z$ have symmetry properties which may be represented by arrows parallel to the x, y, and z axes, respectively, and must therefore be considered to affect the total symmetry of the integral R.

Symmetry [8]

Consideration of the symmetry of a molecule allows the form of its wave functions to be deduced without explicitly solving the wave equation (Eq. 2-1). This suffices for the calculation to determine whether a transition moment integral is zero or nonzero on the basis of symmetry alone. The manipulation of symmetry operations (i.e., any operation which leaves a molecule unchanged) belongs to the realm of *group theory*. Even a brief outline of the general principles of this elegant branch of mathematics is beyond the scope of this text. Only the most important result for our purposes will be considered here: The transition moment integral is identically equal to zero (in the first approximation), if the integrand is an odd function. The operator **R** possesses symmetry properties of its own, as do the wave functions Ψ_m and Ψ_n. The product of the symmetry of these three terms determines whether the integrand is an odd or an even function. If the result is an odd function, integration from plus to minus infinity will lead to a value of zero for R. It should be pointed out that R may equal zero for other reasons, even if the integrand is an even function.

Overlap Requirement

Inspection of R_e (Eq. 3-17) indicates that the spatial properties of the orbitals involved in an electronic transition are also of some importance in the determination of intensities, irrespective of the state symmetries. Transitions are said to be overlap or space forbidden when the two orbitals involved in the transition do not simultaneously possess large amplitudes (either positive or negative) of their wave functions in the same region of space. This notion by itself predicts that π-π^* transitions should be more intense than n-π^* transitions. The latter transitions involve two orbitals which point in different directions and lie in the nodal planes of each other. The wave function of the n orbital has its maximum amplitude where the π^* orbital is zero and vice versa. The resultant transition moment is small as may be seen by consideration of the electronic-transition moment

$$R_e = \int \phi_2(n,\pi^*)\mathbf{R}\phi_1 \, d\tau \qquad (3\text{-}19)$$

which may be shown to be equal to a product of integrals, one of which is of the form

$$\int \phi_{\pi^*}\mathbf{R}\phi_n \, d\tau = 0 \qquad (3\text{-}20)$$

where ϕ_{π^*} and ϕ_n represent the orthogonal one-electron n and π^* orbitals, respectively. The vector $\mathbf{R}$ can affect only the symmetry of these orbitals but not the magnitude of their overlap, so that R_e will be small on the basis of overlap alone. The π and π^* orbitals, however, simultaneously possess relatively large amplitudes of their wave functions in the same region of space, so that the π-π^* transition is not overlap forbidden.

Spin Requirements

An important factor in the determination of the molecular transition moment R is the nature of the electronic spins in states Ψ_1 and Ψ_2. If the spins remain paired during the transition, then the integral $\int S_1 S_2 \, d\tau$ in Eq. 3-17 is unity, but if the spins become unpaired during the transition, the integral $\int S_1 S_2 \, d\tau$ is zero. This selection rule is far more rigorous than the symmetry and overlap requirements. However, singlet-triplet (spin forbidden) transitions *are* observed, and the nature of the process which causes relaxation of this selection rule merits separate discussion.

Spin-Orbital Coupling

In the first approximation, electric dipole transitions between pure singlet and pure triplet states are rigorously forbidden because of the orthogonality of the spin wave functions. A perturbation, external or internal, is required to "mix" pure singlet and pure triplet states, thereby permitting transitions between the "impure" singlet and "impure" triplet.[1] The form of the Hamiltonian which mixes these states is of great interest for the understanding of the processes involving *intercombinational transitions* (singlet-triplet transitions).

The classical operator which corresponds to this perturbation is the spin-orbital operator.[2, 3, 4] Spin-orbital coupling arises from magnetic interactions between the orbital motion of an electron and the electron's spin magnetic moment. The magnetic moment S of the electron is parallel to its axis of spin, and the energy of the spinning electron depends on the relative magnitude of the electron's orbital motion L and the direction of the spin. The net result is that the energy of a molecule depends on the relative orientations of the spin axis and the orbital angular-momentum axis of the electrons. The classical spin-orbital operator for a single electron in a central potential field has the form [2, 3, 4]

$$\mathbf{H}_{SO} = k\zeta(\mathbf{L}\cdot\mathbf{S}) \tag{3-21}$$

where ζ is a term which depends on the field of the nucleus, $\mathbf{L}$ is the electron orbital angular-momentum operator, $\mathbf{S}$ is the spin angular-momentum operator and k is a constant which depends on the given molecule.

A typical wave function which results from spin-orbital coupling may be written in the form

$$\Psi_{SO} = \Psi_T{}^0 + \lambda\Psi_S{}^0 \tag{3-22}$$

where $\Psi_T{}^0$ represents the pure, unperturbed triplet, $\Psi_S{}^0$ represents an appropriate singlet state which may "mix" with the triplet under spin-orbital interaction, and λ is a measure of the extent of mixing. The value of λ is given by

$$\lambda = \left| \frac{\int\Psi_S{}^0\mathbf{H}_{SO}\Psi_T{}^0\, d\tau}{E_T - E_S} \right| \tag{3-23}$$

where E_T is the energy of the triplet $\Psi_T{}^0$, and E_S is the energy of the singlet $\Psi_S{}^0$. We have assumed for the sake of simplicity [3, 4] that only one singlet state is mixing with $\Psi_T{}^0$. If there are more, then λ becomes equal to a sum of terms which have the form of Eq. 3-23.

Under spin-orbital coupling the transition moment R becomes equal to

$$R_{SO} = \int\Psi_{SO}\mathbf{R}\Psi_1\, d\tau \tag{3-24}$$

where Ψ_{SO} is the molecular wave function of the triplet state under spin-orbital perturbation, and Ψ_1 is the molecular wave function of the ground state. Substituting Eq. 3-22 into Eq. 3-24, we have

$$R_{SO} = \int \Psi_T{}^0 \mathbf{R} \Psi_1 \, d\tau + \lambda \int \Psi_S{}^0 \mathbf{R} \Psi_1 \, d\tau \qquad (3\text{-}25)$$

The first term on the right-hand side of Eq. 3-25 is still equal to zero because a transition between a pure singlet and a pure triplet is involved. The second term is identical to a transition moment for singlet-singlet transitions and is therefore finite if not forbidden by symmetry or overlap selection rules (which are only approximate).

From Eqs. 3-21, 3-23, and 3-25 we find that the part of Ψ_{SO} which contributes to the singlet-triplet transition may be written as

$$\Psi_{SO} \propto \left(\frac{\zeta \int \Psi_S{}^0 (\mathbf{L \cdot S}) \Psi_T{}^0}{|E_T - E_S|} \right) \Psi_S{}^0 \qquad (3\text{-}26)$$

It is instructive to note that important contributions to the degree of mixing result from the size of ζ and $|E_T - E_S|$. The term ζ is related to the potential field of the nucleus. Thus, spin-orbital coupling is more pronounced when the electron is in an orbital which has a high probability of being close to the nucleus, especially in an orbital which is

Table 3-1   *Typical values of ζ for atoms*

Atom	$\zeta(cm^{-1})$
Carbon	28
Nitrogen	70
Oxygen	152
Fluorine	272
Chlorine	587
Bromine	2,460
Iodine	5,060
Tin	2,097
Lead	7,294

close to a nucleus of high atomic number. The values of ζ can be calculated from atomic spectral data. Some typical values are given in Table 3-1. Finally, we should note that the magnitude of spin-orbital coupling depends *inversely on the energetic separation of the triplet and the perturbing or mixing singlet.* The values of ζ are accurately known for atoms [2] so that the intercombinational transition probabilities of a molecule may be determined roughly if it is assumed that the ζ value for the molecule is equal to the sum of the values for atoms of which the molecule is composed (see Section 4-5).

3-3. THE FRANCK–CONDON PRINCIPLE [4]

The relative intensities of the vibrational parts of an electronic absorption or emission band are nicely rationalized by the Franck-Condon principle, which states: *Electronic transitions are so fast* (10^{-15} *sec*) *in comparison to nuclear motion* (10^{-12} *sec*) *that immediately after the transition, the nuclei have nearly the same relative position and velocities as they did just before the transition.* This principle implies that the *most probable* transitions between different electronic and vibrational levels will be those transitions for which the momentum and position of the nuclei do not change very much. This principle essentially states that it is difficult to convert electronic energy rapidly into vibrational energy. This principle is best understood by reference to certain potential-energy curves.

The Harmonic Oscillator [4, 5]

The vibrational motions of a diatomic molecule XY may be approximated by a harmonic oscillator for which one nucleus X is regarded as being attached by a spring to a second nucleus Y, and that both nuclei vibrate back and forth with respect to each other along the bond axis. A plot of the potential energy of this system versus the distance between the atoms (XY), is called a *potential-energy curve*. At some particular internuclear separation r_e the potential energy of the system is at a minimum—i.e., the nuclei possess their equilibrium configuration. If the separation is decreased to a value *less* than r_e, the potential energy of the system increases rapidly as a result of internuclear and electronic repulsions. On the other hand, if the internuclear separation is increased to a value *greater* than r_e, the potential energy also increases due to the stretching of the X—Y bond (see Fig. 3-1).

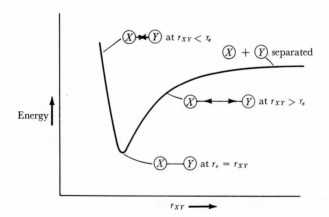

Fig. 3-1   *Potential-energy curve of a diatomic molecule XY.*

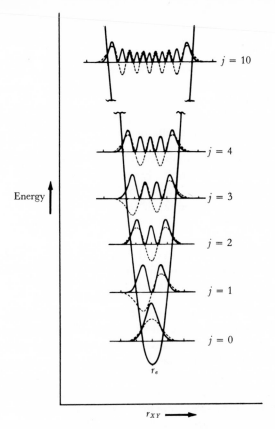

Fig. 3-2   *Energy levels and eigenfunctions of a diatomic molecule which is a harmonic oscillator.*

A simple potential-energy curve for the molecule can be constructed for XY if it is assumed that the vibrational motion of the nuclei may be approximated by a harmonic oscillator, for which the potential energy as a function of distance is

$$\text{P.E.} = \frac{1}{2} kr^2 \tag{3-27}$$

where r is $|r - r_e|$ or the change of internuclear separation from its equilibrium value. Thus, if the restoring force exerted by the atoms X and Y is proportional to r, the potential-energy curve is a parabola, as shown in Fig. 3-2.

Solution of the Schrödinger equation for $V = \frac{1}{2}kr^2$ shows if it is assumed that the eigenfunctions for the harmonic oscillator are single valued, finite, and continuous, then the allowable energies of the system are given by Eq. 3-28

$$E_j = h\nu(j + \tfrac{1}{2}) \tag{3-28}$$

where j is the vibrational quantum number (which can take only integral values, 0, 1, 2, . . .), ν is the vibrational frequency of the *classical* oscillator, and h is Planck's constant.

The important results derived from the quantum mechanical solution of Eq. 2-1 for the harmonic oscillator are:

1. Only the energy values given by Eq. 3-28 for integral values of j are allowed for the harmonically vibrating molecule.

2. The energy of the lowest possible vibration is not zero (as it would be classically) but equal to $\tfrac{1}{2}h\nu$.

3. The vibrational energy levels are equally spaced above the $j = 0$ level in units of $h\nu$.

4. The mathematical form of the eigenfunctions χ_j, which are solutions to Eq. 2-1 for the harmonic oscillator is instructive for the determination of transition probabilities (*vide infra*).

The amplitude of the corresponding *classical vibrational* motion is obtained from Fig. 3-2 from the intersection of the potential-energy curve with the corresponding energy level.   The classical turning points are the positions which define the potential energy—i.e., at the turning points the total energy of the oscillator is potential energy, because the kinetic energy is zero.   This results from the fact that the total vibrational energy X is constant during the stretching and compression motions of the nuclei, but the kinetic energy T and potential energy V are continually changing such that

$$X = T + V \tag{3-29}$$

When the nuclei are close to their equilibrium distance, the potential energy of the system is minimal for that vibration, and the kinetic energy must therefore be maximal.   At points on the curve which correspond to extreme stretching or compression, $T = 0$ since the atoms pause momentarily as the turning point in a vibration is reached, and V must be maximal.

The vibrational eigenfunctions χ_j for $j = 1, 2, 3, 4$, and 10 are plotted in Fig. 3-2 on the corresponding permitted energy levels, which are indicated by horizontal lines.[5]   Above the horizontal line the value of χ_j is positive, and below the line the value of χ_j is negative.   The number of times χ_j goes through zero equals j.

Very important conclusions can be derived from inspection of the relationship of χ_j to the classical potential-energy curve.   It can be seen from Fig. 3-2 that the wave-mechanical probability of finding the nuclei is greatest near the classical turning points (for $j > 0$), but in addition there is a finite, nonnegligible probability that the atoms will vibrate *outside* of this region. Furthermore, the probability of finding the nuclei at a given separation is peculiar for upper vibrational levels in that in addition to the broad maxima of the probability distribution, in the vicinity of the classical turning points, a number of maxima (for $j > 1$) exist in between. As we go to higher and higher values of j, the quantum mechanical situation approximates the classical situation more closely (Bohr's correspondence principle)—i.e., the atoms tend to spend more time near the turning points of vibration and very little time in the region about $r = r_e$.

The probability distribution curve for the $j = 0$ level in Fig. 3-2 contrasts most dramatically with the classical picture. Instead of two turning points, one broad probability maximum at $r = r_e$ exists. Classically, the vibrational state of lowest energy corresponds to the state of rest (point r_e in Fig. 3-2), which is impossible for the quantum mechanical model since the position and velocity of this state would then be exactly defined in violation of the uncertainty principle. Most photoreactions in condensed phases originate from thermally equilibrated vibrational states, which means that the $j = 0$ level will be of great importance in organic photochemistry.

The Anharmonic Oscillator Curves [4, 5]

The harmonic oscillator cannot accurately approximate a real molecule for very short and very long nuclear separations, as can be seen from the following discussion. For the harmonic oscillator the restoring force increases indefinitely and smoothly with increasing or decreasing distance from the equilibrium position (see Fig. 3-2). In a real molecule the potential energy will rise more gradually than predicted by Eq. 3-27 as the internuclear separation is increased because of weakening of the X—Y bond at large r, as is shown in Fig. 3-3. Eventually the potential energy reaches a limiting value as the restoring force disappears, and the bond breaks. This corresponds to the dissociation energy of the molecule and is represented by the asymptote in Fig. 3-3. If the energy of the system just corresponds to the asymptote, the atoms at a great distance from one another will have zero velocity. Above the asymptote the atoms' kinetic energy (which is not quantized) is increased. On the other hand, compression of the nuclei results in a more rapid increase in potential energy than is predicted by Eq. 3-27 because of the sudden rise of coulombic repulsions with decreasing nuclear separation.

The situation described above is best represented by an anharmonic oscillator, the potential curve of which is shown in Fig. 3-3. Such curves are often approximated by Morse curves. In the neighborhood of the equilibrium position such a curve is approximately a parabola—i.e., the potential curve of a harmonic oscillator. The eigenfunctions and probability density distributions of the anharmonic oscillator are quite similar to those of the harmonic oscillator except that they are somewhat unsymmetrical and tend to have greater values of their maxima on the shallower right-hand side of the potential curve than on the steeper left-hand side.

The curves shown in Figs. 3-1, 3-2, and 3-3 represent all the points for which the kinetic energy of the system is equal to zero—i.e., the total vibrational energy of the system X is equal to the potential energy (for a classical system). It is important to realize that at every point on the curve the molecule is at rest and is on the verge of vibrating in the direction opposite to that which brought it to its stationary condition. At all points *between* the end-point vibrations the molecule possesses a certain amount of kinetic energy in addition to its potential energy. At all times, therefore, Eq. 3-29 holds—i.e., the total energy of the system equals the sum of the kinetic and potential energy. For example, in the $j = 3$ vibration level, the anharmonic oscillator shown in Fig. 3-3 possesses 40 kcal mole^{-1} at point A (all potential energy), while at point B the system possesses about 35 kcal mole^{-1} of kinetic energy and 5 kcal mole^{-1} of potential energy (relative to an arbitrary energy of zero for the lowest point in the curve).

In order to describe the energy levels of the anharmonic oscillator an expansion series is required. As a result the vibrational levels, which are still quantized, are no longer equally separated, but their separation

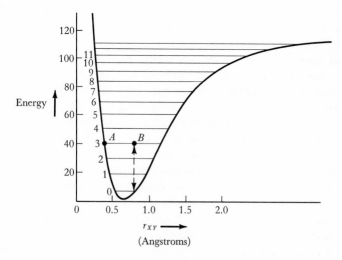

Fig. 3-3   *Potential-energy curve of an anharmonic oscillator.   The internuclear separation is in angstroms, and the energy is in kcal/mole.*

decreases slowly with increasing j, as shown in Fig. 3-3. Note that the energy separation between $j = 0$ and $j = 1$ is about 12 kcal mole^{-1}, while the energy separation between $j = 10$ and $j = 11$ is only about 5 kcal mole^{-1}.

Absorption [4, 6, 7]

Electronic excitation of the diatomic molecule XY causes the over-all electronic distribution of a molecule to change, and a different Morse curve is required to represent the excited state as shown in Fig. 3-4. The upper curve represents the excited state, and, since it possesses an energy minimum, a net attraction between the nuclei still exists. The different electronic configuration of the upper state may cause the equilibrium nuclear separation to be different from that of the ground state. In general, we might expect r_e to be somewhat greater for the excited state than for the ground state because the former state possesses an antibonding electron. The excited state is inherently less stable than the ground state, of course, so that its potential energy is higher.

We have indicated earlier that the Franck-Condon principle tells us that the electronic excitation is so fast compared to vibrational motion that the internuclear distances of a molecule can be regarded as fixed during an electronic transition. The effect of the semiclassical Franck-Condon principle on the vibrational intensities of an electronic transition can now be understood by reference to the three typical dispositions of the potential curves of an excited state (upper curves) with respect to the ground state (lower curves) for a diatomic molecule, as shown in Figs. 3-4, 3-6, and 3-8.

The complete description of a polyatomic molecule requires knowledge of a number of polydimensional energy surfaces, which in turn may be approximated by the superposition of many two-dimensional potential-energy curves. At any rate, the diatomic case is easily visualized, and the conclusions reached from its consideration may be extended to the general case.

In Fig. 3-4 the ground and excited state potential curves have been so chosen that their minima lie at the same internuclear separation. At 25° C absorption occurs from the $j = 0$ vibrational level of Ψ_1. The Franck-Condon principle requires that the internuclear distances and motions remain fixed during the transition, so that the absorptions to the vibrational levels in the shaded area in Fig. 3-4 are allowed. Thus, the 0-0 and 0-1 transitions (i.e., transitions which start from the $j = 0$ level of Ψ_1 and terminate at the $j = 0$ and $j = 1$ level of Ψ_2) from Ψ_1 to Ψ_2 do not involve large changes in the nuclear distances or motions. They begin and end with nearly the same r value and have similar kinetic energy (close to zero). Vertical transition will intersect the upper curve

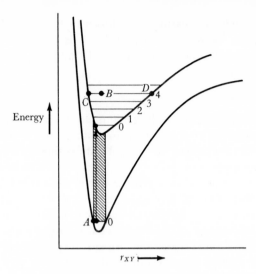

Fig. 3-4   *Franck-Condon potential curves of the ground and lowest excited states (with similar equilibrium separations) of a diatomic molecule XY.*

near turning points where the nuclei have paused momentarily. On the other hand, transition to the $j = 4$ vibrational level would be possible only if the position $(A$ to $C)$ or momentum $(A$ to $B)$ or both changed appreciably at the moment of absorption.   At point B the molecule has four quanta of excess kinetic energy over that of the $j = 0$ level.   The Franck-Condon principle thus predicts that the 0-0 vibrational band should be the most intense in the spectrum of XY, and that the probabilities and intensities for the 0-1, 0-2, 0-3, etc., transitions should fall off rapidly, as shown in Fig. 3-5.   Since there are no other general restrictions

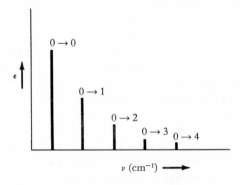

Fig. 3-5   *Typical absorption spectrum of a diatomic molecule whose potential-energy curves correspond to Fig. 3-4.*

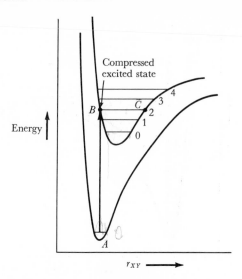

Fig. 3-6 *Franck-Condon potential curves of the ground and excited states of a diatomic molecule XY in which the equilibrium separation in the excited state is slightly larger than that of the ground state.*

on the changes in j for electronic transitions, the Franck-Condon principle alone correctly predicts the relative intensities of vibrational bands.

In Fig. 3-6 the minimum of the potential curve of the excited state is at a greater value of r than the ground state. Again the most probable transitions are those close to vertically upward from the $j = 0$ level of the ground state. The 0-0 band is no longer very intense because the internuclear distance alters somewhat for such a transition. The most probable transitions are now the 0-2 and 0-3 transitions, which require little change in internuclear distance at the time of the electron jump, and

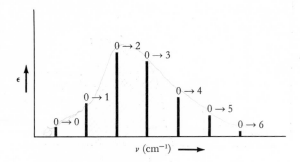

Fig. 3-7 *Typical absorption spectrum of a diatomic molecule whose potential-energy curves correspond to Fig. 3-6.*

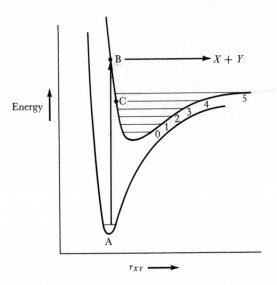

Fig. 3-8   *Franck-Condon potential curves of the ground and excited states of a diatomic molecule XY whose equilibrium separation is much greater in the excited state than the ground state.*

little change in nuclear velocity. Thus, immediately after the electron jump, the nuclei are essentially the same distance apart as they were in the ground state and possess zero relative velocity.   Since the equilibrium distance is now different in the excited state, the nuclei start to vibrate between B and C. Transitions from $j = 0$ of the ground state to the vibrational levels whose left turning points are close to A are also relatively intense, as is shown in Fig. 3-7.

Finally, in Fig. 3-8 the minimum of the excited state is at such a large internuclear distance that a Franck-Condon (vertical) transition from the

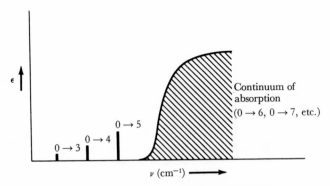

Fig. 3-9   *Typical absorption spectrum for a diatomic molecule whose absorption spectrum corresponds to Fig. 3-8.*

$j = 0$ level of the ground state intersects the excited state potential curve above the asymptote, and, as the molecule XY begins to vibrate immediately after excitation, the atoms experience no restoring force and fly apart. Transitions to the region of discrete levels below the asymptote are possible but not very probable, while transitions to points above the asymptote lead to continuous absorption (no vibrational structure), as is shown in Fig. 3-9.

One can see that the relative intensity distributions of vibrational levels lead to an estimation of the difference between the minimum inter-nuclear distances in the ground and excited states.[10-13]

Emission [4]

In condensed phases the rate of vibrational- and electronic-energy relaxation among excited states is very rapid compared to the rate of emission. As a result, emission will occur from the $j = 0$ vibrational level of the lowest excited states. Let us apply the Franck-Condon principle to emission (Fig. 3-10).

The most probable emissions will be the ones which occur vertically. In contrast to absorption, the displacement of the ground-state potential-energy curve minimum is to the left of the minimum of the excited state curve, so that the most probable emissions produce an elongated ground state, while absorption produces a compressed excited state immediately

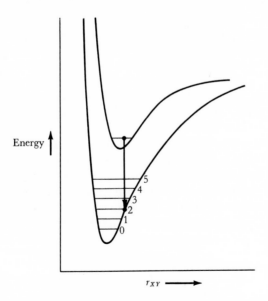

Fig. 3-10   *Typical Franck-Condon emission from an excited state whose equilibrium separation is slightly greater in the excited state than in the ground state.*

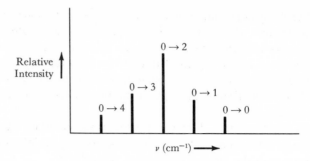

Fig. 3-11   *Typical emission spectrum for a diatomic molecule whose Franck-Condon curves are disposed as shown in Fig. 3-10.*

after transition. The frequency of emission cannot be greater than the frequency of the 0-0 emission, of course, since the 0-1, 0-2, etc., emissions correspond to lower energies than the 0-0 emission. The emission spectrum expected from a molecule whose potential-energy curves are similar to those in Fig. 3-10 is shown in Fig. 3-11.

Quantum Mechanical Formulation of the Franck-Condon Principle [4, 5]

Quantum mechanics confirms the basic assumption of the Franck-Condon principle and predicts that the most probable transitions occur vertically upward in the potential-energy diagram. Recall that the oscillator corresponding to a real molecule is never at rest and that in the $j = 0$ vibrational level a probability distribution describes the internuclear separation.

This means that transitions may originate from $j = 0$ over a certain range of r values. This explains why *more* than one band originating from $j = 0$ is observed. The extent of the band series, of course, will depend on the steepness of the upper potential curve which lies directly above the range of r values for the $j = 0$ vibration.

A more quantitative refinement of the preceeding qualitative discussion leads to an interesting result concerning the probabilities of transitions which involve changes in j between different electronic states. The probability of a transition between Ψ_1 and Ψ_2 is proportional to Eq. 3-17. If the electron spins do not become unpaired during the transition (i.e., $\int S_1 S_2 \, d\tau = 1$), then we have from Eq. 3-17

$$R \cong \int \phi_2 \mathbf{R}_e \phi_1 \, d\tau \int \chi_1{}^j \chi_2{}^{j'} \, d\tau \qquad (3\text{-}30)$$

which is merely the electronic transition moment R_e times the overlap integral of the vibrational eigenfunctions of the initial level $\chi_1{}^j$, and the final level $\chi_2{}^{j'}$.

From Eqs. 3-4, 3-8, and 3-30 we have for absorption

$$I_a \cong \left(\frac{\rho N_1 8\pi^3 \nu}{3hc}\right) |R_e|^2 \left| \int \chi_1{}^j \chi_2{}^{j'} \, d\tau \right|^2 \qquad (3\text{-}31)$$

and for emission from Eqs. 3-7, 3-9, and 3-30 we have

$$I_e \cong \frac{N_2 64\pi^4 \nu^4}{3} |R_e|^2 \left| \int \chi_1{}^j \chi_2{}^{j'} \, d\tau \right|^2 \qquad (3\text{-}32)$$

For a given frequency ν and electronic transition, Eqs. 3-31 and 3-32 become 3-33 and 3-34, respectively

$$I_a \cong k\nu \left| \int \chi_1{}^j \chi_2{}^{j'} \, d\tau \right|^2 \qquad (3\text{-}33)$$

$$I_e \cong k'\nu^4 \left| \int \chi_1{}^j \chi_2{}^{j'} \, d\tau \right|^2 \qquad (3\text{-}34)$$

where k and k' are constant for a given set of experimental conditions.

The intensity of the vibrational patterns of transitions corresponding to the situations described in Figs. 3-4, 3-6, 3-8, and 3-10 can now be rationalized from the standpoint of quantum mechanics. For example, in Fig. 3-4 the value of $\int \chi_2{}^j \chi_1{}^{j'} \, d\tau$ is maximal for $j = j' = 0$ because the overlap is maximal. The overlap dwindles for the 0-1, 0-2, etc. transitions, however, because the negative and positive contributions of $\chi_2{}^{j'}$ tend to cancel the completely positive contribution from $\chi_1{}^{j=0}$ (see Fig. 4-11). Therefore, the 0-0 transitions for *both* emission and absorption will be the most probable.

If the potential curve of the upper state is shifted to the right relative to the lower curve, as in Fig. 3-6, the vibrational function overlap integral has a maximal value when the maximum of the upper vibrational eigenfunction $\chi_2{}^{j'}$ lies vertically above the maximum of $\chi_1{}^{j=0}$. The overlap integral will have maximal values for the 0-2 absorption or 0-3 absorption as well as the 0-2 and 0-4 emissions which will have appreciable probability.

Thus, the Franck-Condon principle stated in quantum mechanical terms would be: In a series of absorption (or emission) vibrational bands originating from a $j = 0$ level, the most intense peaks will be observed for those transitions to upper (or lower) vibrational levels whose eigenfunctions have *terminal* maxima which lie vertically above the maximum of the eigenfunction of the initial state. The width of the vibrational progression will be determined mainly by the range of r values scanned by the nuclei in the $j = 0$ level—i.e., ultimately by the uncertainty principle.

Summary

The Franck-Condon Principle will be seen below (Section 4-3) to be of great importance in processes involving electronically excited states. We see from Eqs. 3-33 and 3-34 that the intensity of absorption and emission bands are dependent on the square of the Franck-Condon overlap integral

$$\int \chi_1{}^j \chi_2{}^{j'} \, d\tau$$

From Eqs. 3-7 and 3-34 we have

$$A_{21} = k''\nu^3 \left| \int \chi_1{}^j \chi_2{}^{j'} \, d\tau \right|^2 \tag{3-35}$$

and from Eq. 3-12

$$\tau = \frac{1}{k''\nu^3 \left| \int \chi_1{}^j \chi_2{}^{j'} \, d\tau \right|^2} \tag{3-36}$$

Thus, the *smaller* the Franck-Condon overlap integral, the *longer* the radiative lifetime of the corresponding state, and the larger the Franck-Condon overlap integral, the *shorter* the radiative lifetime of a state, if all other factors are more or less equal.

PROBLEMS

1. The relative quantum yield ($\phi_f \sim 0.3$) and spectral distribution of benzene-vapor fluorescence are invariant from 5×10^{-3} to 10^{-1} mm pressure. What conclusion can be made about collisional perturbation of the $S_1 \rightsquigarrow T_1$ crossing for benzene under these conditions?

2. Explain the following phenomena in terms of the Franck-Condon principle:

1. An emission spectrum possesses a 0-0 transition as the most intense band.
2. A molecule possesses a broad and structureless absorption band, but the related emission spectrum is relatively sharp and shows fine structure.
3. The $n \rightarrow \pi^*$ absorption and emission band of ketones shifts to shorter wavelengths with increasing solvent polarity.
4. The 0-0 bands of an absorption and related emission spectrum tend to coincide.
5. Intramolecular energy transfer from one state to another occurs isoenergetically.

3. Predict which one of the following pairs of molecules will possess the greater amount of spin-orbital coupling (i. e., possesses more probable intercombinational transitions):

1. fluorine or iodine
2. benzophenone ($E_{T_1} = 69$ kcal mole^{-1}, $E_{S_1} = 74$ kcal mole^{-1}) or benzene ($E_{T_1} = 84$ kcal mole^{-1}, $E_{S_1} = 115$ kcal mole^{-1})
3. naphthalene or quinoline.

4. Do you expect the lowest triplet state of most molecules to "mix" significantly with the ground state? Explain.

5. Predict the vibrational structure for the molecule described in Fig. 3-4, if absorption is mainly from the $j = 1$ level of the ground state.

REFERENCES

1. See references at the end of Chapter 2.
2. D. S. McClure, *J. Chem. Phys.*, **17,** 905 (1949).
3. E. U. Condon and G. H. Shortley, *Theory of Atomic Spectra* (London: Cambridge University Press, 1959), p. 120 ff.
4. G. W. Robinson, in *Experimental Methods of Physics*, ed. L. Marton and D. Williams (vol. III, New York: Academic Press, 1962) p. 155 ff.
5. W. Kauzmann, *Quantum Chemistry* (New York: Academic Press, 1957).
6. J. N. Pitts, Jr., F. Wilkinson, and G. S. Hammond, in *Advances in Photochemistry*, ed. W. A. Noyes, Jr., G. S. Hammond, and J. N. Pitts, Jr. (vol. I, New York: Interscience, 1963), p. 1.
7. H. Sponer and E. Teller, *Rev. Mod. Phys.*, **13,** 75 (1941).
8. W. West in *Technique of Organic Chemistry*, ed. A. Weissberger, (vol. IX, New York: Interscience, 1956), p. 707.
9. F. A. Cotton, *Chemical Applications of Group Theory* (New York: Interscience, 1963).
10. C. Sandorfy, *Electronic Spectra and Quantum Chemistry* (Englewood Cliffs, N.J.: Prentice-Hall, 1964).
11. G. M. Barrow, *Molecular Spectroscopy* (New York: McGraw-Hill, 1962).
12. G. W. King, *Spectroscopy and Molecular Structure* (New York: Holt, Rinehart & Winston, 1964).
13. R. P. Bauman, *Absorption Spectroscopy* (New York: Wiley, 1962).

The Nature of Electronically Excited States

chapter four

4-1. MOLECULAR ELECTRONIC ABSORPTION SPECTRA

The *absorption spectrum* [1, 2, 3] of a molecule provides important information concerning the lifetimes, energies and electronic configurations of the excited singlet states. For reactions in condensed phases, the lowest excited singlet state S_1 is of great interest to the organic photochemist because the extremely rapid rate of internal conversion from upper singlets to S_1 makes photochemical reactions unlikely from these upper excited states. If the properties of S_1 can be deduced from the absorption spectrum, we have obtained information concerning the most probable starting point of a photochemical sequence.

Typical Absorption Spectra

An electronic absorption spectrum is usually presented as a plot of absorption (expressed as ϵ or log ϵ) versus frequency ν (usually expressed in wave numbers or reciprocal centimeters) or wavelength λ (usually expressed in angstroms or millimicrons). Electronic spectra arise from the absorption of light (which causes transitions between electronic states). Most electronic transitions of interest to the organic photochemist result from absorption in the ultraviolet and visible regions of the spectrum (about 2,000 Å or 50,000 cm^{-1} to 7,000 Å or 14,200 cm^{-1}).

If the electronic energy alone changed during a transition, then a sharp absorption line would result; however, for molecules in solution absorption causes not only changes in electronic energy, but also invariably in the vibrational and rotational energy. As a result, a set of closely

44

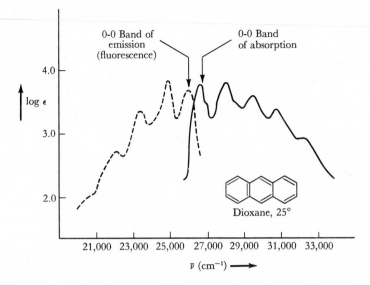

Fig. 4-1   *Absorption (right) spectrum and emission (left) of anthracene in dioxane solution.[34]   The intensity of the emission spectrum is in relative units.   Notice the mirror-image relationship between the emission (fluorescence) spectrum and the absorption spectrum.*

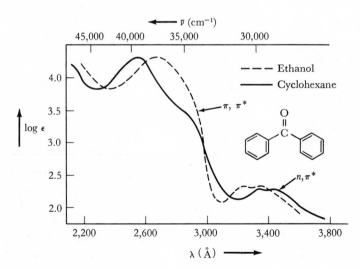

Fig. 4-2   *Absorption spectrum of benzophenone in ethanol [1] at 25° C.   Notice the lack of a clearly defined 0-0 band.*

packed lines corresponding to an electronic transition appear as an absorption *band* in solution spectra.

The absorption spectra of anthracene and benzophenone are shown in Figs. 4-1 and 4-2, respectively. Both spectra manifest differing intensities for the various electronic transitions shown in the figures. Furthermore, notice that the vibrational structure of the anthracene absorption bands is considerably better resolved than those of benzophenone.

Assignment of n,π^* and π,π^* Configurations [4–7]

The term *chromophore* refers to the group mainly responsible for a given absorption band. For anthracene, the molecule as a whole must be

Table 4-1   *Comparison of the features of n-π^* and π-π^* transitions* [4, 7]

Property	n-π^*	π-π^*
Maximum ϵ	Less than 100	Greater than 1,000
Vibration band structure	Sharp in nonpolar solvents, broad in polar solvents. Possesses localized vibrational progressions (e.g., C=O)	Moderately sharp in most solvents. Possesses C=C vibrational progression
τ_f and ϕ_f	$\tau_f > 10^{-6}$ sec, $\phi_f < 0.01$	$\tau_f \sim 10^{-9}$–10^{-7} sec $\phi_f \sim 0.5$–0.05
τ_p and ϕ_p	$\tau_p \sim 10^{-3}$ sec, $\phi_p \sim 0.5$–0.05	$\tau_p \sim 0.1$–10 sec $\phi_p \sim 0.5$–0.05
Direction of transition moment	Perpendicular to molecular plane for singlet-singlet transitions	Parallel to molecular plane for singlet-singlet transitions
Effect of increasing solvent polarity or electron donating substituents	Transition shifts to shorter wavelengths	Transition shifts to longer wavelengths

considered as the absorbing group, but for benzophenone both the carbonyl group and the extended conjugated system may be considered as independently absorbing systems. The long wavelength, low intensity absorption of benzophenone is the result of a n-π^* transition which is mainly localized on the carbonyl group, while the short wavelength, high intensity band is the result of a π-π^* transition, for which the excited electron is delocalized over the entire molecule. A number of empirical criteria[4] which have been proposed as a means of differentiating n-π^* from π-π^* transitions in carbonyl compounds are listed in Table 4-1. The position and intensity of the longest wavelength absorption (transition to S_1) strongly depends on the electronegativity of the elements [1, 2, 3] making up the bond, the extent of conjugation, and the presence or absence of n orbitals on one of the partners (see Table 4-2).

Table 4-2 *Long wavelength absorption of typical chromophores*

Chromophore	λ_{max} (Å)	ϵ_{max}
C=C	1,800	10,000
C=O	2,800	20
N=N	3,500	100
C=C—C=C	2,200	20,000
C=C—C=O	3,200	100
N=O	6,600	10
Benzene	2,600	200

Energies of Electronically Excited States

At 25° or lower, a thermally equilibrated S_1 state will be in its $j' = 0$ vibrational level. The energy of this state is therefore given by the energy of the $S_0(j = 0)$ to $S_1(j' = 0)$ transition which corresponds to the 0-0 band in the absorption spectrum. It is usually assumed that the longest wavelength vibration absorption band is the 0-0 band. If the electronic absorption band does not possess vibrational fine structure at 25° C, lowering the temperature or changing solvent may help resolution.

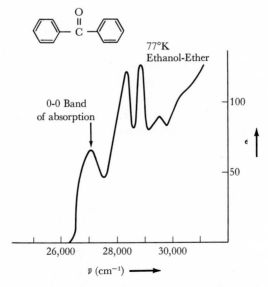

Fig. 4-3 *Absorption spectrum of benzophenone [8] in ethanol at −198° C. Notice the increase in vibrational fine structure.*

The absorption spectrum of benzophenone [8] at $-198°$ C is shown in Fig. 4-3. The longest wavelength band is at 26,700 cm^{-1} (3,750 Å) and corresponds to 76.5 kcal/mole from Eq. 1-2.

In the following discussions the energy of the lowest excited singlet state S_1 and the lowest triplet T_1 will be expressed in kcal mole^{-1} unless specified and correspond to the 0-0 band for the corresponding transition in an absorption or emission spectrum.

Lifetimes of Electronically Excited States

The *"allowedness"* of the electronic transition to S_1 as measured by the integrated intensity of the corresponding absorption band is related approximately to the "allowedness" of the reverse process, *fluorescence*, by the equation (see Section 3-2)

$$\tau^0 = \frac{3.5 \times 10^8}{\bar{\nu}_m{}^2 \int \epsilon \, d\bar{\nu}} \tag{4-1}$$

where τ^0 is the inherent *radiative* lifetime in seconds of S_1 (in the absence of other paths of deactivation), $\bar{\nu}_m$ is the mean frequency for the absorption band (in reciprocal centimeters), and $\int \epsilon \, d\bar{\nu}$ is the experimental extinction coefficient integrated over the width of the absorption band.[9] For a symmetrical band this equation may be approximated by

$$\tau^0 = \frac{3.5 \times 10^8}{\bar{\nu}_m{}^2 \epsilon_m \Delta \bar{\nu}_{1/2}} \tag{4-2}$$

where ϵ_m is the maximum extinction coefficient of the band, and $\Delta \bar{\nu}_{1/2}$ is the half-width of the band in reciprocal centimeters.

As an example, consider the 0-0 band for benzophenone absorption given in Fig. 4-3. The half-width of this band is about 1,000 cm^{-1}, ϵ_m is 65, and $\bar{\nu}_m$ is about 27,000 cm^{-1}. Equation 4-2 gives as the radiative lifetime the $S_1(n,\pi^*)$ state of benzophenone

$$\tau^0 \sim \frac{3.5 \times 10^8}{(27,000)^2 (65)(1,000)} = 7 \times 10^{-6} \text{ sec}$$

It is clear from Eq. 4-1 that while *"forbiddenness"* in absorption is manifested by a low extinction coefficient of the band corresponding to the transition, in emission, forbiddenness appears as a long radiative lifetime. This merely means that a state which is difficult to *populate* by direct absorption is equally difficult to *depopulate* by emission of radiation. However, if no radiationless paths for the deactivation of a forbidden excited state exist, it must eventually emit with a mean emission life of τ^0.

This is the basis of the long radiative lifetime of a triplet state. Thus, the absorption band corresponding to the $S_0 + h\nu \rightarrow T_1$ process is so weak that it is usually buried under the tail of the intense $S_0 + h\nu \rightarrow S_1$ absorption. Let us calculate the radiative lifetime of a triplet which possesses the same frequency position and half-width as benzophenone but with $\epsilon_m = 10^{-3}$. The mean lifetime for such a state from Eq. 4-2 (multiplied by the factor of three because of the threefold degeneracy of the triplet) [9] is

$$\tau^0 = \frac{(3)(3.5 \times 10^8)}{(27,000)^2(10^{-3})(1,000)} = 1.4 \times 10^{-2} \text{ sec}$$

These are the radiative lifetimes expected if only the 0-0 transitions were involved in absorption and emission. A more accurate estimate of the lifetime can be had by integrating over the entire electronic absorption band and including all vibrational transitions.[11–13]

Organic molecules which contain only light atoms possess extinction coefficients for singlet-triplet absorption [16, 17] comparable to that given in the above example, while singlet-singlet transitions usually have extinction coefficients at maximum absorption greater than 10. This result is of utmost importance for organic photochemistry since, if all factors are equal, the triplet will have a far greater probability of undergoing reaction than the corresponding singlet on the basis of its inherently longer radiative lifetime—i.e., T_1 persists for a longer time than S_1, before it *must* radiate (Eq. 4-1).

Experimental tests of a slightly modified form of Eq. 4-1 have been made and are given below in Tables 4-3 and 4-4. The results show that

Table 4-3   *Experimental and calculated lifetimes in seconds for singlet-singlet transitions* [11–15]

Compound	τ ($\times 10^9$) [a]	τ ($\times 10^9$) [b]
Rubrene	22.0	16.0
Anthracene	13.5	16.7
Perylene	5.1	5.6
9,10-Diphenylanthracene	8.9	8.8
9,10-Dichloroanthracene	11.0	15.4
Acridone	15.9	15.1
Quinine sulfate[c]	27	3.6
Fluorescein	4.7	5.0
9-Aminoacridine	15.6	15.3
Rhodamine B	6.0	6.0

[a] Calculated from singlet-singlet absorption spectrum.
[b] Measured experimentally from observed τ_f and ϕ_f.
[c] Acid-base reactions may cause this compound to be peculiar.

Table 4-4   *Experimental and calculated lifetimes in seconds for triplet-singlet transitions* [10, 16, 21]

Compounds	τ ($\times 10^3$) [a]	τ ($\times 10^3$) [b]
Anthracene	90.0	0.1
1,4-Dibromobenzene	1.5	0.3
1,3,5-Tribromobenzene	1.2	0.7
1,2,4,5-Tetrabromobenzene	0.6	0.5
Bromobenzene	3.0	1.0
Chlorobenzene	6.0	4.0
2-Bromonaphthalene	10.0	20.0
2-Iodonaphthalene	2.0	3.0

[a] Calculated from singlet-triplet absorption measurements.
[b] Measured experimentally from lifetime and quantum yield data.

Eq. 4-1 holds reasonably well for intense singlet-singlet transitions [11-15] but gives only order of magnitude agreement for singlet-triplet transitions,[10] perhaps because of difficulties in the accurate measurement of singlet-triplet absorption spectra.[10, 17]

Forbidden Transitions [6, 45]

Transitions between singlet and triplet states (*intercombinational transitions*) require a finite amount of *spin-orbital coupling* (Section 3-2) in order to "mix" the singlet and triplet states. Spin-orbital coupling is greatest if one of the electrons involved in the transition is in an orbital which is close to a heavy atom. Therefore, both an intramolecular and intermolecular heavy-atom effect on the probability of the singlet-triplet transitions are expected.[6]

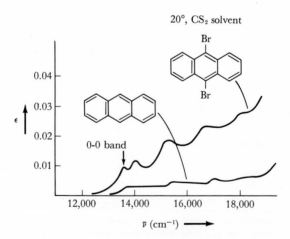

Fig. 4-4   *Singlet-triplet absorption spectra of anthracene and 9,10-dibromoanthracene.*[16]

The nature of the *intramolecular heavy-atom effect* may be seen from examination of Fig. 4-4 in which the singlet-triplet absorption spectra of anthracene and 9,10-dibromoanthracene are shown.[16] An example of the *intermolecular heavy-atom effect* is shown in Fig. 4-5 in which the absorption spectrum of 1-chloronaphthalene is shown in the pure liquid and in ethyl iodide solution.[16, 18] Although both of these substances are individually colorless, their binary solution is yellow. This is due to an enhancement of spin-orbital coupling induced by ethyl iodide in the halonaphthalene, which causes sufficient enhancement of the usually unmeasureable $S_0 + h\nu \rightarrow T_1$ transition (0-0 band about 20,500 cm^{-1}) to produce a yellow color. An analogous phenomenon operates in the *intramolecular* enhancement of the $S_0 + h\nu \rightarrow T_1$ process for 9,10-dibromoanthracene.[16] Several important criteria should be met in order to establish that the enhancement is in fact due to an increase in the probability of the $S_0 + h\nu \rightarrow T_1$ process[6]:

1. The position and shape (mirror-image relationship) of the presumed absorption spectrum should be compared to the phosphorescence spectrum, and there should be a near overlap of the 0-0 bands of the two spectra.

2. The intensity of the $S_0 + h\nu \rightarrow S_1$ transition should be relatively

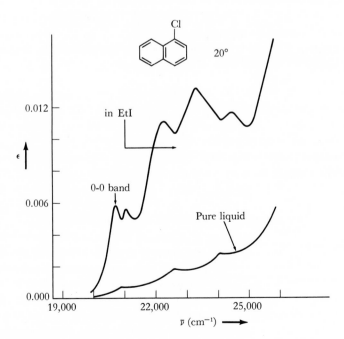

Fig. 4-5 *Absorption spectrum of 1-chloronaphthalene in ethyl iodide.*[16, 18]

unaffected by heavy-atom perturbation, while the $S_0 + h\nu \rightarrow T_1$ absorption should rise dramatically.

3. The possibility that the new absorption is due to impurities or complexation must be eliminated.

Certain *paramagnetic materials* are known to enhance spin-orbital coupling. Thus, measurement of the absorption spectra of a number of organic molecules under a high pressure of oxygen (a ground-state triplet and therefore a paramagnetic molecule) has been employed to enhance the $S_0 + h\nu \rightarrow T_1$ absorption of these compounds. Such spectra are called *oxygen-perturbation spectra*.[19] The success of this method may be evaluated by inspection of Table 4-5 where the energies of a number of

Table 4-5 *Comparison of triplet energies achieved by oxygen perturbation and phosphorescence* [19, 35]

Compound	$E_T{}^a$	$E_T{}^b$
Quinoline	63.0	62.4
Benzene	84.0	84.0
Fluorene	67.4	67.8
1-Bromonaphthalene	59.0	59.2
Anthracene	42.5	42.0

[a] Energy in kcal/mole measured from oxygen-perturbation experiments.
[b] Energy in kcal/mole measured from phosphorescence experiments.

0-0 bands (for $S_0 + h\nu \rightarrow T_1$ absorption) obtained by oxygen perturbation are compared with other methods of determining the energy required for this transition. Unfortunately, this method is not very convenient for routine determination of singlet-triplet absorption spectra, but it is useful for the measurement of triplet excitation energies of compounds for which no phosphorescence data are available.

4-2. MOLECULAR ELECTRONIC EMISSION SPECTRA

Electronic emission spectra have been of great assistance for the elucidation of the theory of electronically excited states—e.g., the concepts of singlet and triplet states,[20] the rates and mechanisms of excited-state interconversions, etc. The emission spectrum of a molecule may yield direct information concerning the energy, lifetime, and nature of S_1 and/or T_1. Since the latter states are the starting points for most photoreactions in condensed phases (solution or solid), investigation of an emission spectrum (or the observation that a molecule fails to emit light even under the most favorable conditions) allows certain conclusions to be made concerning the probable course of the photochemistry of the emitting (or nonluminescent) molecule.

Fluorescence and Phosphorescence [9, 20]

When the total luminescence spectrum of a complex organic molecule is measured (under ultraviolet excitation at low temperatures in a glass), two distinct emissions are often observed.[20]   One occurs at higher frequency (shorter wavelengths), is relatively short-lived and is called *fluorescence*, the reverse of normal singlet-singlet absorption process.   The second emission occurs at lower frequencies (longer wavelengths), is relatively long-lived, is the reverse of the strongly forbidden singlet-triplet absorption process, and is called *phosphorescence*.

The essential distinction between these two emissions was not clearly understood until the work of Lewis [21–23] and Terenin [24] who proposed that the triplet state was responsible for the long-lived emission.   Subsequently, this assignment has been confirmed by theoretical calculations,[25] the observation of singlet-triplet [16] and triplet-triplet [26, 66, 67] absorptions, heavy-atom effects,[5, 6, 16] and (most convincingly) by paramagnetic studies.[22, 23, 28, 38]

Empirical Rules [5, 45]

Exceedingly interesting conclusions concerning the fate of electronic excitation energy may be drawn from studies of the emission properties of molecules at low temperature in rigid media—i.e., under conditions such that bimolecular quenching and thermal collisional deactivation of electronically excited states is minimized.   Under such conditions the following generalizations may be made:

1. The rate of radiationless conversion from upper vibrational and electronic states to the $j = 0$ levels of S_1 or lowest triplet T_1 is so rapid, compared to the rate of light emission from these upper levels, that the $j = 0$ levels of S_1 and/or T_1 are generally the emitting levels (a few exceptions are known—e.g., azulene).

2. Radiative and radiationless intercombinational (triplet-singlet) transitions are 10^3 to 10^6 times less probable than corresponding singlet-singlet transitions.

3. Heavy atoms (and certain paramagnetic species) strongly increase the probability of intercombinational processes.

4. Even under optimum conditions radiationless processes are important and can compete with radiative processes for the deactivation of electronically excited molecules.

Fluorescence emission of moderate intensity is occasionally observed for certain organic molecules even at room temperature and in *fluid solution*. Phosphorescence is only rarely observed under these conditions, even though many organic molecules phosphoresce strongly at room temperature in a rigid glass. For example, triphenylene, in a boric acid glass at 25° C, phosphoresces with a mean lifetime [28, 59] of about 12 sec, whereas in an EPA† glass at 77° K its phosphorescent lifetime is about 16 sec; nevertheless, triphenylene is nonphosphorescent in fluid solution. An enormous amount of evidence is now available which indicates that for a given molecule *the triplet state is as highly populated in fluid solutions as it is in rigid glasses* (Section 5-4). The lack of phosphorescence in fluid solution merely reflects the rapid rate of *bimolecular diffusional quenching* of triplets by impurities (compared to the relatively slow rate of emission from the triplet).

Emission Lifetimes and Quantum Yields [5, 29, 35]

The mean intrinsic emission lifetime of S_1 and T_1 may be calculated indirectly from Eq. 4-1 on the basis of absorption data alone or may be measured directly. The unimolecular lifetime τ of an excited state may be defined in general as the time in seconds required for the concentration of molecules in the state to decay to $1/e$ of an initial value. The inherent radiative lifetime τ^0 of an excited state is the mean time it would take to deactivate the state *if no radiationless processes occurred*. The measured lifetime τ of an excited state is not in general equal to the true radiative lifetime τ^0 because of competing radiationless deactivations. If it is assumed (Section 5-3) that all radiationless deactivations of electronic energy occur from T_1 and not from S_1, then the following relationships hold [29]

$$\Phi_f \tau_f^0 = \tau_f \tag{4-3}$$

$$\tau_p \left(\frac{1 - \Phi_f}{\Phi_p} \right) = \tau_p^0 \tag{4-4}$$

where Φ, τ^0 and τ are the quantum yield, intrinsic emission lifetime, and measured lifetime, respectively, for fluorescence (f) and phosphorescence (p).

The effect of competing radiationless unimolecular steps on τ may be seen from the following discussion.[21] Suppose a radiationless process (internal conversion, intersystem crossing, chemical reaction, etc.) and emission are the sole processes available for the deactivation of an excited state A^*. Then,

$$A^* \xrightarrow{k_1} A_0 + h\nu \tag{4-5}$$

$$A^* \xrightarrow{k_2} A_0 + \text{heat} \tag{4-6}$$

† Ether-isopentane-alcohol.

so that

$$-\frac{d[A^*]}{dt} = (k_1 + k_2)[A^*] \qquad (4\text{-}7)$$

or

$$[A^*] = \exp - (k_1 + k_2)t \qquad (4\text{-}8)$$

where $[A^*]$ is the concentration of the excited state at time t. The relative concentrations of A^* at time $t = 0$ and a later time t are given by

$$\ln \frac{[A^*]_t}{[A^*]_{t=0}} = -(k_1 + k_2)t \qquad (4\text{-}9)$$

so that the mean lifetime τ of A^* is

$$\ln \frac{1}{e} = -(k_1 + k_2)\tau \qquad (4\text{-}10)$$

or

$$\tau = \frac{1}{(k_1 + k_2)} \qquad (4\text{-}11)$$

which simply states that the measured unimolecular radiative lifetime is given by the reciprocal of the sum of the unimolecular rate constants for the deactivation processes. In general we have

$$\tau = \frac{1}{\sum_i k_i} \qquad (4\text{-}12)$$

where τ is the measured radiative lifetime, and the rate constants (k_i) represent unimolecular or pseudo-unimolecular processes which deactivate A^*.

Typical Emission Spectra [5, 30, 33]

Emission generally results from a radiative transition from the $j = 0$ vibrational level of S_1 or T_1 to the ground-state vibrational levels. An emission spectrum is usually presented as a plot of the *relative* intensity (relative number of photons emitted per unit frequency or wavelength) of the vibrational bands against frequency or wavelength. The total emission spectra [30] of naphthalene and benzophenone are shown in Figs. 4-6 and 4-7, respectively. These spectra were taken at 77° K in a solvent of ether-isopentane-ethanol (EPA) and are independent of the wavelength of exciting radiation.[31]

It is frequently noted that the fluorescence spectrum is related to the lowest frequency absorption band in that it occurs at lower frequencies and its vibrational structure bears a "mirror-image" relationship.[34] Since the lowest frequency absorption band is a result of transition from the

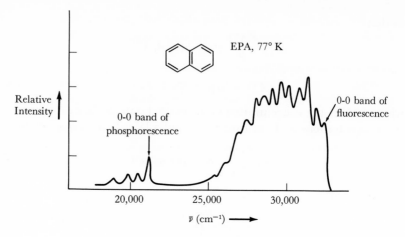

Fig. 4-6   *Total-emission spectrum of naphthalene* [10] *at 77° K.*

$j = 0$ vibrational level of S_0 to the various vibrational levels of S_1 while the fluorescence spectrum is the result of transitions from S_1 ($j = 0$) to the various vibrational levels of S_0, the mirror-image correspondence holds only if the vibrational spacings in both states are related to one another. At any rate, the 0-0 band for both the fluorescence and absorption should nearly coincide, since the same two vibrational levels are involved in both transitions (see Fig. 4-1).   A slight separation in the two bands is expected

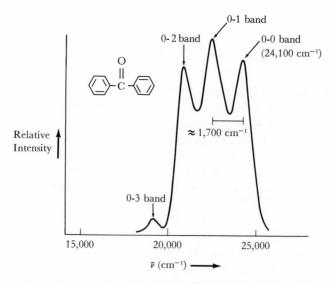

Fig. 4-7   *Total-emission spectrum of benzophenone* [10] *at 77° K.*

if the equilibrated S_1 state is solvated differently from the Franck-Condon S_1 state which is reached immediately after absorption.[13, 34]

Spin-Orbital Coupling and Emission [6, 20, 45]

External and internal perturbations are known to increase the amount of spin-orbital coupling in organic molecules.[6] The external or inter-molecular effects result when a heavy atom or paramagnetic atom on one molecule interacts with the electronic structure of a second molecule and enhances the probability of intercombinational processes.[35] The internal spin-orbital effect is observed when the heavy atom is chemically affixed to the molecular framework whose intercombinational transitions it perturbs.[16]

In emission three intercombinational processes should be influenced by spin-orbital coupling perturbations:

$$S_1 \overset{k_{ST}}{\rightsquigarrow} T_1$$

$$T_1 \overset{k_t}{\rightsquigarrow} S_0$$

$$T_1 \overset{k_p}{\longrightarrow} S_0 + h\nu$$

We therefore expect, in the presence of enhanced spin-orbital coupling,

1. a greater population of T_1 due to a larger k_{ST}
2. a greater yield of phosphorescence relative to fluorescence
3. a shorter phosphorescence lifetime.

The effect of spin-orbital coupling on the intrinsic fluorescence lifetime, however, should be negligible.

The halonaphthalenes[36] and benzene derivatives[35] of group IV and V elements nicely fulfill these predictions for an internal heavy-atom effect,

Table 4-6   *Phosphorescence lifetimes in seconds of naphthalene and its 1-halo derivatives in heavy-atom solvents* [36, 45]

Emitter	EPA [a]	PrCl [b]	PrBr [c]	PrI [d]
Naphthalene	2.5	0.52	0.14	0.076
1-Fluoronaphthalene	1.4	0.17	0.10	0.029
1-Chloronaphthalene	0.23	0.075	0.06	0.023
1-Bromonaphthalene	0.014	0.0073	0.007	0.006
1-Iodonaphthalene	0.0023	0.001	0.001	0.001

[a] EPA is a mixture of ethanol, isopentane, and ether.
[b] Propyl chloride.
[c] Propyl bromide.
[d] Propyl iodide.

MOLECULAR PHOTOCHEMISTRY

as shown by the data in Tables 4-6 and 4-7. The nature of the external heavy-atom effect on naphthalene [40] is shown by the data in Table 4-8. The ratio ϕ_p/ϕ_f steadily increases, although the total emission yield is constant, as the heavy-atom population increases either internally or externally. At the same time τ_p decreases regularly. The results indicate that the rate constants k_{ST} and k_p are influenced the most by spin-orbital coupling.[40–43]

Table 4-7 *Effects of heavy-atom substituents on spectra of benzene derivatives* [35]

Compound	τ_p (sec)	E_{S_1} [a]	E_T [b]
$(C_6H_5)_3CH$	5.4	110	81.5
$(C_6H_5)_4Si$	1.2	110	81.0
$(C_6H_5)_4Sn$	3×10^{-3}	110	81.5
$(C_6H_5)_3N$	4×10^{-1}	94	73.0
$(C_6H_5)_3P$	1.4×10^{-2}	110	72.0
$(C_6H_5)_3As$	1.6×10^{-3}	115	73.0

[a] Energy of lowest singlet-singlet transition in kcal/mole.
[b] Energy of lowest triplet-singlet transition in kcal/mole.

Table 4-8 *Variation of ϕ_p, ϕ_f, and τ_p in heavy-atom solvents for naphthalene* [36, 45]

Solvent	ϕ_f	ϕ_p	τ_p [a]
EPA	0.55	0.05	1.0
Propyl chloride	0.44	0.08	0.9
Propyl bromide	0.13	0.24	0.7
Propyl iodide	0.03	0.35	0.3

[a] Lifetimes are relative to naphthalene in EPA ($\tau_p = 2.3$ sec).

A rather striking demonstration that intermolecular spin-orbital coupling is derived from physical polarizability and field effects rather than chemical reaction was found in a study of the lifetime of the benzene triplet in rare gas solvents.[37] The results of this study are given in Table 4-9.

The nature of the orbitals involved in electronic transitions greatly influences the amount of spin-orbital coupling in a molecule which does not possess heavy atoms.[25] For example, most carbonyl compounds undergo intercombinational transitions at rates 10 to 10^4 times faster than analogous unsaturated hydrocarbons. The true radiative lifetime of benzophenone phosphorescence is about 10^{-2} sec, while for benzene it is about 28 sec.   The intersystem crossing process $S_1 \rightsquigarrow T_1$ completely dominates fluorescence from carbonyl compounds.   These facts are explained by reference to Eq. 3-23.

The energy difference between S_1 and T_1 is about 6 kcal/mole for benzophenone and about 30 kcal/mole for benzene.   The smaller energy gap favors intersystem crossing in benzophenone.   Furthermore, S_1 for benzene is π,π^*, so that in a good approximation neither orbital involved in the transition has significant probability at the nucleus of the carbon atoms where spin-orbital interaction is greatest.   The n orbital in benzophenone, in addition to being located on the heavier oxygen atom, has more s character (when higher approximations are made) than π orbitals —i.e., it spends more time near the nucleus, where terms which determine

Table 4-9   *Phosphorescence lifetimes of benzene in various solvents at 4.2° K* [37, 57]

Solvent	C_6H_6		C_6D_6
	τ_p (sec)	ϕ_p/ϕ_f	τ_p (sec)
Methane	16.0	1	22.0
Argon	16.0	20	26.0
Krypton	1.0	∞	1.0
Xenon	0.07	∞	0.07
EPA	7.0 [a]	1	28.0 [a]

[a] From the data of Reference 57 at 77° K.

the magnitude of the mixing coefficient λ are large.   Finally, transition to $S_1(n,\pi^*)$ for benzophenone is forbidden somewhat by symmetry and over- lap which make $\tau_f{}^0$ sufficiently long so that intersystem crossing will deplete S_1 before fluorescence can occur.

The nature of the lowest singlet state is a factor in determining the rate constant for the radiationless $S_1 \rightsquigarrow T_1$ process (see Section 4-3). For example, in quinoline the $^1(n,\pi^*)$ and $^1(\pi,\pi^*)$ states lie so close to one another in energy that their relative energetic dispositions may be inverted by change of solvent [30] (recall that $^1(n,\pi^*)$ states undergo blue shifts with increasing solvent polarity, while $^1(\pi,\pi^*)$ states undergo red shifts as the solvent becomes more polar).   In hydroxylic solvents the $^1(\pi,\pi^*)$ state is lower in energy and the yields of fluorescence and phos- phorescence are comparable ($\phi_p/\phi_f = 2$).   In hydrocarbon solvents, in which the $^1(n,\pi^*)$ state is lower, ϕ_p/ϕ_f is greater than 100 (the total emis- sion yields are comparable in both solvents).   Thus, we may conclude that k_{ST} increases by about two orders of magnitude (in the same mole- cule) when the lowest singlet is switched from π,π^* to n,π^*.

The effectiveness of n,π^* states in facilitating the intersystem crossing process appears to be related to the factors discussed above and also results from the greater coulombic potential of oxygen (which perturbs the π system more) over carbon. The n electrons also sense solvent perturbations more than the π electrons and then transmit these perturbations to the π system. Recent quantum mechanical calculations, however, indicate that the neglect of σ interactions may lead to erroneous conclusions. These calculations indicate that the n and σ orbitals are not as localized as was formerly thought.[40]

The Effect of Charge-Transfer Complexing on Intersystem Crossing [40−43]

When aromatic hydrocarbons bound in strong donor-acceptor complexes are excited by absorption in the charge-transfer band, (a transition which involves nearly complete transfer of charge between loosely bonded separate molecules), two emissions may result: one from the triplet level of the uncomplexed aromatic and one from the reverse of charge-transfer absorption. These processes are possible if the aromatic (donor) component of the complex possesses a triplet level which is energetically below the S_1 charge-transfer state of the complex and if the $S_0 \rightarrow S_1(CT)$ absorption is followed by intersystem crossing and a dissociation process which populates the triplet level of the aromatic hydrocarbon portion of the complex, i.e.,

$$(D \cdots A)_0 \xrightarrow{h\nu} {}^1(D \cdots A) \rightsquigarrow {}^3(D \cdots A) \rightsquigarrow {}^3D + A_0$$

where D is the donor aromatic compound, and A is the acceptor (e.g., trinitrofluorene).

The over-all process is a "sensitized" phosphorescence, which results from presumed transfer of energy between the triplet level of the complex and the lowest triplet level of the emitter. The process is important because the relative yield of phosphorescence of the donor under these conditions may be considerably higher than that for the uncomplexed material.

For example, an increase of the ratio ϕ_p/ϕ_f and a decrease of the phosphorescence lifetime τ_p of naphthalene occurs when the naphthalene is codissolved with *sym*-trinitrobenzene (TNB) in a rigid solution at 77° K (see Table 4-10). A number of other compounds have been shown to exhibit a decrease in τ_p when the acceptor partner of the complex has no heavy atoms, and a further decrease in τ_p occurs when heavy atoms are attached to the acceptor. This means that the charge-transfer complexing inherently causes a decrease in τ_p of the donor and may allow a heavy atom effect, due to the close contact of the donor-acceptor pair, to reduce τ_p further.

Table 4-10   *Relative ϕ_p/ϕ_f for various naphthalene-acceptor pairs* [40]

Acceptor	ϕ_p/ϕ_f
None	0.05
sym-Trinitrobenzene (TNB)	0.17
tetra-Chlorophthalic anhydride (TCPA)	0.50
tetra-Bromophthalic anhydride (TBPA)	0.64
tetra-Iodophthalic anhydride (TIPA)	1.32

The increase in the rate of radiationless singlet-triplet transitions may be considered to be a result of an enhancement of molecular environmental coupling in the complex relative to the uncomplexed material and an associated increase in the ease of energy dissipation—i.e., the stronger the coupling of the excited molecule with its environment, the faster the rate of radiationless processes, which require the dissipation of energy by thermal transfer of energy to the surroundings. Also, complexing will in general deform the MO's and mix σ and π orbitals, thereby providing more s character (as a result of σ mixing) and a greater amount of spin-orbital coupling.

There are several mechanisms which might account for the relative increase in ϕ_p/ϕ_f which occurs with different heavy-atom acceptors (see Table 4-10):

1. an increase in the probability of the $S_1 \leadsto T_D$ process;
2. an increase in the probability of the $S_1 \leadsto {}^3CT$ process;
3. an increase in the probability of the $T \to S_0 + h\nu$ process.

The major effect of complexing appears to be an increase in the rate of intersystem crossing, mechanism 1.

Azulene's Anomalous Fluorescence [44-47]

The blue hydrocarbon, azulene, and its simple derivatives are the sole confirmed examples of molecules which violate the general rule [5, 31] that the emitting level of a molecule is the lowest level of a given multiplicity—i.e., either S_1 of T_1. Azulene, 1, and its simple alkyl derivatives,

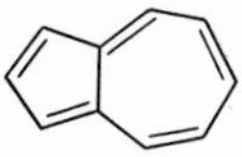

1

which were obtained from widely differing sources, all showed the same phenomena of unique emission from $S_2 \to S_0$. No phosphorescence was detected for any of these compounds. This may be due to the fact that such emission might have occurred in the infrared and would have been

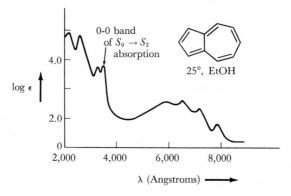

Fig. 4-8   *Absorption spectrum of azulene.*[44, 45]

missed by the experimenters, whose equipment could not detect emission in regions below 10,000 cm^{-1}.   Azulene's absorption and emission spectra are given in Figs. 4-8 and 4-9.

All of the reasons for azulene's anomalous behavior are probably not known, but some features of its absorption spectrum indicate one of the important factors is the large splitting between S_2 and S_1 (about 40 kcal mole^{-1}, cf. naphthalene where $\Delta E_{S_2-S_1}$ is about 10 kcal mole^{-1}).

Since there is a much wider spacing between the zero-point vibrational levels of the first two excited states of azulene compared to the analogous spacing in naphthalene, it is not completely surprising that

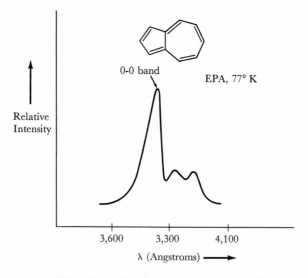

Fig. 4-9   *Emission spectrum of azulene.*[44, 45]

internal conversion from $S_2 \rightsquigarrow S_1$ fails to compete with emission from the S_2. However, it should be pointed out that such large separations (40 kcal/mole) also occur in numerous other molecules, which possess "normal" emissive properties. It is therefore of great importance for the unambiguous interpretation of the azulene emission spectrum that the positions of the *triplet levels* be ascertained since, if a triplet level lay close to the S_2 state, $S_2 \rightsquigarrow T_2$ may be very fast compared to $S_2 \rightsquigarrow S_1$, and this would be an alternative explanation of the lack of S_1 emission. Triplet-triplet absorption studies would clarify this point, but to date all attempts to observe azulene [48] triplets by direct methods—i.e., phosphorescence or flash photolysis, have failed. Interestingly, deuteration *enhances* the yield of fluorescence of azulene-d_8 (see Section 4-3).

Indirect evidence, however, has been obtained which leads to an estimation of an upper limit for the energy of the lowest triplet level of azulene,[48] and recent experiments show hope of "sandwiching" in the value by energy-transfer methods (see Chapter 5). The latter technique has been useful for the location of triplet levels which are not accessible by direct methods. Transfer of energy of the type

$$D(\text{triplet}) + A_0(\text{singlet}) \rightarrow A(\text{triplet}) + D_0(\text{singlet})$$

is very efficient if the energy gap between the donor and acceptor levels is more than a few calories, the donor level being higher (see Chapter 5). The rate of energy transfer is *diffusion controlled* (i.e., transfer occurs on every encounter of donor and acceptor) under these conditions, whereas no transfer (or at best a very slow rate of transfer) is observed when the triplet level of the acceptor is greater than that of the donor.

When anthracene triplets [48] are used as a donor and azulene as an acceptor the rate constant for the transfer was found to be 1.3×10^{10} M^{-1} sec^{-1}—i.e., diffusion controlled. Therefore, it can be assumed that the triplet of azulene lies below that of anthracene which is located 42 kcal/mole above its ground state. Preliminary experiments [49] indicate that naphthacene ($E_T = 29$ kcal/mole) *does not* transfer excitation to azulene. This leads to a bracketing of azulene's lowest triplet between 42 and 29 kcal/mole.

A sole possible exception to the rule that only the lowest triplet state emits has been found and deserves further study.[50] The molecule investigated was ferrocene, for which no emission was observed upon excitation into the lowest energy absorption band, but emission did occur upon excitation into the next higher energy band. The luminescence is long lived (2 sec) and was therefore assumed to be phosphorescence. No nickelocene emission of any type was detected.*

No emission is obtained by excitation of ferrocene at 4,400 Å, so that

* See, however, Note Added in Proof, p. 72.

perhaps S_1 and S_0 cross, and deactivation to S_0 competes favorably with emission. Otherwise, the $S_2 \leadsto S_1$ and $S_1 \leadsto T_1$ transitions must be very slow compared to the $S_2 \leadsto T_2$ transition. One other possibility is that $T_2 \rightarrow S_0 + h\nu$ occurs, while $T_1 \rightarrow S_0 + h\nu$ does not, analogous to the conversion of singlet states in azulene. More molecules which emit from upper excited states will probably be uncovered if careful searches for such emissions are made.

Summary

The "forbiddenness" or "allowedness" of electronic transition is determined by selection rules, which are only approximations. Experimental evidence determines the rigorousness of selection rules by the measurement of extinction coefficients or lifetimes. The most intense transitions are those that are completely allowed and possess maximum extinction coefficients of the order of 10^5 and radiative lifetimes of the order of 10^{-9} sec. The degree of forbiddenness may be estimated by the factor which separates a measured ϵ or τ^0 from these upper limits. Table

Table 4-11   *Experimental manifestation of selection rules*

Rule	Prohibition factor	Example	ϵ
Spin	10^{-6}	$S_0 \underset{}{\overset{h\nu}{\rightleftarrows}} T_1$	$\sim 10^{-2}$
Space	10^{-2} to 10^{-3}	$n \rightarrow \pi^*$	10^3 to 10^2
Symmetry	10^{-1} to 10^{-3}	$n \rightarrow \pi^*$	10^2 to 10^4

4-11 lists the three main types of selection rules which are important for organic molecules. The approximate prohibition factor and an example are also given.

4-3. RADIATIONLESS TRANSITIONS [5, 6]

In the absence of irreversible photochemical reactions, internal conversion from S_1 to S_0 and intersystem crossing from T_1 to S_0 are the main processes which cause the total emission yield to be less than unity. Furthermore, the intersystem crossing process $S_1 \leadsto T_1$ is required for the population of triplets. An understanding of radiationless processes and a method of estimating their importance is a prerequisite for a detailed interpretation of photochemical reactions.

Internal Conversion and Intersystem Crossing [5]

The rate of *internal conversion* among excited singlet states (S_2, S_3, S_4, etc.) to S_1 is known to be of the order of 10^{11} to 10^{13} because this process dominates fast fluorescence from upper electronic levels. *Presumably,* excited triplets cascade to T_1 at a similar rate; however, there is relatively little evidence to demand this conclusion. On the other hand, the internal conversion $S_1 \rightsquigarrow S_0$ and the intersystem crossing $T_1 \rightsquigarrow S_0$ are relatively slow. The high density of excited states above S_1 results in frequent crossings or near crossings of excited-state potential surfaces and thus enhances the rate of internal conversion. The large energy gap between S_0 and S_1 or T_1 is responsible in part for the slower rate of the $S_1 \rightsquigarrow S_0$ and $T_1 \rightsquigarrow S_0$ transitions.

The intersystem crossing process $S_1 \rightsquigarrow T_1$, however, is between two excited states of similar energy and would occur at a rate similar to internal conversion among excited singlets *except for spin prohibitions.* Spin selection rules slow down this process by a factor of 10^2 to 10^6, which means the rate for the $S_1 \rightsquigarrow T_1$ process will be 10^{11} to 10^7—i.e., often fast enough to compete with fluorescence for deactivation of S_1.

Theory of Radiationless Transitions [5, 6, 51–56]

The potential-energy curves described in Chapter 3 can be used to gain some theoretical insight into the nature of radiationless transitions. In Fig. 4-10 typical dispositions of the potential-energy curves of S_1, T_1,

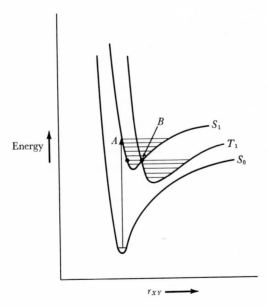

Fig 4-10 *Franck-Condon principle and radiationless conversions: intersystem crossing. In principle, the potential-energy curves of states of the same symmetry do not "cross," but interact strongly in the "crossing" region to produce two states whose energetic separation depends on the magnitude of interaction.*

and S_0 are shown for a diatomic molecule. Absorption of a photon to populate an upper electronic level will be followed by a rapid cascade of energy until a vibrational level of S_1 is reached at point A in the figure. (The same level may be reached by direct absorption.) Rapid vibrational relaxation to the $j = 0$ vibrational level of S_1 follows, and the excitation pauses here momentarily. The potential-energy curves of S_1 and T_1 intersect at point B. In the presence of spin-orbital coupling the molecule will spend part of the time in S_1 $(j = 0)$ and another part of the time in the isoenergetic $j = 3$ vibrational level of T_1, setting up an equilibrium between molecules in S_1 and T_1. In the figure, the equilibrium separation for T_1 is greater than for S_1. This is neither necessary nor general, but simply for convenience in the drawing.

Since the vibrational internal conversion T_1 $(j = 3)$ ⤳ T_1 $(j = 0)$ is extremely rapid, if the energy gap between the $j = 0$ levels of S_1 and T_1 is large, then the molecule will be "stuck" in the forbidden triplet as thermal energy is insufficient to pop it back into S_1. Point B, it should be noted, is simultaneously a turning point of a vibration for S_1 and T_1 so that the nuclear configuration, potential energies, and kinetic energies of the two states are identical, and the vibration has paused momentarily (kinetic energy at the turning points of vibration is zero). All that is needed for the energy to continue cascading to T_1 $(j = 0)$ is a relaxation of spin restriction.

Similar arguments applied to upper electronic levels explain the rapid rate of internal conversion among excited states because many crossing points such as B exist, and, furthermore, spin restrictions do not prohibit such transitions. For polyatomic molecules similar arguments hold, but in this case polydimensional energy surfaces rather than two-dimensional potential curves are required to describe the molecule.[52] The simple two-dimensional diagrams will suffice for the purposes of our discussion. In addition, they are far easier to draw.

One might ask at this point why emission of infra-red radiation is not found to be a significant path for transitions between the rotational and vibrational levels. Experimentally, infra-red emission (loss of a few quanta at a time) does not compete with radiationless deactivation, but ultraviolet and visible emission do. This result follows theoretically from the relationship [32, 53]

$$A_{21} = \frac{64\pi^4}{3h} \bar{\nu}^3 |R_{21}|^2 \tag{3-9}$$

where $\bar{\nu}$ is the wave number of the photon which is emitted upon passing from state 2 to state 1, R_{21} is the electric dipole matrix element for the transition and A_{21} is the probability coefficient for spontaneous emission.

Since $\bar{\nu}$ is usually 1,000 to 3,000 cm^{-1} for infra-red transitions, while $\bar{\nu} \sim 30,000$ cm^{-1} for ultraviolet transitions, the $\bar{\nu}^3$ term in Eq. 3-9 places a prohibition factor of about 10^{-3} or greater on the relative rate of infra-red emission compared to ultraviolet-visible emission. Furthermore, the dipole-moment changes involved in pure vibrational transitions are usually small compared to those which occur upon passing from one electronic state to another. This factor may apply another order of magnitude prohibition on the rate of infra-red emission.

Franck-Condon Principle and Radiationless Transitions [53, 55–58]

The semiclassical and quantum mechanical formulations of the Franck-Condon principle both correctly predict the relative rates of radiationless conversions from one electronic state to another. Figure 4-11 depicts a typical disposition of the S_0 and S_1 states of a diatomic molecule. If a radiationless transition from S_1 to S_0 is to occur during the vibrational motion between points A and B, then an amount of electronic energy between that corresponding to AC or BD would have to be instantaneously converted into kinetic energy, or the internuclear separation would have to alter suddenly to some value between AE and BE. Both processes are unlikely according to the Franck-Condon principle which prohibits

1. the conversion of large amounts of electronic energy into kinetic energy of the nuclei (vibrations);
2. a large change in nuclear position during an electronic transition (therefore, radiationless conversion from an excited state to S_0 is expected to be slow).

Figure 4-11 also depicts two excited states S_2 and S_1 whose potential curves intersect at point F. As discussed above for the $S_1 \rightsquigarrow T_1$ conversion, a transition from S_2 to S_1 can occur without an appreciable alteration of position or momentum of the nuclei, if the transition occurs at crossing points such as F.

Since the intrastate loss of vibrational energy is so rapid, most molecules will undergo radiationless conversion to S_0 from the lowest (temperature equilibrated) vibrational level. For efficient radiationless conversion from one state to another, many crossings should occur near the zero-point levels of the higher electronic states to some upper level of the lower electronic states. Thus, the potential-energy curve of any excited electronic state must be crossed radiationlessly to that of a lower state within the region described by the upper state in its zero-point level. Internal conversion and intersystem crossing can therefore be visualized as occurring at a rate which depends on the shortest distance between the zero-point region of the upper state and the isoenergetic section of the lower state. Internal conversion between two such states is expected to be very rapid when they are disposed in the manner of S_2 and S_1 in Fig. 4-11.

Let us consider how quantum mechanics seeks to estimate the probability of radiationless transitions. For example, there is some perturbation operator $\mathbf{P}$ such that the probability of the radiationless transition from S_1 to S_0 is given by

$$P = |\int \Psi_{S_1} \mathbf{P} \Psi_{S_0} \, d\tau|^2 \qquad (4\text{-}13)$$

where Ψ_{S_1} and Ψ_{S_0} are the wave functions for S_1 and S_0, respectively. A factor which depends only on the vibrational motion of the nuclei

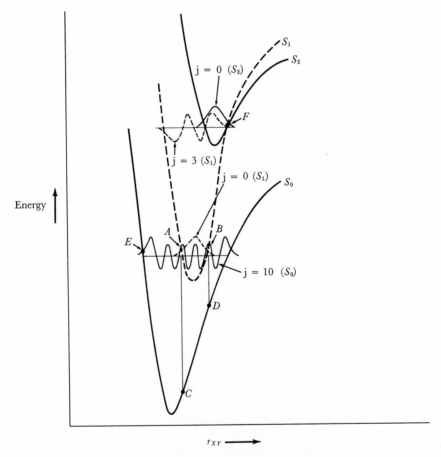

Fig. 4-11   *Radiationless transitions and the Franck-Condon principle: internal conversion.*

may be split out of each Ψ (see Section 3-2), so that

$$P = |\int \phi_{S_1} \mathbf{P} \phi_{S_0} \, d\tau \int \chi_{S_1} \chi_{S_0} \, d\tau_v|^2 \qquad (4\text{-}14)$$

where ϕ_{S_1} and ϕ_{S_0} are the electronic portions of the total wave functions for S_1 and S_0, and χ_{S_1} and χ_{S_0} are the vibrational eigenfunctions for these two states. From Fig. 4-11, it can be seen that the vibrational eigenfunctions for χ_{S_0} (a high-energy vibrational level of S_0) oscillates from negative to positive values rapidly in the region where χ_{S_1} (assumed to be in the $j = 0$ state) is always positive, so that the integral $\int \chi_{S_1} \chi_{S_0} \, d\tau_v$ is very small and the $S_1 \rightsquigarrow S_0$ probability is low. In Fig. 4-11, on the other hand, in the region of interaction about point F, χ_{S_1} and χ_{S_2} (assumed to be in the $j = 0$ state) are so situated that $\int \chi_{S_2} \chi_{S_1} \, d\tau_v$ has a considerable value. The $S_2 \rightsquigarrow S_1$ transition is therefore more probable than the $S_1 \rightsquigarrow S_0$ transition, if the electronic part of the molecular wave functions for the two transitions are comparable.

It has been long known that many organic compounds which possess rigid cyclic structures and/or long conjugated systems of π electrons tend to fluoresce strongly. We may now rationalize this result theoretically from the standpoint of the Franck-Condon principle for radiationless transitions. The Franck-Condon principle tells us that for rigid structures the conversions $S_1 \rightsquigarrow S_0$ and $T_1 \rightsquigarrow S_0$ will be difficult because of the restraints placed on the molecule tending to hold the nuclei together. From Eq. 4-1 we see that if a long conjugated system tends to have intense transitions to S_1, it will also tend to have a *short* fluorescence lifetime. Rigidity will in general inhibit radiationless processes relative to radiative processes, all other factors being equal.

In aromatic hydrocarbons, for example, all other factors *are not equal* if the molecules possess a high degree of symmetry. In these cases, the absorption to S_1 is often forbidden by symmetry which leads to a low extinction coefficient for absorption and, correspondingly, a relatively long fluorescence lifetime. As a result, conversion to the triplet competes favorably with fluorescence.

An example of the operation of Franck-Condon factors in radiationless transitions [55–59] is the difference in the radiative lifetimes of perprotiated and deuterated aromatic hydrocarbons, as shown in Table 4-12. The limits to the radiative lifetimes of benzene [57] and naphthalene [55–59, 37–39] given by Eq. 4-4 are about 28 and 20 sec, respectively. The radiative lifetime of the deuterated hydrocarbons nearly equals the maximum radiative lifetime—i.e., in the deuterated materials nearly every triplet emits, whereas only a fraction of the perprotio-benzene triplets emit. This striking result derives from Franck-Condon factors. [58] The triplet states of both perprotio- and perdeutero-benzene lie at 85 kcal above S_0. This corresponds to about ten vibrational quanta for C-H vibrations.

The lower amplitude of the C-D vibrations requires a much larger number of vibrational quanta to equal 85 kcal. Therefore, a higher j level is reached when the deuterated material converts from T_1 to S_0, and intersystem crossing from T_1 to S_0 is inhibited.

An empirical relationship between the rate constants of radiationless conversions from S_1 and T_1 to S_0 with a parameter extracted from spectroscopic data has been proposed.[58] This relationship supposes that the rates of radiationless transitions are determined by the width of the barrier to be "tunnelled" through in going from the zero-point motion region of

Table 4-12　　*Variation of phosphorescence lifetime with E_T and deuteration* [55-59]

Compound	E_T [a]	τ_p [b]
Benzene	85	7.0
Benzene-d_6	—	26.0
Triphenylene	67	16.0
Triphenylene-d_{12}	—	23.0
Biphenyl	65	3.1
Biphenyl-d_{10}	—	11.3
Phenanthrene	62	3.3
Phenanthrene-d_{10}	—	16.4
Naphthalene	60	2.3
Naphthalene-d_8	—	22.0
Pyrene	48	0.2
Pyrene-d_{10}	—	3.2
Anthracene	42	0.06
Anthracene-d_{10}	—	0.10

[a] Energy of the lowest triplet state in kcal/mole. The E_T values of the deuterated compounds differ by about 1 kcal/mole from the perprotio-compounds.
[b] Phosphorescence lifetime in seconds.

the upper state to the upper vibrational levels of the lower state. Thus, deuteration is pictured as inhibiting tunnelling through large barriers and therefore slowing down the rate of internal conversion from S_1 or T_1 to S_0. On the other hand, no significant deuterium effect on these rates is expected if the energy gap between the initial and final states is small (e.g., the $S_1 \rightsquigarrow T_1$ process). This prediction is also made by consideration of Franck-Condon effects and has been verified for phenanthrene, naphthalene, and triphenylene.[29]

Note that these theories do not consider the possibility that reversible photochemical reactions may be significant deactivation paths in certain cases.

Influence of Environment [58–61]

In condensed phases the environment provides a thermal reservoir with which an excited solute may interact by collisions. Excited molecules in the vapor phase are known to lose their excess energy in the following order: rotational $\gg$ vibrational $>$ electronic. The same order is preserved in solution, which may be approximated as a gas at infinite pressure—i.e., a constant state of collision exists between the excited molecule and the environment. However, in liquids the notion of a collision must be replaced by that of an encounter which is a "sticky" collision in the sense that on each encounter molecules suffer a number of collisions before they diffuse apart.

In quantum mechanical terms the environment may be considered to provide many energy levels for which many near-resonance conditions with the excited solute may occur. The environment also may serve as a perturbation which couples with the electronic system of the solute and into which energy in the form of heat may flow. This perturbation can also "mix" states in the solute, as occurs in the external heavy atom effect, or may make new intersections of potential-energy surfaces of the solute possible.[60]

Radiationless conversions are difficult to treat quantitatively from the standpoint of quantum mechanics. Robinson and Frosch [55–58] have pointed out the dominating factors for the rates of transitions which are slow compared to vibrational relaxation—i.e., the $S_1 \rightsquigarrow S_0$ and $T_1 \rightsquigarrow S_0$ processes. A major result of their treatment is the relationship

$$P_r = k \left(\frac{\beta^2}{\alpha}\right) \sum_n (\chi_n|\chi_0)^2 \qquad (4\text{-}15)$$

where P_r is the probability of a radiationless conversion between two given states, β is a measure of the intramolecular interaction between an initial state and all available final states, α (which is related to the density of states available to the system) is a measure of the solvent interaction which connects the two states undergoing transition in the solute, and $\sum_n (\chi_n|\chi_0)^2$ is the Franck-Condon term connecting the vibrational eigenfunction χ_0 ($j = 0$) of the initial state to the vibrational eigenfunctions of all of the final states χ_n. This result is in complete accord with our earlier picture of the influence of Franck-Condon factors on the rates of radiationless processes because, as the energy gap between the initial ($j = 0$) and final states increases, higher vibrational numbers of the lower state are required at the point of transition, and the vibrational overlap integral becomes smaller.

Symmetry Considerations [53]

Symmetry considerations indicate that in general the $S_1 \rightsquigarrow T_1$ process should be more rapid than the $T_1 \rightsquigarrow S_0$ or $S_1 \rightsquigarrow S_0$ processes. For centrally symmetric aromatic molecules the ground-state wave function is symmetrical (also called gerade g), whereas S_1 and T_1 are usually antisymmetrical (also called ungerade u). The nature of the operator, $\mathbf{P}$ (which is symmetrical) in Eq. 4-14 is such that the following selection rules for nonradiative transitions exist

$$
\begin{array}{ll}
\begin{aligned} u &\longleftrightarrow u \\ g &\longleftrightarrow g \end{aligned} & \quad S_1 \rightsquigarrow T_1 \quad \text{allowed} \\[2em]
u \longleftrightarrow g & \quad \begin{aligned} S_1 &\rightsquigarrow S_0 \\ T_1 &\rightsquigarrow S_0 \end{aligned} \quad \text{forbidden}
\end{array}
$$

El-Sayed [54] has shown that (in the first-order approximation) for nitrogen heterocycles no spin-orbital coupling occurs between the singlet and triplet states *of the same* electronic configuration. This result predicts that spin-orbital coupling between $^3(n,\pi)$ and $^1(n,\pi)$ states will be about 100 to 1,000 times less than that between $^{1\text{ or }3}(\pi,\pi^*)$ and $^{1\text{ or }3}(n,\pi^*)$ states. In other words the following rule for radiationless processes prevails for the nitrogen heterocycles:

$$
\begin{array}{ll}
\begin{aligned} ^1(n,\pi^*) &\longleftrightarrow ^3(\pi,\pi^*) \\ ^1(\pi,\pi^*) &\longleftrightarrow ^3(n,\pi^*) \end{aligned} & \quad \text{allowed} \\[2em]
\begin{aligned} ^1(n,\pi^*) &\longleftrightarrow ^3(n,\pi^*) \\ ^1(\pi,\pi^*) &\longleftrightarrow ^3(\pi,\pi^*) \end{aligned} & \quad \text{forbidden}
\end{array}
$$

These results may be of limited application, but are of fundamental interest and further calculations are needed.

Note added in proof: A study of the fluorescence, phosphorescence, and triplet-triplet absorption spectrum of biphenylene has led to the conclusion that *both the second excited singlet and the second excited triplet levels emit* (J. Hilpern, *Trans. Faraday Soc.*, **61**, 605 (1965)). The separation of S_2 and S_1 (and T_2 and T_1) appears to be normal for this molecule so that the explanation given for the anomalous emission of azulene cannot apply here. However, the peculiar emission properties of biphenylene are nicely rationalized on the basis of the selection rules for radiationless transitions. On the basis of spectroscopic and theoretical calculations, S_2 is ungerade, while S_1 and S_0 are gerade. As a result of the $u \leftrightarrow g$ selection rule for radiationless transitions (which is precisely the opposite of the selection rule for radiative transitions), the rate of the radiationless process $S_2 \rightsquigarrow S_1$ is slowed down and allows emission from S_2 to be observed. Similar arguments together with MO calculations rationalize the lone emission from T_2, *whose lifetime is 4 sec at 77° K!* If correct, this result demands that internal conversion from T_2 to T_1 is enormously inhibited in this molecule. However, recent work indicates an impurity is responsible for the observed emission [*Physics Letters*, **20**, 386 (1966)].

4-4. KINETIC INFORMATION FROM SPECTRAL DATA

Under certain assumptions, values for the rate constants of a number of processes involving the electronic states can be calculated from spectral data. The validity of these calculations depends on the accuracy of the measurements and the extent to which the assumptions are appropriate. Nevertheless, such calculations, in addition to being instructive and useful, yield qualitative information concerning the "dark" photochemical processes and point out the areas where extensive experimental data are needed.

Calculation of the Rates of Radiationless Processes [5, 82]

Knowledge of the rates of interconversions and lifetimes of excited states is of great importance in photochemical problems. The following scheme will allow us to estimate these rates from spectral data alone. In the absence of irreversible photochemical reaction and specific bimolecular quenching the following reaction steps describe the important paths of a deactivation molecule which is excited to its lowest singlet S_1:

	Step	*Rate*
$h\nu + S_0 \rightarrow S_1$	Excitation	I
$S_1 \rightsquigarrow S_0 + \text{heat}$	Internal Conversion	$k_s[S_1]$
$S_1 \rightsquigarrow T_1 + \text{heat}$	Intersystem Crossing	$k_{ST}[S_1]$
$T_1 \rightsquigarrow S_0 + \text{heat}$	Intersystem Crossing	$k_t[T_1]$
$T_1 \rightarrow S_0 + h\nu$	Phosphorescence	$k_p[T_1]$
$S_1 \rightarrow S_0 + h\nu$	Fluorescence	$k_f[S_1]$

The processes involved are shown in Fig. 4-12.

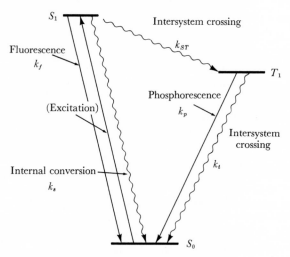

Fig. 4-12   *Typical energy diagram.*

The steady-state approximation in excited singlet states leads to

$$I = (k_{ST} + k_f + k_s)[S_1] \tag{4-16}$$

where I is the rate of absorption of light in einsteins/liter sec, and $[S_1]$ is the concentration of excited singlets. Similarly for triplets we have

$$k_{ST}[S_1] = (k_t + k_p)[T_1] \tag{4-17}$$

or

$$[T_1] = \frac{k_{ST}[S_1]}{(k_p + k_t)} \tag{4-18}$$

From Eq. 4-16 we have

$$[S_1] = \frac{I}{(k_{ST} + k_f + k_s)} \tag{4-19}$$

Substituting Eq. 4-19 into Eq. 4-18

$$[T_1] = \frac{k_{ST}I}{(k_t + k_p)(k_{ST} + k_f + k_s)} \tag{4-20}$$

From the definition of quantum yield we find

$$\phi_f = \frac{\text{rate of fluorescence}}{\text{rate of absorption}} = \frac{k_f[S_1]}{I} \tag{4-21}$$

$$\phi_p = \frac{\text{rate of phosphorescence}}{\text{rate of absorption}} = \frac{k_p[T_1]}{I} \tag{4-22}$$

Therefore, the ratio ϕ_p/ϕ_f from Eqs. 4-21 and 4-22 is

$$\phi_p/\phi_f = \frac{k_p}{k_f}\left(\frac{k_{ST}}{k_t + k_p}\right) \tag{4-23}$$

All of the quantities in Eq. 4-23 are measureable except for k_{ST} and k_t. However, we may now make some assumptions about the rate of k_t and calculate k_{ST}.

For example, if the total quantum yield of emission is high, then $k_p \gg k_t$, and Eq. 4-23 becomes

$$\frac{\phi_p}{\phi_f} = \frac{k_{ST}}{k_f} = \tau_f k_{ST} \tag{4-24}$$

In actual practice the condition that $\phi_p + \phi_f \sim 1$ is rarely met. If the total phosphorescence emission yield is less than unity but greater than one-tenth, we can arrive at results which should be within an order of magnitude of the true values since k_t must be less than ten times k_p under these conditions. Furthermore, *we may assume* that all molecules which do not emit are deactivated in T_1 (see Section 5-3) so that k_t may be approximated by

$$k_t \sim k_p \left(\frac{1 - (\phi_p + \phi_f)}{\phi_p} \right) \qquad (4\text{-}25)$$

i.e., the rate of phosphorescence times the ratio of radiationlessly deactivated triplets to phosphorescing triplets. We can now calculate limiting values of k_{ST} from a knowledge of ϕ_f, ϕ_p, and τ_f, as is done in Table 4-13.

Table 4-13 *Order of magnitude values of k_{ST} from emission and absorption data*

Compound	$\phi_f{}^a$	$\phi_p{}^a$	$k_f{}^b$	$k_p{}^c$	$k_t{}^d$	$k_{ST}{}^e$
Benzene	0.20	0.20	2	0.035	0.1	8×10^6
Chlorobenzene	0.00	0.06	3	15	250	4×10^{10}
Bromobenzene	0.00	0.02	3	20	10^4	4×10^{10}
Naphthalene	0.55	0.05	1	0.044	0.35	1×10^6
1-Fluoronaphthalene	0.84	0.06	3	0.27	0.46	5×10^5
1-Chloronaphthalene	0.06	0.54	3	1.7	1.4	5×10^7
1-Bromonaphthalene	0.002	0.55	3	28	22	2×10^9
1-Iodonaphthalene	0.000	0.70	2	350	150	3×10^{10}
Benzophenone	0.000	0.90	1	160	18	1×10^{10}
Acetophenone	0.000	0.63	0.4	76	50	5×10^9
Biacetyl	0.001	0.25	0.1	125	375	2×10^7
Quinoline	0.10	0.20	10	0.15	0.5	8×10^7

[a] Fluorescence and phosphorescence quantum yields in EPA at 77° K from References 29 and 62. The results of recent measurements indicate that some of these values are probably too high by about a factor of two (*J. Chem. Phys.*, **41**, 3042 (1964)). For the purposes of these calculations, if the fluorescence yield is too small to measure, a yield < 0.0001 is assumed.

[b] Approximate fluorescence rates ($\times 10^6$ sec^{-1}) calculated from Eqs. 3-11 and 3-14 from the data in Reference 35.

[c] Measured phosphorescence decay rates (sec^{-1}) at 77° K in EPA from Reference 35.

[d] Calculated from Eq. 4-25 on the assumption that all electronic deactivation occurs in the lowest triplet.

[e] Calculated from Eq. 4-23.

Population of Triplet States [51, 63]

The data in Table 4-13 indicate that only the fastest fluorescence rates are comparable to the rate of the $S_1 \rightsquigarrow T_1$ process. It is important to point out that a low quantum yield of phosphorescence ϕ_p *does not necessarily imply a low yield of triplets*. In fact, there is evidence that every S_1 which does not fluoresce, passes to T_1 (see Section 5-3). A low quantum yield of emission then implies quenching in the triplet level. The lower the energy E_T of T_1 the less stringent the Franck-Condon prohibi-

tion.   Indeed, the fraction of the triplet molecules which actually phosphoresce is expected to decrease steadily as E_T decreases.   Some examples
of this phenomenon are shown in Table 4-12.   Thus, a low value of ϕ_p
cannot be construed to mean the triplet state is not populated after excitation of S_1, especially if ϕ_f is also low, but it may instead imply that rapid
quenching of T_1 occurs.   The proposal that all radiationless deactivation
occurs in T_1 and not S_1 (for aromatic hydrocarbons, at least) derives
from the observation that certain deuterated aromatics have total emission yields close to unity as a result of an increase in phosphorescence
alone.[29]

Construction of State Diagrams [30, 33]

A detailed state diagram of a molecule can now be constructed on the
basis of spectral data alone.   Such a diagram will show at a glance the
energies, lifetimes, and populations of the S_1 and T_1 states.   Armed with
such information the interpretation of photoreactions can be greatly
simplified and even predicted in favorable cases.

Figure 4-13 shows the absorption and emission spectra of 1-chloro-
naphthalene.   The fluorescence ($\phi_f = 0.06$, $\tau_f = 10^{-6}$ sec, calculated
from the absorption spectrum) and phosphorescence ($\phi_p = 0.54$, $\tau_p = 0.30$ sec) are well separated.   The 0-0 band for fluorescence is at 31,500
cm^{-1} (90 kcal/mole) and for phosphorescence is at 21,000 cm^{-1} (60 kcal/
mole).   Both S_1 and T_1 are identifiable by the criteria listed in Table 4-1.
Thus, the ϵ_{max} for absorption is 1,000, the vibrational structure of the
absorption and emission spectra are similar to those expected for an
aromatic hydrocarbon, the phosphorescence lifetime is of the order of
1 sec, and the spectral bands shift to longer wavelengths upon increasing
the polarity of the solvent.   If we assume that every molecule which does
not fluoresce passes to T_1, then we arrive at the relative distribution of
approximately 5% S_1 and 95% T_1 for the bipartition of quanta of excitation.   The rate constant k_p^0 is given by Eq. 4-4 (superscript zeros refer
to inherent lifetimes or rate constants)

$$k_p^0 = \frac{1}{\tau_p^0} = \frac{1}{\tau_p}\left(\frac{\phi_p}{1 - \phi_f}\right) = \frac{1}{0.30}\left(\frac{0.55}{0.95}\right)$$

$$k_p^0 \sim 1.9 \text{ sec}^{-1}$$

The rate constant k_t^0 may now be calculated from Eq. 4-25 as

$$k_t^0 = k_p^0\left(\frac{1 - (\phi_p + \phi_f)}{\phi_p}\right) = 1.9(0.73) = 1.4 \text{ sec}^{-1}$$

and k_{ST} may be calculated from Eq. 4-23 as

$$k_{ST} = \phi_p/\phi_f \left(\frac{k_f^{\,0}}{k_p^{\,0}}\right)(k_t^{\,0} + k_p^{\,0}) = \left(\frac{0.54}{0.06}\right)\left(\frac{3 \times 10^6}{1.9}\right)(3.3) \cong 5 \times 10^7 \text{ sec}^{-1}$$

The state diagram for 1-chloronaphthalene is given in Fig. 4-14.

As a final example, consider Figs. 4-3 and 4-7. Benzophenone is nonfluorescent ($\phi_f < 10^{-4}, \tau_f = 10^{-6}$ sec, calculated from the absorption spectrum) but phosphoresces strongly ($\phi_p = 0.90$, $\tau_p = 0.006$ sec). The 0-0 band for absorption is at 27,000 cm^{-1} (77.2 kcal/mole) and for emission is at 24,100 cm^{-1} (69.0 kcal/mole). Both S_1 and T_1

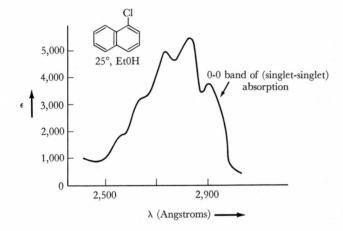

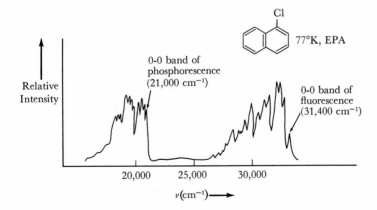

Fig. 4-13   *Absorption spectrum [upper from J. Ferguson, J. Chem. Soc., 304 (1954)] and emission spectrum (lower) of 1-chloronaphthalene.*

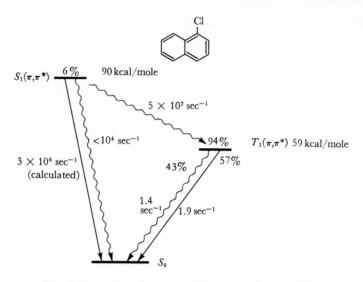

Fig. 4-14   *State diagram for 1-chloronaphthalene at 77° K.*

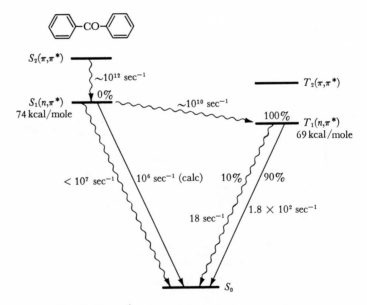

Fig. 4-15   *State diagram for benzophenone at 77° K.*

are n,π^* states, and S_2 can be seen to be π,π^* from the criteria listed in Table 4-1. The vibrational progression of emission is especially striking since the $\sim$1,700 cm^{-1} separation is close to the C=O stretching frequency, which indicates that excitation in T_1 is localized on the carbonyl group. From Eqs. 4-4, 4-25, and 4-23 we may calculate $k_p{}^0$, $k_t{}^0$, and k_{ST}, respectively, as

$$k_p{}^0 = \frac{1}{6 \times 10^{-3}} \left(\frac{0.90}{1.00}\right) = 1.5 \times 10^2 \text{ sec}^{-1}$$

$$k_t{}^0 = 1.5 \times 10^2 \left(\frac{1 - 0.90}{0.90}\right) = 17 \text{ sec}^{-1}$$

$$k_{ST} \geq \left(\frac{0.9}{0.0001}\right)\left(\frac{10^6}{150}\right) 167 \sim 10^{10} \text{ sec}^{-1}$$

The state diagram for benzophenone is given in Fig. 4-15.

4-5. FLASH SPECTROSCOPY

Phosphorescence spectra have been of great importance for the development of triplet-state theory, but they are of extremely limited use in the direct study of triplets in fluid solution for the simple reason that phosphorescence is rarely observed under these conditions. Flash spectroscopy (usually called flash photolysis) overcomes this handicap and allows observation of triplet states in fluid solution by the direct measurement of their absorption spectra. When a molecule is in an excited state such as T_1, it is a distinct (metastable) molecular species possessing physical and chemical properties which are, in general, different from S_0. Triplet-triplet absorption (which is *not* forbidden by spin restrictions) is different from the normal singlet-singlet absorption and in principle can be distinguished from the latter.

Principles of the Technique [64, 65]

The basic principles of this powerful method are easily seen from inspection of Figs. 4-16 and 4-17. An extremely intense flash (the photolysis flash) is employed to excite a large number of molecules to upper singlet states. Internal conversion rapidly converts these states to S_1 from which intersystem crossing to T_1 may occur. Intersystem crossing from the upper excited singlets to upper triplets followed by internal conversion to T_1 is also possible. A second spectroscopic (low intensity) flash is triggered from 1 to 50 μsec after the photolysis flash, and the absorption spectrum of the lowest triplet state, as it passes to upper triplets, is recorded. Once the absorption spectrum has been established, triplet

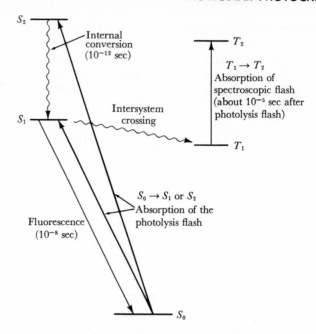

Fig. 4-16   *Transitions involved in flash-photolysis studies of the triplet state.   The horizontal scale has no physical meaning.*

decay kinetics and effects of the medium can be studied.   Furthermore, if the depletion of S_0 can be measured simultaneously, the concentration of triplets may be estimated, and a calculation of the extinction coefficient of triplet-triplet absorption is possible.   No spin restrictions exist for triplet-triplet absorptions, so that they are expected to be as intense as singlet-singlet absorption.

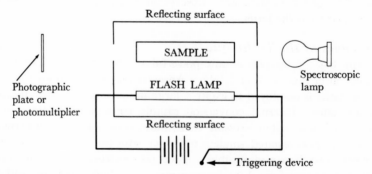

Fig. 4-17   *Schematic description of a simple flash-photolysis apparatus.   The photolysis flash is obtained by discharging a high capacity condenser bank through a flash lamp.   About ten μsec after the flash the sample is analyzed spectroscopically as a function of time.*

Although this technique is applicable to all three phases, certain limitations exist:

1. A measurable concentration of triplets must be produced by the photolysis flash.

2. The lifetime of T_1 must be longer than the duration of the photolysis flash.

3. The triplet-triplet absorption spectrum must occur at an experimentally accessible frequency and must be measurably distinct from the normal singlet-singlet absorption spectrum.

4. Photolysis products must be carefully eliminated as the source of the observed absorption.

Good evidence that the observed triplet-triplet absorption is authentic is possible if it can be shown that the decay of absorption is identical to the lifetime of phosphorescence when both are measured under similar conditions. A comparison of triplet lifetimes measured by flash photolysis [66] and phosphorescence [35] is given in Table 4-14.

Table 4-14 *Comparison of triplet lifetimes in seconds measured by flash photolysis and phosphorescence [35, 66]*

Compound	$\tau_T{}^a$ (20° C)	$\tau_T{}^b$ (77° K)	$\tau_p{}^c$ (77° K)
Naphthalene	2.3	3.3	2.3
2-Bromonaphthalene	10^{-2}	5×10^{-2}	2×10^{-2}
Anthracene	1.4×10^{-2}	10^{-1}	0.1
Fluorene	—	4.9	4.9
Quinoline	—	0.5	1.4
Phenanthrene	—	3.3	3.3
Pyrene	—	0.7	0.2

^{a} Unimolecular lifetimes by flash photolysis (extrapolated to 20°) in isopentane.
^{b} Unimolecular lifetimes by flash photolysis in isopentane or EPA.
^{c} Unimolecular phosphorescence lifetimes in EPA.

Lifetimes of Triplets in Fluid Solutions [67–70]

Flash photolysis has helped to solve the enigma posed by the lack of phosphorescence in fluid solutions. The triplet state can be highly populated in liquids, but radiationless deactivation, *especially bimolecular diffusion controlled impurity quenching*,[68] completely dominates emission from T_1. Thus, whereas the rates of triplet decay of a number of halonaphthalenes are nearly identical to one another, the rates of decay of anthracene and its derivatives show a reasonable dependence on the number and position of the substituted halogens.[69, 70] The decay rate of the naphthalene is attributed to some common bimolecular quenching process

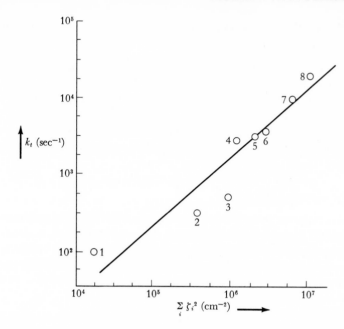

Fig. 4-18   *Plot of k_t (measured by flash photolysis) versus $\Sigma_i \zeta_i^2$. 1. Anthracene; 2. 1-chloroanthracene; 3. 1,5-dichloroanthracene; 4. 9,10-dichloroanthracene; 5. 2,9,10-trichloroanthracene; 6. 1,5,9,10-tetrachloroanthracene; 7. 9-bromoanthracene; 8. 9,10-dibromoanthracene.*

and is not a true unimolecular rate for the $T_1 \rightsquigarrow S_0$ process.   On the other hand, the rates of decay of anthracene derivatives are those expected if the function of the heavy atom is to increase spin-orbital coupling of the electrons involved in the transition.   In fact a qualitative correlation between the rate constant of unimolecular decay k_t and the spin-orbital coupling factor ζ^2 (see Section 3-2) is shown in Fig. 4-18, in which k_t is plotted against $\Sigma_i \zeta_i^2$, the sum of the square of the spin-orbital coupling factor for the heaviest atoms in the molecule.

4-6. PROPERTIES OF EXCITED STATES

Although the properties of the ground state of a stable molecule are easily deduced on the basis of standard chemical and physical techniques, the inherently low concentration of excited states makes their characterization difficult.   Furthermore, the quantitative application of quantum mechanical methods to the elucidation of the properties of excited states has not been particularly successful.   A detailed analysis of an absorption or emission spectrum allows calculation of some of the properties of the state reached by absorption or from which emission occurred, but such analyses are usually complex and limited in applicability. However, one important result of such analyses is the fact that the properties of excited states are in general quite different from those of the ground state.[40, 71]

Structure of Excited States [1, 53, 71]

As an example, consider the excited acetylene molecule.[72] Analysis of the absorption spectrum of acetylene vapor shows that excitation of a π-bonding electron of acetylene into an antibonding π^* orbital is accompanied by extensive rehybridization. A minimum of interaction occurs between the unpaired π and π^* electrons if the CH bonds become sp^2 hybridized and assume a *trans* configuration. The lowest excited singlet state of acetylene is therefore envisioned as a trans-planar species.

Similar analysis shows that, while formaldehyde [73–75] is planar in its ground and n,π^* singlet states, the π,π^* singlet, which possesses one π electron and one π^* electron, is subject to a net destabilization in the planar configuration and therefore tends toward a pyramidal configuration in which the carbon atom is sp^3 hybridized.

Dipole Moments [1, 74, 75]

The calculation of dipole moments may be made from a study of solvent shifts of absorption and emission spectra or rotational analyses of absorption spectra.[74] From Table 4-15, which lists some typical data, it can be seen that the dipole moment may increase or decrease in the excited state. It is interesting to note that the n,π^* singlet state has a dipole whose magnitude changes in the right direction but which is smaller than expected for a transition which promotes an n electron on oxygen into a π^* orbital predominately on carbon,[75] for formaldehyde.

Table 4-15 *Dipole moments of excited states* [75, 81]

	Dipole Moment DU	
Compound	S_0	S_1
4-Amino-4'-nitrobiphenyl	6.4	18.0
2-Amino-7-nitrofluorene	7.0	25.0
4-Dimethylamino-4'-nitrostilbene	7.6	32.0
Formaldehyde	2.3	1.5

Acid and Base Strengths [76, 77]

Excited molecules may undergo acid-base reactions without simultaneous electronic deactivation. The acid and base strengths of excited molecules may therefore be evaluated by spectral measurement of the concentrations of protonated excited molecules as a function of pH. The results [77] of such experiments are summarized in Table 4-16.　The

Table 4-16　　　*Acid and base strengths of singlet and triplet states* [76, 77]

Molecule	pK_G [a]	pK_s [b]	pK_T [c]	pK_T [d]
2-Naphthol	9.5	3.1	8.1	7.7
2-Naphthoic acid	4.2	10 to 12	4.0	4.2
Acridine	5.5	10.6	5.6	—
2-Naphthylamine	4.1	−2.0	3.3	3.1

[a] pK of the ground-state molecule.
[b] pK of the lowest excited singlet state from fluorescence measurements.
[c] pK of the lowest triplet from flash-photolysis studies.
[d] pK of the lowest triplet from phosphorescence studies.

pK of the triplet state can be seen to be remarkably close to that of the ground state rather than the excited singlet state,[76] which possesses the same electronic configuration, according to simple MO theory.　These results serve to emphasize the large difference in chemical reactivity which may exist between a singlet and triplet state.

Reactivity of Excited States [45, 71]

In large polyatomic molecules the excitation of an electron may produce a configuration in which many electrons remain in bonding orbitals, so that a significant change in molecular geometry is not expected, unless the bonding between two or more atoms changes radically.　The latter situation applies to a molecule such as acetylene, which may become reactive in its S_1 state as a result of rehybridization.　The n,π^* state of formaldehyde, while still planar, may be expected to be reactive as a result of the positive "hole" left behind on oxygen.　It should be pointed out that comparisons of reactivities of excited states and ground states must always be tempered by the fact that the excited state usually contains some 40 to 80 kcal/mole excess electronic energy, which may be the controlling factor in a given photochemical reaction.　It should also be noted that much of the data available for structural and electronic elucidation pertains to singlet-singlet analysis and may not necessarily be interpolated to triplets.

In general, the n,π^* state will possess π-bonding properties which are more similar to the ground state than those of the corresponding π,π^* state.　Although the $^1(\pi,\pi^*)$ state will in general possess a shorter fluorescence lifetime than a $^1(n,\pi^*)$ state, the reverse is true for phosphorescence (see Table 4-13). For example, the inherent phosphorescence lifetime of benzophenone is 8×10^{-3} sec, while naphthalene has an inherent phosphorescent lifetime of about 20 sec.

Finally, it should be pointed out that the choice of solvent may play an important role in a photochemical sequence (in addition to serving as a possible reactant). The solvent may exhibit specific quenching or solute-solvent interaction which can affect the rates of internal conversion and intersystem crossing processes [65] (e.g., heavy-atom effects, state switching, etc.).

Singlets and Triplets [45, 60, 63, 78, 79]

According to elementary MO theory, if a molecule possesses no *orbital* degeneracies, singlet and triplet states occur in pairs. The two states are split apart in energy when electron-electron interactions are applied as a perturbation, the triplet becoming the lower energy state. Singlet-triplet splitting depends somewhat on *configuration interaction* [83] which tends to destroy the simple idea that each singlet has an associated triplet. The magnitude of the energy of the (lowest excited) singlet-(lowest) triplet split ΔE_{ST} is given approximately by the expression [78, 79]

$$\Delta E_{ST} = \int \phi_2 \mathbf{H} \phi_1 \, d\tau \qquad (4\text{-}26)$$

where ϕ_2 is the wave function of the excited state and ϕ_1 is the wave function of the initial orbital involved in the transition. The operator $\mathbf{H}$ is merely e^2/r so that Eq. 4-26 may be rewritten as

$$\Delta E_{ST} = e^2 \int \phi_2 \phi_1 \frac{1}{r} \, d\tau \qquad (4\text{-}27)$$

The magnitude of ΔE_{ST} thus depends on the amount of *spatial overlap* of the orbitals ϕ_2 and ϕ_1. Since n and π^* orbitals do not have much spatial overlap, whereas π and π^* orbitals do, the singlet-triplet energy splitting is greater for π,π^* states than n,π^* states. Several examples are given in Table 4-17.

The probability of electrons being at the same point in space is zero for two orbitals containing two unpaired electrons, but it is finite for two orbitals containing two paired electrons. The electrons *tend* to be farther apart in the triplet than the corresponding singlet. Electron repulsions are thus less in the triplet. Triplets have been described as biradicals, but the term is not very descriptive or general. The electrons in an excited singlet may, because of their spatial positions, act as a diradical. We may, on the other hand, conceive of triplet states which are not at all biradical in nature—e.g., triplets of long conjugated systems in which the excited electron may be smeared over the entire molecular frame.

Table 4-17 *Singlet-triplet splittings and Φ_{ST} for π,π^* and n,π^* states* [35, 82]

Compound	ΔE_{ST} [a]	Φ_{ST} [b]
π,π^* *States*		
Anthracene	32	0.70
Benzene	30	0.24
Naphthalene	29	0.40
Fluorene	27	0.31
Chrysene	22	0.67
Phenanthrene	19	0.76
Triphenylene	15	0.96
n,π^* *States*		
Benzophenone	5	1.0
Biacetyl	6	0.99
Quinoline	29	0.32

[a] Energy of S_1-T_1 separation in kcal/mole (Reference 35).
[b] Quantum yield of triplet formation from S_1 (see Section 5-6, Reference 54).

The triplet state of anthracene and acetone may be written as

but the description (in the absence of spin labelling) is also appropriate for that of a singlet state.

The chemical behaviors of lowest excited singlet and triplet states are thus difficult to distinguish from theoretical considerations. However, a major difference in chemical reactivity may result from the longer inherent lifetime of the triplet relative to that of the singlet. All other factors being equal, the triplet has a much better opportunity of reacting since it persists and retains its excitation energy for a long period of time.

Photochemistry and Spectroscopy [45]

In this chapter the methods and results of spectroscopy have been emphasized in their relation to photochemistry. Problems of general interest to both the spectroscopist and photochemist include:

1. inter- and intramolecular energy transfer
2. long- and short-lived excited states
3. electronic density and structure and its change with excitation
4. the effects of inter- and intramolecular environment on the ground and excited states of molecules.

Modern photochemistry should glean the advantages of elegant spectroscopic techniques (such as flash photolysis), which make possible the direct and indirect study of transient species involved in photoreactions. The concepts of the spectroscopists (e.g., energy diagrams, inherent radiative lifetimes, radiationless conversions, etc.) are of fundamental importance for the construction of a basic framework for the understanding of organic photochemistry.

PROBLEMS

1. Estimate a lower limit for the rate of internal conversion k_i from S_2 to S_1 for a molecule whose natural fluorescence lifetime τ_f and yield ϕ_f are 10^{-8} sec and 0.1 sec, respectively. The fluorescence yield and spectrum of the molecule are independent of the exciting wavelength, and a search for a fluorescence yield of 10^{-4} from S_2 could not be detected when the latter state was excited.

2. The transition probabilities for the $S_0 \rightarrow S_1$ absorption and $T_1 \rightarrow S_0$ emission of naphthalene and its 1-halo derivatives are given in the table below. The frequency of absorption and emission remain constant as one goes from naphthalene to 1-iodonaphthalene. What do these results imply about the effect of heavy atoms on singlet-singlet and triplet-singlet processes?

Oscillator strengths and inherent radiative lifetimes in seconds of naphthalene and its halo derivatives [35]

Compound	$10^{-3} \times f$ $(S_0 \rightarrow S_1)$	τ $(T_1 \rightarrow S_0)$
Naphthalene	1.0	20.0
1-Chloronaphthalene	3.7	0.8
1-Bromonaphthalene	3.9	0.04
1-Iodonaphthalene	2.6	0.003

3. Benzene possesses a phosphorescence lifetime of about 10 sec at 77° K, yet no $T_1 \rightarrow T_2$ absorption spectrum of the compound is observed at 25° C in fluid solution. What conclusions can you make concerning the lifetime of benzene triplets in fluid solution?

4. Suppose the electronic density of the highest filled π and lowest unfilled π^* orbitals of anthracene are as shown below. Would you expect a greater spin-orbital interaction to occur in the π,π^* states of 9,10-dibromo or 2,6-dibromo-anthracene?

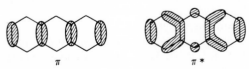

π π^*

5. The absorption spectrum of *trans*-azobenzene shows a band at 4,300 Å ($\epsilon_{max} \sim 500$) and a second band at 3,200 Å ($\epsilon_{max} \sim 25,000$). The compound

is nonluminescent.   To what type of transitions do the bands correspond?   What does the lack of luminescence imply?

6. Why are $S_1 \overset{h\nu}{\rightarrow} S_2$, $S_1 \overset{h\nu}{\rightarrow} S_3$, etc. absorptions not usually observed in flash photolysis?

7. Chlorophyll, in addition to its important property of curbing halitosis, is suspected of being of great importance in the process of photosynthesis.   The fluorescence intensity of chlorophyll is negligible in very dry hydrocarbon solution, but traces of water or hydroxylic solvents cause a relatively intense fluorescence from this molecule.   Rationalize these facts in terms of an energy diagram for the two cases.   (Hint: Remember the effects of polar solvents on $n \rightarrow \pi^*$ transitions.)

8. Predict whether k_{ST}/k_f will be greater than, equal to, or less than one for the following compounds.   Specify your reasoning.

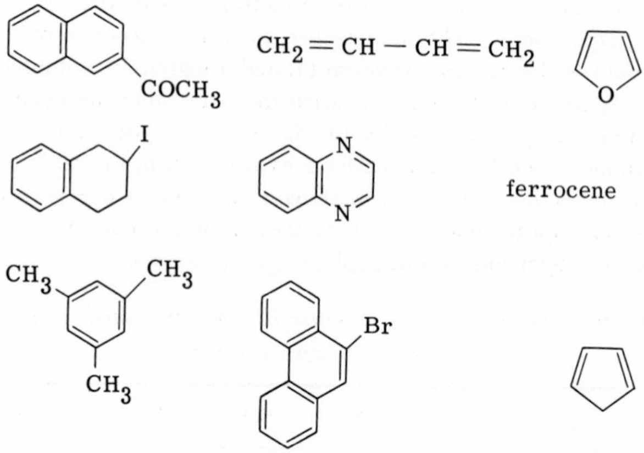

9. Calculate the radiative lifetime of the S_1 state of anthracene at 25° from Fig. 4-1 and Eq. 4-2.

10. Construct detailed state diagrams for the following molecules from the data in Table 4-13.

    1. benzene ($E_{S_1} = 115$, $E_{T_1} = 84$)
    2. naphthalene ($E_{S_1} = 90$, $E_{T_1} = 60$)
    3. biacetyl ($E_{S_1} = 62$, $E_{T_1} = 56$)

REFERENCES*

1. H. H. Jaffe and M. Orchin, *Theory and Applications of Ultraviolet Spectroscopy* (New York: Wiley, 1962).
2. S. F. Mason, *Quart. Rev.*, **15**, 287 (1961).
3. R. P. Bauman, *Absorption Spectroscopy* (New York: Wiley, 1962).
4. M. Kasha, in *Light and Life*, ed. W. D. McElroy and B. Glass (Baltimore, Md.: Johns Hopkins Press, 1961), p. 31.

   * See Addendum for additional references.

5. M. Kasha, *Disc. Faraday Soc.*, **9**, 14 (1950).
6. M. Kasha and S. P. McGlynn, *Ann. Rev. Phys. Chem.*, **7**, 403 (1956).
7. J. W. Sidman, *Chem. Rev.*, **58**, 689 (1958).
8. V. L. Ermolaev and A. N. Terenin, *Soviet Physics*, **3**, 423 (1960).
9. T. Forster, *Fluorezenz Organischer Verbindungen* (Gottingen: Vandenhoech and Ruprech, 1951).
10. G. N. Lewis and M. Kasha, *J. Am. Chem. Soc.*, **67**, 994 (1945).
11. S. J. Strickler and R. A. Berg, *J. Chem. Phys.*, **37**, 814 (1962).
12. W. R. Ware and B. A. Baldwin, *ibid.*, **40**, 1703 (1964).
13. J. B. Birks and D. J. Dyson, *Proc. Royal Soc.*, **A275**, 135 (1963).
14. W. H. Melhuish, *J. Phys. Chem.*, **65**, 229 (1961).
15. R. G. Bennett, *Rev. Sci. Instr.*, **31**, 1275 (1960).
16. S. P. McGlynn, T. Azumi, and M. Kasha, *J. Chem. Phys.*, **40**, 507 (1964).
17. Y. Kand, *et al.*, *Spectrochimia Acta*, **20**, 1387 (1964).
18. M. Kasha, *J. Chem. Phys.*, **20**, 71 (1952).
19. D. Evans, *J. Chem. Soc.*, 1351 (1957); *ibid.*, 2753 (1959); *ibid.*, 1735 (1960); *ibid.*, 1987 (1961).
20. M. Kasha, *Chem. Rev.*, **41**, 401 (1948).
21. G. N. Lewis and M. Kasha, *J. Am. Chem. Soc.*, **66**, 2100 (1944).
22. G. N. Lewis and M. Calvin, *ibid.*, **67**, 1232 (1945).
23. G. N. Lewis, M. Calvin, and M. Kasha, *J. Chem. Phys.*, **17**, 804 (1949).
24. A. N. Terenin, *Acta Physicochim. U.S.S.R.*, **18**, 210 (1943); *C.A.*, **38**, 5149 (1943).
25. D. S. McClure, *J. Chem. Phys.*, **17**, 665 (1949).
26. D. S. McClure, *J. Chem. Phys.*, **19**, 670 (1951).
27. D. S. McClure and P. L. Hanst, *ibid.*, **23**, 1772 (1955).
28. D. F. Evans, *Nature*, **176**, 777 (1955).
29. E. H. Gilmore, G. E. Gibson, and D. S. McClure, *J. Chem. Phys.*, **20**, 829, (1952); and correction, *ibid.*, **23**, 399 (1955).
30. M. Kasha, *Radiation Research*, Supplement 2, 243 (1960).
31. A number of examples of violations of the rule that emission spectrum is invariant with wavelength have appeared; for example, see S. Lipsky and C. L. Braum, *J. Chem. Phys.*, **37**, 190 (1962).
32. G. K. Rollefson and M. Burton, *Photochemistry and the Mechanism of Chemical Reactions* (Englewood Cliffs, N.J.: Prentice-Hall, 1939).
33. M. Kasha, in *Comparative Effects of Radiation*, ed. M. Burton, J. S. Kirby-Smith, and J. L. Magee (New York: Wiley, 1960), p. 72.
34. E. J. Bowen, in *Advances in Photochemistry*, ed. W. A. Noyes, Jr., G. S. Hammond, and J. N. Pitts, Jr. (vol. I, New York: Interscience, 1963), p. 23.
35. D. S. McClure, *J. Chem. Phys.*, **17**, 905 (1949).
36. S. P. McGlynn, M. J. Reynolds, G. W. Daigre, and N. D. Christodouleos, *J. Phys. Chem.*, **66**, 2499 (1962).
37. G. W. Robinson, *J. Mol. Spectroscopy*, **6**, 58 (1961).
38. C. A. Hutchingson, Jr. and B. W. Magnum, *J. Chem. Phys.*, **32**, 1261 (1960); M. S. DeGroot and J. H. Van der Waals, *Molec. Phys.*, **4**, 189 (1961).
39. R. S. Berry, *J. Chem. Phys.*, **38**, 1934 (1963); L. E. Orgel, *J. Chem. Soc.*, 121 (1955).

40. N. Christodouleas and S. P. McGlynn, *J. Chem. Phys.*, **40,** 166 (1964).
41. S. P. McGlynn, *Chem. Rev.*, **58,** 1113 (1958).
42. S. P. McGlynn, *et al.*, *J. Chem. Phys.*, **32,** 357 (1960); S. P. McGlynn and J. D. Boggus, *J. Am. Chem. Soc.*, **80,** 5096 (1958).
43. K. B. Eisenthal and M. A. El-Sayed, *J. Chem. Phys.*, **42,** 794 (1965).
44. M. Beer and H. C. Longuet-Higgins, *J. Chem. Phys.*, **23,** 1390 (1955); G. Viswangth and M. Kasha, *ibid.*, **24,** 574 (1955).
45. S. P. McGlynn, F. J. Smith, and G. Cilento, *Photochem. Photobio.*, **3,** 269 (1964).
46. J. Sidman and D. S. McClure, *ibid.*, **24,** 757 (1955).
47. R. Praiser, *ibid.*, **25,** 1112 (1956).
48. W. R. Ware, *J. Chem. Phys.*, **37,** 923 (1963).
49. A. A. Lamola, W. G. Herkstroeter, J. C. Dalton, and G. S. Hammond, *J. Chem. Phys.*, **42,** 1715 (1965).
50. D. R. Scott and R. S. Becker, *J. Chem. Phys.*, **35,** 516 (1961).
51. C. Reid, *Excited States in Chemistry and Biology* (London: Butterworth, 1957).
52. E. Teller, *J. Chem. Phys.*, **41,** 109 (1947).
53. G. Herzberg, *Spectra of Diatomic Molecules*, 2d ed. (Princeton: Van Nostrand, 1950).
54. M. A. El-Sayed, *J. Chem. Phys.*, **38,** 2834 (1963).
55. M. R. Wright, R. P. Frosch, and G. W. Robinson, *J. Chem. Phys.*, **33,** 934 (1960).
56. M. R. Wright, R. P. Frosch, and G. W. Robinson, *ibid.*, **38,** 1187 (1963).
57. E. C. Lim, *J. Chem. Phys.*, **36,** 3497 (1962).
58. G. W. Robinson and R. P. Frosch, *ibid.*, **37,** 1962 (1962).
59. R. E. Kellogg and R. P. Schwenker, *J. Chem. Phys.*, **41,** 2860 (1964).
60. G. W. Robinson, in *Light and Life*, ed. W. D. McElroy and B. Glass (Baltimore, Md.: Johns Hopkins Press, 1961), p. 11.
61. M. Gouterman, *J. Chem. Phys.*, **36,** 2846 (1962).
62. V. L. Ermolaev and K. J. Svitashev, *Opt. and Spect.*, **7,** 399 (1959).
63. G. W. Robinson, *Proc. Natl. Acad. Sci., U.S.A.*, **49,** 521 (1963).
64. G. Porter, in *Technique of Organic Chemistry*, 2d ed., ed. A. Weissberger (vol. 8, New York: Interscience, 1963), p. 1055.
65. G. Porter, *Proc. Chem. Soc.*, 291 (1959).
66. D. P. Craig and I. G. Ross, *J. Chem. Soc.*, 1589 (1954).
67. G. Porter and M. W. Winsor, *Disc. Faraday Soc.*, **17,** 178 (1954).
68. R. Livingston and W. R. Ware, *J. Chem. Phys.*, **39,** 2539 (1963).
69. H. W. Helpern, G. Porter, and L. J. Stief, *Proc. Royal Soc.*, **A277,** 437 (1964).
70. M. F. Hoffman and G. Porter, *ibid.*, **A268,** 46 (1962).
71. J. P. Simons, *Quart. Rev.*, **13,** 3 (1959).
72. C. K. Ingold and G. W. King, *J. Chem. Soc.*, 2702 (1953) and subsequent papers.
73. J. N. Shoolery and A. H. Sharbough, *Phys. Rev.*, **82,** 95 (1951).
74. G. W. Robinson and W. E. DiGiorgio, *Can. J. Chem.*, **36,** 31 (1958).
75. D. E. Freeman and W. Klemperer, *J. Phys. Chem.*, **40,** 604 (1964).
76. A. Weller, *J. Phys. Chem.*, **3,** 238 (1955).
77. G. Jackson and G. Porter, *Proc. Royal Soc.*, **A260,** 13 (1961).

78. M. A. El-Sayed and G. W. Robinson, *J. Chem. Phys.*, **34,** 1840 (1961).
79. M. A. El-Sayed and G. W. Robinson, *ibid.*, **35,** 1896 (1961).
80. C. A. Parker, in *Advances in Photochemistry*, ed. W. A. Noyes, Jr., G. S. Hammond, and J. N. Pitts, Jr. (vol. II, New York: Interscience, 1964), p. 305.
81. E. Lippert, *Z. Electrochem.*, **61,** 962 (1957).
82. A. A. Lamola and G. S. Hammond, *J. Chem. Phys.*, **43,** 2129 (1965).
83. H. Eyring, J. Walter, and G. E. Kimball, *Quantum Chemistry* (New York: Wiley, 1944).

chapter five

Electronic Energy Transfer

5-1. PHOTOCHEMICAL KINETICS

Study of the rates of photochemical processes allows the formation of certain conclusions concerning the mechanism of photoreactions, which do not require knowledge of the detailed path of the reaction. In Section 4-4 we considered mainly unimolecular processes and were able to estimate the rates of the "dark" reactions—i.e., radiationless transitions. We shall now consider bimolecular processes which deactivate excited states. The basic problem which concerns us in this chapter is the determination of the mechanism of these bimolecular quenching (energy transfer) processes.

Rates of Deactivation of Excited States [1, 2]

The concentration of a particular excited state A^* is constant with time under conditions of continuous, uniform excitation, so that

$$\frac{dA^*}{dt} = 0 \tag{5-1}$$

The inherent spontaneous-emission lifetime τ^0 of A^* fixes the time scale for photochemical processes which may occur from A^*. If no other process is capable of deactivating A^* before the time τ^0, the excited molecule must emit a photon and become deactivated. Obviously, paths other than emission do exist in general because total emission yields are rarely equal to unity even under the most favorable conditions.

If A^* is the lowest excited singlet state S_1, for example, its rate of disappearance is given by

$$\frac{dS_1}{dt} = k_f[S_1] + k_{ST}[S_1] + k_s[S_1] + \sum_i k_i[S_1][Q_i] + \sum_j k_j[S_1] \quad (5\text{-}2)$$

where k_f, k_{ST}, k_s, k_i, and k_j are the specific rate constants for fluorescence, intersystem crossing to T_1, internal conversion to S_0, bimolecular quenching (or reaction), and unimolecular reaction, respectively, and $[S_1]$ is the steady-state concentration of singlets. The steady-state approximation and other known facts about the relative rates of the processes indicated in Eq. 5-2 will allow the simplification of the kinetic scheme needed to explain the mechanism of the reaction. Occasionally, an analogy to a reaction of established mechanism may be immediately apparent, so that the temptation to assign a similar mechanism to the system under study is great. Prudence gleaned from past experience suggests that this "quick" answer should be reinforced by the performance of other critical experiments. These critical experiments should employ any and all of the various physical techniques now available to the modern organic chemist and spectroscopist. The classical methods of measuring emission spectra and lifetimes should be augmented by a search for intermediates (i.e., by flash photolysis, electron-spin resonance, etc.).

Quenching of Excited States [1, 2]

Quenching of excited states is, in the broad sense, any deactivation which results from interaction of the excited molecules with the components of a system. If a particular molecular component is considerably more effective at promoting the quenching process, it is sometimes possible to neglect paths of deactivation which involve other species of the system.

As a specific example, consider quenching of the emission of an excited molecule D^* by the addition of a second molecule A. Let us assume the following mechanism [1, 2] for formation and disappearance of D^*

Process		*Rate*
Absorption	$D_0 + h\nu \rightarrow D^*$	I_a (einsteins/liter sec)
Emission	$D^* \rightarrow D_0 + h\nu$	$k_1 [D^*]$
Quenching	$D^* + A_0 \rightarrow A^* + D_0$	$k_2 [D^*][A]$
Deactivation	$D^* \rightarrow D_0 + \text{heat}$	$k_3 [D^*]$

where absorption produces a thermally equilibrated S_1 state, I_a is the rate of light absorption = rate of formation of D^* (which may be a singlet or triplet) and k_1, k_2, and k_3 are the specific rate constants for emission from D^*, energy transfer from D^* to A, and thermal deactivation of D^*, respectively.

Under conditions of steady illumination and no irreversible photo-chemical reactions, we have

$$\frac{[dD^*]}{dt} = I_a - (k_1 + k_2[A] + k_3)[D^*] \qquad (5\text{-}3)$$

Assuming the steady state in $[D^*]$ is achieved, then

$$I_a = (k_1 + k_2[A] + k_3)[D^*] \qquad (5\text{-}4)$$

The quantum yield for emission from D^* in the absence of A is given by

$$\Phi_0 = \frac{k_1[D^*]}{I_a} = \frac{k_1}{k_1 + k_3} \qquad (5\text{-}5)$$

When a concentration of A equal to $[A]$ is added, the quantum yield of emission from D^* is

$$\Phi_A = \frac{k_1[D^*]}{I_a} = \frac{k_1}{k_1 + k_3 + k_2[A]} \qquad (5\text{-}6)$$

Dividing Eq. (5-5) by Eq. (5-6) we arrive at the Stern-Volmer expression

$$\frac{\Phi_0}{\Phi_A} = \frac{k_1 + k_3 + k_2[A]}{k_1 + k_3} \qquad (5\text{-}7)$$

or in the more familiar form

$$\frac{\Phi_0}{\Phi_A} = 1 + \frac{k_2}{k_1 + k_3}[A] \qquad (5\text{-}8)$$

that is,

$$\frac{\Phi_0}{\Phi_A} = 1 + k_2\tau[A] \qquad (5\text{-}9)$$

where

$$\tau = \frac{1}{k_1 + k_3} \qquad (5\text{-}10)$$

Here τ is the *measured lifetime* of D^* in the absence of A. If the assumed mechanism above is operating, then a plot of (Φ_0/Φ_A) vs $[A]$ will produce a straight line with a slope of $k_2\tau$. Since the value of τ can be measured in the absence of A, k_2, the bimolecular quenching constant for deactivation of D^* by A energy transfer, can be derived. If such a Stern-Volmer plot is found experimentally, we have obtained *prima facie* evidence that a mechanism in which there is competition between a bimolecular quenching process and unimolecular processes (e.g., emission) for deactivation of D^* is operating.

As an example of the use of Eq. 5-9 consider the concentration $[A]_{1/2}$ which reduces Φ_0 to one-half of its original value so that

$$\frac{\Phi_0}{\Phi_A} = \frac{1}{0.5} = 2 = 1 + k_2\tau[A]_{1/2} \qquad (5\text{-}11)$$

or

$$k_2\tau[A]_{1/2} = 1 \qquad (5\text{-}12)$$

An upper limit to k_2 may be set for diffusion-controlled quenching. The rate constant k_q for a diffusion-controlled reaction is approximately [3]

$$k_q = \frac{8\,RT}{3,000\eta} \text{ liters mole}^{-1} \text{ sec}^{-1} \qquad (5\text{-}13)$$

where η is the solvent viscosity in poise. For typical organic solvents† at 25° C, k_q is of the order 10^9 to 10^{10} liter mole^{-1} sec^{-1}. Table 5-1 shows the half-quenching concentration of A as a function of k_2 for slow and fast emission and as a function of k_1 if the quenching is diffusion controlled—i.e., quenching occurs at every encounter of D^* and A. Several interesting conclusions may be reached from inspection of Table 5-1:

1. If $[A]_{1/2} < 10^{-3}\ M$, most fluorescent singlets will not be quenched, even if $k_2 = 10^{10}$ liter mole^{-1} sec^{-1}, since $k > 10^6$ sec^{-1} for fluorescence.

2. If $[A]_{1/2} > 10^{-4}\ M$, then all phosphorescent triplets will be quenched if $k_2 = 10^{10}$ liter mole^{-1} sec^{-1}.

3. If $[A]_{1/2} \sim 10^{-1}\ M$, all emission will be suppressed if $k_2 = 10^{10}$ liter mole^{-1} sec^{-1}.

† A system which is not in thermodynamic equilibrium (e.g., an irradiated solution containing an absorbing solute molecule) may be considered to have a net flux of potentially reactive molecules diffusing towards one another. When a molecule D^* and A accidentally happen to be nearest neighbors, such an event is called an *encounter*. The two partners are surrounded by a solvent "cage" at the moment of the encounter, and will suffer from 10 to 100 collisions with one another before they diffuse sufficiently far apart so that a solvent molecule separates them.[3, 33] The exact magnitude of the effect of nonrandom forces that the solvent molecules will exert when D^* and A are separated by distances of the order of a molecular diameter or less is not known. Such effects could conceivably be important at very close approach of D^* and A, and may create a small yet significant potential barrier to the separation or approach of the two potentially reactive species, i.e., an energy barrier beyond that expected for diffusion of the two molecules through a solvent continuum may exist when D^* and A are very close to one another. Thus, depending on whether the magnitude of the energy required for reaction or diffusion is greater, the rate of quenching of D^* by A may be proportional to either the rate of encounters or to the rate of collisions of the two partners. In the following discussions, diffusion-controlled rates will be considered as collision-controlled rates unless experimental evidence to the contrary is available.

Table 5-1   *Typical values of quenching concentrations for a range of rate constants*

$[A]_{1/2}$ in M	$k_2 \ (M^{-1} \ \sec^{-1})$ (if $k_1 = 10^8 \ sec^{-1}$)	$k_2 \ (M^{-1} \ \sec^{-1})$ (if $k_1 = 10^3 \ sec^{-1}$)	$k_1 \ (sec^{-1})$ (if $k_2 = 10^{10} \ M^{-1} \ \sec^{-1}$)
10	10^7	10^2	10^{11}
1	10^8	10^3	10^{10}
10^{-1}	10^9	10^4	10^9
10^{-2}	10^{10}	10^5	10^8
10^{-3}	10^{11}	10^6	10^7
10^{-4}	10^{12}	10^7	10^6
10^{-5}	10^{13}	10^8	10^5
10^{-6}	10^{14}	10^9	10^4
10^{-7}	10^{15}	10^{10}	10^3

5-2. INTERMOLECULAR ENERGY TRANSFER

The nonradiative transfer of excitation absorbed by a molecule D and passed on to another molecule A is of great importance in the photochemistry of organic molecules in solution. The term *intermolecular energy transfer* as used below refers specifically to the radiationless, one-step transfer of electronic excitation from a donor molecule D^* to an acceptor molecule A. The transfer process may be schematically represented by the equations

$$D + h\nu \rightarrow D^* \tag{5-14}$$

$$D^* + A \rightarrow A^* + D \tag{5-15}$$

where the asterisks designate excited electronic states.

Mechanisms of Energy Transfer [16]

We expect that the energy of the excited state A^* must be lower than that of D^* if the energy-transfer process is to be efficient. Furthermore, the sensitized excitation of A by D^* must occur within the time τ that the molecule D remains in the excited state.

Two different mechanisms of electronic energy transfer are suggested by theoretical and empirical considerations:

1. transfer which can take place only if the two molecules approach each other so closely that they may be considered to be in molecular contact—i.e., their centers are separated by the sum of their molecular radii;

2. transfer which occurs between molecules separated by distances which considerably exceed their collision diameters.

Clearly, the rates of transfers which proceed by mechanism 1, are limited by the diffusion of molecules in solution and should decrease as one goes from fluid to viscous media because of the slower rate of diffusion in the latter. The rates of transfer occurring by mechanism 2, are not so limited and would be expected to be independent or insensitive to the viscosity of the solution or by transition to the glassy state. In other words, the quenching of D^* by A is not associated with diffusion or direct encounter during the lifetime of the excited state for mechanism 2.

Consider the following model of an electronically excited molecule D^* in a thermal bath capable of rapidly removing excess vibrational energy of any state.[4, 5] If the excited state formed by absorption of a photon has a higher vibrational energy than the surrounding medium (which is the solvent in a solution), thermal relaxation will occur, and the energy of the state will fall to lower vibration levels until thermal equilibrium is established, which usually takes about 10^{-12} sec. The electronically excited molecule D^* now stays in its lowest vibrational level until it becomes deactivated by either emission or some nonradiative process.

If another molecule A with a low-lying state is in the neighborhood of the first one, excitation transfer may take place. A consideration of the energy levels involved in such a process is given in Fig. 5-1. If the energy difference for a deactivation process in D^* corresponds to that for a possible absorption transition in a nearby molecule of A, then with sufficient energetic coupling between these molecules, both processes

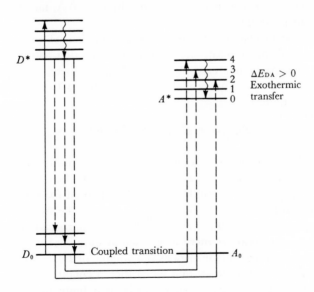

Fig. 5-1   *Coupled energy transfer between excited donor (D^*) and acceptor (A).*

may occur simultaneously, resulting in a transfer of excitation from sensitizer to acceptor by either a radiative or radiationless mechanism.

The broad spectra of polyatomic molecules in solution guarantees sufficient coincidence between D^* and A transitions if the absorption spectrum of A overlaps the emission spectrum of D^*.

Resonance-Excitation Transfer [4, 5, 6]

Under certain conditions an excited molecule D^* can transfer its excitation to a suitable acceptor over distances (e.g., 50 to 100 Å) much greater than collisional diameters. Several theoretical treatments have appeared concerning the mechanism of excitation transfer between well-separated molecular electronic states, such as the case of two distinct molecules separated in space. The problem is to calculate the probability that electronic excitation on the molecule D^* will appear at a later time as excitation on the molecule A.[4, 5, 6]

Classically, the electronic systems of D^* and A may be approximated by mechanical oscillators (such as two tuning forks) both of which are capable of vibrating with a common frequency ν. The oscillating electric charges of D^* and A will interact with one another as two dipoles—i.e., with an interaction energy which falls off as the inverse third power of the distance separating the interacting centers.[7, 8] When A is in the vicinity of D^* there is a probability that excitation will be transferred from D^* to A before it can be emitted as radiation. This simple treatment predicts average transfer distances greater than 1,000 Å, far greater than observed experimentally.[7]

A quantum mechanical treatment of the problem of energy transfer considers a long-range, weak intermolecular interaction between D^* and A, which is a particular case of the more general exciton mechanism for energy transfer.[6] The probability of transfer is then given by an expression of the form

$$P_{D^* \to A^*} = \rho \left| \int \Psi_{D^*} \Psi_A \mathbf{H}' \Psi_D \Psi_{A^*} \right|^2 \tag{5-16}$$

where $\Psi_{D^*} \Psi_A$ represents the wave function for the initial state, $\Psi_D \Psi_{A^*}$ represents the wave function of the final state, ρ is the density of states available for interaction, and $\mathbf{H}'$ is the Hamiltonian for suitable interaction between initial and final states. As soon as the two states represented by $\Psi_{D^*} \Psi_A$ and $\Psi_A \Psi_{D^*}$ are coupled by an appropriate interaction, they become degenerate *if* there is an excited state of A which requires exactly the same excitation energy as is available in D^*. Time-dependent perturbation theory shows that when such a condition exists, excitation of one of the degenerate states leads to a finite probability that excitation will appear in the other. This probability increases with time but falls off as the sixth power of the distance separating the centers of the two molecules.

Forster [6] showed that the necessary interaction occurs between the quantum mechanical transition moments which also determine the absorption and emission properties of individual molecules. This interaction is strongest if the corresponding dipole transitions in both D^* emission and A absorption are allowed—i.e., singlet-singlet or triplet-triplet transitions. The dipole-dipole energy is dependent on the inverse third power of the molecular separation, and probability of excitation transfer (which falls off as the square of the interaction energy) decreases with the inverse sixth power of the distance. Forster [4, 6] was able to relate the probability of energy transfer, which occurs as a result of dipole-dipole interaction, to the emission spectrum of D^* and the absorption spectum of A by the equation

$$\text{Rate constant } (D^* \rightarrow A^*) = \frac{k}{\tau_D{}^0 R^6} \int f_{D^*} \epsilon_A \frac{d\bar{\nu}}{\bar{\nu}^4} \qquad (5\text{-}17)$$

where $\bar{\nu}$ is the wave number, and ϵ_A is the extinction coefficient of the acceptor absorption f_{D^*} the emission distribution of the donor (in quanta on a wave-number scale and normalized to one), R is the distance between the centers of D^* and A, $\tau_D{}^0$ is the inherent radiative lifetime of the donor, and k is an experimental constant.

Equation 5-17 is derived assuming that thermal relaxation occurs before excitation transfer, that the dominant interaction can be expressed in terms of electric dipole transitions of D^* and A, and that the solvent does not interact strongly with the solute. The rate of excitation transfer predicted by Eq. 5-17 is merely expected to be smaller for "forbidden" transitions than for "allowed" ones. For a given donor, the transfer rate will increase as the extinction coefficient of the acceptor (averaged over the emission spectrum of the donor) increases.

It is important to note that Eq. 5-17 predicts that if the transition is forbidden in D^* but is allowed in A, excitation transfer may still occur with high probability by the resonance mechanism because the slower transfer rate is compensated by a longer mean lifetime of D^*. On the other hand, if the rate given by Eq. 5-17 is small because emissive transition in D^* is allowed, but absorptive transition in A is forbidden, then transfer by the resonance mechanism is unlikely because of the short radiative life of D^* and the slow rate of excitation transfer.

The integral

$$\int f_{D^*} \epsilon_A \frac{d\bar{\nu}}{\bar{\nu}^4}$$

is large if the emission spectrum of D^* overlaps strongly with the absorption spectrum of A—i.e., precisely the conditions required of the purely radiative emission-reabsorption mechanism. The latter is called the "trivial" reabsorption mechanism and can be shown to be negligible for properly chosen donor-acceptor pairs. Two important distinctions between the resonance and trivial mechanisms are that the former process occurs *before* D^* emits and that resonance interaction is effective only over limited distances, whereas the trivial mechanism may occur over extremely large distances. The trivial process may be excluded experimentally if the donor emission lifetime can be shown to depend on the concentration of A but that the nature of the emission spectrum is independent of the concentration of A.

Forster [4, 6] has shown that the rate constant of resonance-energy transfer as a function of distance is given by

$$\text{Rate constant } (D^* \rightarrow A^*) = \frac{1}{\tau_D} \left(\frac{R_0}{R} \right)^6 \qquad (5\text{-}18)$$

where τ_D is the *actual mean lifetime* of D^*, R is the separation between the centers of D^* and A, and R_0 is the critical separation of donor and acceptor for which energy transfer from D^* to A and emission from D^* are equally probable. Thus, the rate of energy transfer at $R_0 = R$ is equal to $1/\tau_D$, and if $R < R_0$, energy transfer dominates.

The *theoretical* transfer [4, 6] distance R_0 may be calculated from an approximate equation, where the emission spectrum of the donor is expressed in terms of the absorption spectrum of the donor by using the assumed mirror-image symmetry of these spectra (see Section 4-2):

$$R_0^6 \sim \frac{k\tau_D}{\bar{\nu}_0^2} \int_0^\infty \epsilon_A(\bar{\nu})\epsilon_D(2\bar{\nu}_0 - \bar{\nu}) \, d\bar{\nu} \qquad (5\text{-}19)$$

where $\bar{\nu}_0$ represents the wave number of the 0-0 donor transition. From Eq. 5-18 an *experimental* value [4, 6] of R_0 may be calculated by measuring the concentration of A required to make excitation transfer and spontaneous deactivation of D^* equally probable—i.e.

$$k_{et}[D^*][A]_{1/2} = k_d[D^*] \qquad (5\text{-}20)$$

where k_{et} and k_d are the specific rate constants for excitation transfer, and spontaneous deactivation, respectively, and $[D^*]$ and $[A]_{1/2}$ are the concentration of donor and acceptor, respectively. The concentration of $[A]_{1/2}$ required to fulfill Eq. 5-20 is found experimentally when the decay of D^* in the presence of A is equal to one-half of its value in the absence of A—i.e., $[A] = [A]_{1/2}$. Once $[A]_{1/2}$ is known, the experimental value of

R_0 may be calculated from the equation (N is Avogadro's number)

$$R_0 = \sqrt[3]{\frac{3,000}{4\pi N[A]_{1/2}}} = \frac{7.35}{\sqrt[3]{[A]_{1/2}}} \quad \text{in Å} \qquad (5\text{-}21)$$

This corresponds to an average of one molecule of A in a sphere with radius R_0 and D^* as the center. Equations 5-18, 5-19, and 5-21 hold for the case in which vibrational relaxation is fast compared to energy transfer. The transfer probability is then independent of the wavelength of the exciting radiation and increases, for a given donor molecule, as the extinction coefficient of the acceptor and the overlap of the donor emission spectrum and acceptor absorption spectrum increases. Consideration of Fig. 5-1 indicates the reason for the latter result. The emission spectrum of the donor will result from transitions from the $j = 0$ vibrational level of D^* to the $j' = 0, 1, 2$, etc. levels of the ground state, whereas the absorption spectrum of A will be from its $j' = 0$ level to the $j = 0, 1, 2, 3$, etc. levels of A^*. A coupled transition which spontaneously deactivates D^* and produces A^* requires an energy matching in the levels of the two molecules. If D^* undergoes a 0-0 emissive transition, A must undergo a 0-4 absorption. Clearly, the greater the amount of overlap of the D^* emission spectrum with the absorption spectrum of A, the greater the number of possibilities of energy matchings for coupled transitions.

Figure 5-2 shows a situation in which the 0-0 transition for the D^*

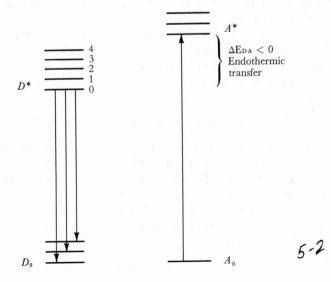

Fig. 5-2   *Unfavorable conditions for energy transfer between donor and acceptor.*

emission band is of lower energy than the 0-0 transition for the A absorption band. There is therefore *no overlap* of the two spectra and no chance for energy matching. Equation 5-17 predicts that the rate of transfer from D^* to A will be zero because the overlap integral is zero. The overlap restriction is obviously related to the energy of transitions available from D^* and A, so that for efficient energy transfer the molecule A must possess an excited state of lower energy than D^*.

Exchange-Energy Transfer [5, 16]

A second type of energy transfer which is in principle different from the resonance-energy transfer is possible when D^* and A are close enough for overlap of their electron clouds. In the region of overlap the electrons are indistinguishable so that an excited electron on D^* may also appear on A—i.e., an exchange mechanism for energy transfer operates.

Dexter [5] has shown that the probability of energy transfer by the exchange mechanism is proportional to the square of an exchange integral—i.e.,

$$P(D^* \to A^*) \propto \left| \int \Psi_{D^*} \Psi_A \mathbf{H}' \Psi_D \Psi_{A^*} \, d\tau \right|^2 \tag{5-22}$$

where $\Psi_{D^*} \Psi_A$ and $\Psi_D \Psi_{A^*}$ are the wave functions of the initial and final states, respectively, and $\mathbf{H}' = e^2/r_{12}$ where r_{12} is the distance between the electrons involved in the transition. This integral represents the electrostatic interaction between the electron clouds of the donor and acceptor. Since the molecular boundary surfaces of the electron clouds fall off rapidly as the separation of the D^* and A increases, this integral has small values except for very close separations.

Dexter [5] has also shown that the exchange mechanism becomes probable for a type of energy transfer which is prohibited from occurring by a resonance mechanism, namely triplet-triplet energy transfer. Since $\mathbf{H}'$ does not operate on spin wave functions, the latter may be factored out of Eq. 5-22:

$$P \propto \left| \int \phi_{D^*} \phi_A \mathbf{H}' \phi_{A^*} \phi_D \, d\tau_{12} \int S_{D^*} S_{A^*} \, d\tau_1 \int S_D S_A \, d\tau_2 \right|^2 \tag{5-23}$$

where the integration of spin functions is made over the spin coordinates of electron one and electron two. The spin integrals will equal zero unless the spin function of D^* is equal to that of A^*, and the spin function of D is equal to that of A because different spin functions are orthogonal. However, *the spin function of* D^* *or* A^* *need not be equal to that of* A *or* D. This assures us that the following energy transfer process is not forbidden by the exchange mechanism

$$D_T + A_0 \to A_T + D_0 \tag{5-24}$$

where D_T and A_T represent donor and acceptor triplets, respectively, while A_0 and D_0 represent acceptor and donor ground states.

The transfer probability may be written in a form [5] similar to that of Eq. 5-17

$$P(D^* \rightarrow A^*) = kz^2 \int\int f_{D^*} \epsilon_A \, d\bar{\nu} \qquad (5-25)$$

where z is proportional to the exchange integral given in Eq. 5-22, k is an experimental constant, and $\int\int f_{D^*} \epsilon_A \, d\bar{\nu}$ is again a measure of the overlap of donor emission and acceptor absorption. Only when D^* and A are close in space will z be sizeable—i.e., in the region where r_{12} is small, so that the exchange mechanism is predicted to occur only when D^* and A are essentially in molecular contact. Even if this condition is met, the emission-absorption overlap requirement demands that the energy of D^* emission transition must equal or be greater than for absorption transition.

Equation 5-23 predicts that both singlet-singlet transfer and triplet-triplet transfer are possible by an exchange mechanism.

5-3. PHYSICAL METHODS FOR THE DETECTION OF ENERGY TRANSFER

When energy transfer is detected by physical methods, the donor D is usually excited by radiation not absorbed by the acceptor A, and then physical evidence for the formation of A^* is sought. Equation 5-17 implies that only acceptors possessing strong singlet-singlet absorption will participate in resonance-excitation transfer, although the donor may be in a singlet or triplet state. Strong singlet-singlet absorptions results in a fast fluorescence rate from A^* (see Eq. 3-14), so that in most experimental examples of resonance transfer the appearance of the fluorescence of A^*, under conditions that only D absorbs the exciting radiation, is investigated.

Singlet-Singlet Transfer by Resonance Mechanism [9–11]

In order to establish that a resonance mechanism is operating, it must be shown that since resonance excitation transfer does not require collisions, it

1. must be able to occur efficiently over distances considerably greater than molecular diameters;
2. must be insensitive to the viscosity of the solvents or medium.[9–11]

Complex formation and the "trivial" mechanism must also be carefully eliminated as the mechanism responsible for excitation transfer.

An example of a system for which the resonance mechanism operates [9] is the acceptor-donor pair, perylene ($\phi_f^p = 0.50$) and 1-chloroanthracene ($\phi_f^c = 0.05$). Simultaneously, the fluorescence yield of 1-chloroanthracene decreases, and the total fluorescence yield of the system increases, as the relative concentration of 1-chloroanthracene to perylene increases, even though the former absorbs most of the exciting radiation. This result demands that the 1-chloroanthracene singlet is quenched *before* it fluoresces and that excitation transfer to perylene is faster than the internal quenching processes which cause the inherently low fluorescence efficiency of 1-chloroanthracene.

Table 5-2 lists some relevant data of three donor-acceptor pairs [9, 10]

Table 5-2   *Singlet-singlet transfer by the resonance mechanism* [9, 10]

Donor	Acceptor	k_{et} [a]	R_0 [b]
1-Chloroanthracene	Perylene	2×10^{11}	41
1-Chloroanthracene	Rubrene	2×10^{11}	38
9-Cyanoanthracene	Rubrene	3×10^{11}	84

[a] The rate constants for energy transfer are in liter mole^{-1} sec^{-1} and were found to be constant over a 100-fold change of solvent viscosity and 200° (20° to −180°) range of temperatures.
[b] Experimental critical separation distance in angstroms.

which have been shown to take part in resonance-excitation transfer. The rate of diffusion of the molecules studied should vary over a factor of more than 100 for the solvents employed, and yet the experimental values of k_{et}, the rate constant for excitation transfer, and R_0, the "critical" distance between the centers of D^* and A (see Section 5-2), remained constant within the experimental error. The quenching of D^* by A cannot be explained by a direct encounter of the two molecules during the lifetime of D^* since the rate of energy transfer would then be dependent on the rates of diffusion. Furthermore, k_{et} and R_0 were found to be nearly the same in liquid and solid solution. Diffusion is virtually prohibited in the latter phase, so that quenching must result from a remote interaction between D^* and A. Indeed, the experimental critical distances R_0^e, listed in Table 5-2, compare favorably with the values R_0^t, calculated from theory. The experimental transfer rate constants are of the order 2×10^{11} liter mole^{-1} sec^{-1}, about an order of magnitude larger than the rate constant expected for a diffusion-controlled transfer.[9, 10]

Triplet-Singlet Resonance Excitation Transfer [12-14]

At first sight we might expect any energy transfer process which involves a "spin-flip" will occur with such low probability that such occurrences could be neglected. However, although the rate of triplet-singlet transfer (Eqs. 5-17 and 5-19) is very small, the radiative lifetime of a triplet molecule is very long, so that a process such as energy transfer from a long-lived triplet donor to the singlet level of an acceptor may compete with triplet deactivation under certain conditions. We see therefore from Eq. 5-17 that a *slow rate* of triplet-singlet transfer is not

Table 5-3 *Critical separation distances for energy transfer from donor triplet to acceptor singlet* [12–14]

Donor	Acceptor	$R_0{}^e$	$R_0{}^t$	$\phi_s{}^a$	$\phi_s{}^b$
Phenanthrene	Fluorescein	35	—	8	7
2-Acetonaphthone	Fluorescein	43	—	20	20
Triphenylamine	Chlorophyll a	54	33	—	—
4-Phenylbenzaldehyde	Chrysoidine	33	32	—	—
N,N-Dimethylamine	9-Methylanthracene	24	—	—	—

[a] Measured value of sensitized acceptor fluorescence.
[b] Calculated value of sensitizer fluorescence from Eq. 5-27.

necessarily incompatible with a large value of R_0 for transfer—i.e., transfer by a resonance mechanism.[4] In general, an energy transfer process which is "forbidden" can become important if competing processes for energy dissipation of donor excitation are similarly forbidden.

In fact, the presence of triplet donor-singlet acceptor resonance transfer has been found for a number of systems, some of which are reported in Table 5-3.   A typical energy diagram for this phenomenon is given in Fig. 5-3.   The experiments [12–14] which established triplet-singlet transfers were conducted under conditions such that the donor absorbed most of

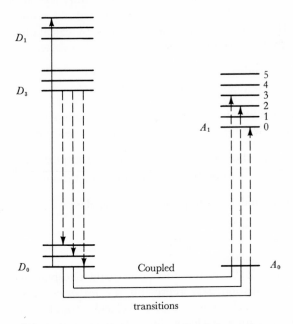

Fig. 5-3   *Energy diagram for triplet-singlet transfer.*

the exciting radiation. The lifetime τ_p and quantum yields ϕ_p of donor triplet emission at 77° K in solid ethanol solution were then measured for various concentrations of different acceptors. The triplet-singlet transfer was detected by the following methods:

1. reduction of τ_p in the presence of acceptor;
2. appearance of the fluorescence of the acceptor but *with a lifetime close to that of the triplet donor;*
3. experimental calculation of R_0, which was then compared to the theoretical R_0 expected from resonance transfer.

The sensitized fluorescence spectrum of the acceptor was identical to the spectrum obtained by direct excitation. Since the sensitized fluorescence decayed *at a much slower rate than normal fluorescence,* the latter could easily be eliminated by use of a phosphoroscope (which detects only long-lived emission). Triplet-singlet excitation transfer did not occur if the phosphorescence spectrum of the donor did not overlap the singlet-singlet absorption spectrum of the acceptor. Furthermore, the large value of R_0 eliminates the exchange mechanism from consideration. Similar experiments employing plastics as solvent, have led to similar results.[14]

A study of the absolute emission quantum yields allows the conclusion that *most of the degradation of electronic excitation energy within the donor and acceptor takes place from the lowest triplet to the ground state in competition with phosphorescence.*[12] This conclusion was reached by employing *acceptors* whose fluorescence yields are nearly one and by calculating the yields of sensitized fluorescence under the assumption that either:

1. all deactivation occurs in the S_1 state;
2. all deactivation occurs in the T_1 state.

Under the first assumption, each donor triplet emits or transfers, so that the quantum yield for *sensitized acceptor fluorescence* ϕ_s must be unity, where

$$\phi_s = \frac{\text{number of sensitized fluorescent acceptor molecules}}{\text{number of quenched triplet donors}} \qquad (5\text{-}26)$$

On the other hand, if assumption 2 is made, then

$$\phi_s = \frac{1 - \phi_f{}^D}{\phi_p{}^D} \qquad (5\text{-}27)$$

where $\phi_f{}^D$ and $\phi_p{}^D$ are the fluorescence and phosphorescence yields of the donor. Equation 5-27 represents the *maximum* yield of sensitized fluorescence if each donor triplet molecule transfers since $1 - \phi_f{}^D$ equals the maximum yield of donor triplets formed (no quenching of donor singlets to ground state being assumed) and $\phi_p{}^D$ represents the minimum number capable of transferring. As shown in Table 5-3, the value of ϕ_s predicted under assumption 2 closely corresponds to the experimentally measured value of ϕ_s. To the extent that the over-all assumptions for making this deduction are correct and within the accuracy of the experiments (15 to 20%), it appears that in solid solu-tion the internal-energy degradation of the excited molecules studied occurs through the lowest triplet state.[12-16] There is not enough experi-mental evidence available at this time to demand the conclusion that thermal quenching of S_1 will be unimportant for compounds other than simple aromatic hydrocarbons. For example, in the case of fluorescein derivatives, there is reason to believe that internal conversion from S_1 to S_0 is an important path of fluorescence quenching.[64]

Triplet-Triplet Energy Transfer [16]

The occurrence of energy transfer from the triplet level of a donor D_T to the triplet level of an acceptor A_T may be described by Eq. 5-28.

$$D_T + A_0 \rightarrow A_T + D_0 \tag{5-28}$$

The longer a molecule remains in an excited state the greater the proba-bility that it will transfer energy to a suitable acceptor if one happens to be in its vicinity. Because of its relatively long lifetime, the triplet state of a molecule is, in general, a more likely candidate to participate in energy transfer processes than the relatively short-lived singlet state of the same molecule. Indeed, the involvement of triplets in important energy transfer processes has been amply demonstrated by a number of physical and chemical techniques.[17-32]

The optimum conditions for detection of triplet-triplet transfer can be deduced from a consideration of Fig. 5-4. If the lowest singlet state of the donor D_{S_1} lies *below* that of the acceptor A_{S_1} but the lowest triplet level of the donor D_T lies *above* that of the acceptor A_T, the selective excitation of the donor in the presence of the acceptor is possible by employing exciting radiation which is totally absorbed by the donor. (The $S_0 \rightarrow T$ absorptions of donor and acceptor are negligible.) Under such conditions, singlet-singlet transfer is unlikely because of the unfavor-able energetic positions of the D_{S_1} and A_{S_1}. Triplet-triplet transfer, which is unlikely by a resonance mechanism *since forbidden transitions in both the donor and acceptor are involved*, is quite probable by an exchange mechanism *if the molecules D_T and A_0 are within collisional diameters of one another*. The advantage of selectively exciting the donor is that any process which occurs through the triplet acceptor (which does not pass through S_1) arises from the energy transfer process in Eq. 5-28.

Rigid Media [16]

The first experiments to establish the occurrence of triplet-triplet

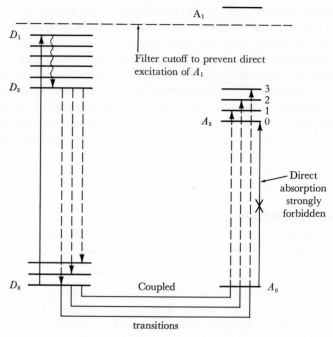

Fig. 5-4   *Triplet-triplet excitation transfer.*

energy transfer were performed by Terenin and Ermolaev.[17]   These authors studied the quenching of donor phosphorescence by various triplet energy acceptors in rigid media at 90° K.   The donors and acceptors were selected so as to conform to Fig. 5-4.   Let us point out again that triplet-triplet transfer is completely allowed by spin-selection rules, since the *total* spin momentum of the system is conserved.   Table 5-4 lists some compounds which were effective as sensitizers of acceptor

Table 5-4   *Triplet-triplet transfer in rigid media at 77° K* [17]

Donor [a]	E_T [b]	E_S [c]	R_0 [e]	Acceptor [a]	E_T [b]	E_{S_1} [c]	k_{et} [d]
Benzophenone	69	74	13	Naphthalene	61	89	2×10^2
Benzaldehyde	72	76	12	Naphthalene	61	89	2×10^2
Carbazole	70	84	15	Naphthalene	61	89	3×10^{-1}
Diphenylamine	72	89	13	Biphenyl	65	97	—

[a] Donor and acceptor concentration about 1.0 M in ethanol and ether solvent. Excitation provided by 3,660 Å light.

[b] Energy of lowest triplet level in kcal mole^{-1}.

[c] Energy of lowest singlet level in kcal mole^{-1}.

[d] Pseudo-unimolecular rate constants (in sec^{-1}) for the rate of excitation transfer.

[e] Critical separation distance in angstroms calculated from Eq. 5-21.

phosphorescence. For example, if an ethanol-ether solution which is 0.5 M in each acetophenone and naphthalene, is irradiated with 3,660 Å light (78.0 kcal mole^{-1}) only acetophenone singlets are excited. However, under these conditions the naphthalene phosphoresces strongly, and the acetophenone phosphorescence is strongly quenched.[16, 17] The lowest singlet state S_1 of acetophenone lies at 78 kcal mole^{-1}, while that of naphthalene lies at 90 kcal mole^{-1} making singlet-singlet transfer energetically impossible. However, the lowest triplet state of acetophenone T_1 lies at 74 kcal mole^{-1} above its ground state, while that of naphthalene lies at 61 kcal mole^{-1} making triplet-triplet transfer energetically favorable. Consideration of Fig. 5-4 shows that these are precisely the requirements for good overlap of the phosphorescence spectrum of donor with the singlet-triplet absorption spectrum of the acceptor. The trivial emission-reabsorption mechanism is completely ruled out in this case, however, because of the negligible extinction of intercombinational absorption for the molecules studied.[16, 17]

Measurement of the quantum yields of sensitized triplet-triplet transfer [21, 22] has led to some interesting conclusions concerning the nature of the excitation transfer process and the mechanism of electronic-energy degradation from the lowest excited singlet and triplet states. The quenching of donor phosphorescence follows Eq. 5-29

$$\frac{\phi_0}{\phi} = \exp{(NV[A])} \tag{5-29}$$

where ϕ_0 is the phosphorescence yield of the excited donor triplet D_T in the absence of the acceptor A_0, ϕ is the donor phosphorescence yield in the presence of an acceptor of concentration $[A]$, and $V = \frac{4}{3}\pi R^3$ (where R is the radius of a quenching sphere which depends solely on the donor-acceptor pair but not on their concentration). Equation 5-29 was derived from the quenching of an excited molecule which is surrounded by a well-defined "quenching sphere of influence" V. If a molecule of A happens to fall within the bounds of this sphere, an instantaneous quenching of the excited molecule is assumed. All the molecules of A which lie outside of the quenching sphere have no effect whatsoever on the excited molecule. Since Eq. 5-29 is followed by systems studied for triplet-triplet transfer in rigid media, the probability of such energy transfer must fall off very rapidly as the distance between the interacting donor and acceptor increases. This is exactly what is predicted by the exchange-energy transfer mechanism because of the rapid decrease of electronic boundary surfaces as one goes beyond collisional diameters. Further evidence [22-24] that a collisional mechanism operates in these systems derives from the critical transfer distances R_0, which are calculated from Eq. 5-30 (see Table 5-4):

$$V = \frac{\ln \dfrac{\Phi_0}{\Phi}}{N[A]} \tag{5-30}$$

where V is the volume of the sphere of radius R_0 in cubic centimeters, N is 6.02×10^{20} and $[A]$ is the concentration of acceptor in moles per liter which is required to reduce the donor phosphorescence yield from an initial value of Φ_0 to Φ.

Pseudo-first-order rate constants k_{et} for the energy-transfer process may be calculated from the lifetime of the donor phosphorescence as a function of $[A]$ if it is assumed that a linear dependence between the rate of energy transfer and $[A]$ exists.[16, 17]

Table 5-4 lists some typical rate constants in the last right-hand column. These rate constants are about 10^{10} times lower than those for singlet-singlet resonance transfer under similar conditions (see Table 5-2). The quenching of D_T must therefore only occur when an excited donor happens by accident to have a suitable acceptor molecule as a nearest neighbor. It should be noted that relatively high concentrations of donor and acceptor (about $0.5\ M$) are required to demonstrate this effect in rigid media.

Measurement of the quantum yield of sensitized phosphorescence ϕ_s where

$$\phi_s = \frac{\text{number of sensitized phosphorescent acceptor molecules}}{\text{number of quenched phosphorescent donor molecules}} \tag{5-31}$$

provides an important conclusion to be reached concerning the utilization of excitation energy imparted to the acceptor.[21-24] First of all, it is found that the yield of sensitized phosphorescence ($\phi_s = 0.12$) from naphthalene with benzophenone as donor is higher than the yield for naphthalene upon direct excitation ($\phi_p = 0.07$). More importantly, two limiting cases again can be tested to determine if electronic excitation is degraded to the ground state in S_1 or T_1 of the donor and acceptor. Case 1 assumes all quenching to the ground state occurs in the T_1 states. The yield of sensitized phosphorescence is then

$$\phi'_s = \left(\frac{\phi_p{}^A}{1 - \phi_f{}^A}\right)\left(\frac{1 - \phi_p{}^D}{\phi_p{}^D}\right) \tag{5-32}$$

where $\phi_p{}^A/(1 - \phi_f{}^A)$ is the fraction of phosphorescent acceptor molecules out of all those which form triplets and $(1 - \phi_p{}^D)/\phi_p{}^D$ is the fraction of donor triplets which are quenched by A. Case 2 assumes that all quenching occurs in the S_1 states. This case predicts

$$\phi''_s = 1 \tag{5-33}$$

since each phosphorescent donor which is quenched must produce a
phosphorescent acceptor triplet (see Table 5-5).

Table 5-5   *Quantum yields of sensitized phosphorescence in rigid media*
at 77° K [16, 22-24]

Donor [a]	Acceptor [a]	ϕ_s [b]	ϕ_s [c]	ϕ_s [d]
Benzophenone	Naphthalene	0.07	0.06	1
Benzophenone	1-Chloronaphthalene	0.12	0.22	1
Benzophenone	1-Bromonaphthalene	0.20	0.19	1
Benzophenone	1-Iodonaphthalene	0.35	0.29	1
Phenanthrene	Naphthalene	0.30	0.30	1
Phenanthrene	1-Chloronaphthalene	0.73	1.0	1
Phenanthrene	1-Bromonaphthalene	0.99	0.94	1

[a] Donor and acceptor concentrations about 0.1 M in alcohol-ether solvent.   Excitation provided by 3,660 Å light.   The acceptors do not absorb at this wavelength,
i.e., E_{S_1} (acceptor) $> E_{S_2}$ (donor).
[b] Experimental value of Φ_s (uncertainty about 10 to 15%).
[c] Value of ϕ_s calculated from Eq. 5-32, assuming all quenching occurs in T_1.
[d] Value of ϕ_s calculated from Eq. 5-33, assuming all quenching occurs in S_1.

Comparison of the experimental value of ϕ_s with the calculated values
in the last two columns shows that satisfactory agreement for the values
from Eq. 5-32 but large discrepancies for the values from Eq. 5-33, except
for the case in which phenanthrene is donor, where either fits the data.[22-24]
If we tentatively assume these data are typical of simple aromatic compounds, then we conclude that

1. transfer of electronic energy between triplet states occurs by
quenching of the donor triplet and simultaneous excitation of the
acceptor triplet;
2. the processes of nonradiative transfer to the ground state in
simple aromatic molecules occur in the triplet state and are independent
of the path required to populate the triplet state.

Such results are consistent with the observation that, on irradiation
with flash or even ordinary lamps of solid solutions of organic compounds,
appreciable concentrations of molecules in the triplet state are obtained,
but the same compounds may show only a negligibly small phosphorescence yield.   These conclusions, of course, are completely consistent
with those derived from triplet-singlet resonance transfer (see earlier).
It should be pointed out that the experimental uncertainty of the data
given in Table 5-5 (15 to 20%) may obscure a significant amount of
$S_1 \rightsquigarrow S_0$ deactivation.   It is of fundamental importance that the generality and accuracy of these data be extended.

It may be that the slow rate of thermal quenching of the excited singlet state is due to its higher energy (compared to the triplet) which causes it to have a smaller probability of radiationless transition to the ground state because of the Franck-Condon principle. In other words, the greater the energy of an excited state, the greater the amount of electronic energy which must be converted into ground-state vibrational energy when a radiationless transition from the excited state to the ground state occurs. Also, as we have seen, crossing of excited-state potential-energy surfaces are less frequent with the ground state than with other excited states. This places a prohibition factor on the rate of the singlet-ground radiationless process, relative to the favored singlet-triplet inter-system crossing. Once the molecule is in the triplet state, which is invariably the lowest excited state of the molecule, it must either emit or undergo intersystem crossing to the ground state. Since the radiative lifetime of triplets is relatively long, it is not surprising that thermal quenching in the triplet may be important. This is precisely the interpretation of the remarkable effect of perdeuteration of benzene and naphthalene described in Section 4-3. The radiationless degradation of T_1 to ground is hindered by the deuterium substitution which allows nearly every triplet formed to emit.[14,25]

A study of the relationship of the strength of the singlet-triplet absorption spectrum of the acceptor on the efficiency of quenching donor phosphorescence showed that there is no difference in the efficiency of transfer in going from naphthalene to iodonaphthalene as quenchers of benzophenone phosphorescence. However, $\epsilon(S_0 \to T)$ is expected to differ by a factor of 1,000 for these compounds,[26] judging from their phosphorescence lifetimes (see Table 5-6). In these cases, the $S_0 \to T$

Table 5-6   *Quenching efficiencies of naphthalene and its haloderivatives in rigid media at 77° K* [26]

Donor [a]	Acceptor [a]	Quenching Efficiency of Acceptor [b]	$\epsilon_A(S_0 \to T)$ [c]
Benzophenone	Naphthalene	0.20	1
Benzophenone	1-Chloronaphthalene	0.16	10
Benzophenone	1-Bromonaphthalene	0.20	100
Benzophenone	1-Iodonaphthalene	0.20	1000

[a] Concentration of donor = 2.1×10^{-2} M; acceptor = 3.2×10^{-1} M in ethanol-ether. Excitation provided by 3,660 Å light (E_T (Donor) = 69).

[b] Ratio of donor emission in the presence of acceptor to donor emission in the absence of acceptor (E_T (Acceptor) < 61).

[c] Relative (approximate) extinction coefficients for singlet-triplet absorption of the acceptor from lifetime data in Reference 26.

absorption spectrum of the quenchers are approximated by extension of the 0-0 phosphorescence band of these molecules to higher energies.[47] These results imply that resonance-excitation transfer is negligible, and that exchange transfer, since it is already fully allowed when the donor and acceptor are nearest neighbors, is unaffected by the $S_0 \rightarrow T_1$ transition probability of the acceptor.

In all of the systems studied, no spectral perturbations indicative of complexing between donors and acceptors were detected. Furthermore, the fluorescence of donors such as carbazole was not affected by the presence of triplet acceptors, although phosphorescence was strongly quenched. Finally, the phosphorescence spectra and lifetimes of the sensitized molecules were identical to those for the same molecule directly excited.

The requirement of a favorable energetic disposition of donor and acceptor triplet levels was confirmed by the fact that none of the acceptors listed in Table 5-5 are capable of exciting the phosphorescence of any of the donors. Finally, singlet donor to triplet acceptor was rendered unlikely as a mechanism for the energy transfers described in this section because naphthalene is incapable of quenching the fluorescence of anthracene derivatives which strongly overlap the (expected) singlet-triplet absorption spectrum of naphthalene.

Recently, electron spin resonance (esr) has been used to confirm these results for triplet-triplet transfer.[18] In this case, the esr signal of the triplet of the acceptor, naphthalene, was found to appear when solutions of benzophenone and naphthalene were irradiated with light absorbed only by the ketone.

Finally, a favored geometry has been found for energy transfer from benzophenone to phenanthrene. Such studies are of great theoretical interest, although relatively few have been made.[20]

Summary of Conclusions from Sensitized Triplet-Triplet Transfer in Rigid Media [16]

The results of sensitized phosphorescence studies are of great fundamental importance and are probably responsible for the motivation behind many of the important extensions of this work to fluid solution. Let us list these conclusions here:

1. The exchange mechanism very adequately explains the small values of R_0 which conform closely to the molecular diameters of the molecules studied.[17]

2. A method is available for populating the T_1 state of an acceptor bypassing the S_1 state. This implies that the triplet state of certain molecules, which undergo very inefficient intersystem crossing from

S_1, can be populated efficiently by employing a donor which forms and transfers triplets in good yield.[17]

3. The efficiency of an acceptor or quencher is not determined by molecular structure but rather by the position of the lowest triplet levels.[21]

4. The degradation of electronic states to ground states probably occurs in T_1 for the molecules studied.[22–24]

5. Excitation transfer is efficient only if the E_T of the donor is greater than the E_T of the acceptor.

5-4. COLLISIONAL OR EXCHANGE–ENERGY TRANSFER IN FLUID SOLUTION

The phenomenon of exchange-energy transfer between singlet states also has been noted by several workers.[27–32] The technique employed to detect such a process in liquids is to observe the emission spectrum of biacetyl which both fluoresces and phosphoresces in fluid solutions at room temperature. The yield of phosphorescence Φ_p is much greater than the yield of fluorescence Φ_f, under these conditions, Φ_p/Φ_f being about 60. The intense phosphorescence can be completely eliminated, however, by working with solutions saturated with oxygen. In such aerated solutions the fluorescence spectrum is unaffected but the phosphorescence spectrum is completely quenched, which makes measurements of the less intense fluorescence quite easy.

Singlet-Singlet Energy Transfer [27–34]

The energy-transfer experiment is conducted as follows: An aerated solution of donor (sensitizer) and biacetyl are irradiated under conditions such that the intensity of biacetyl fluorescence in the presence of sensitizer may be compared with intensity of biacetyl fluorescence in the absence of sensitizer.[27, 28] The sensitizer and wavelength of the exciting radiation are so chosen that the biacetyl only absorbs a small fraction of the incident light. If an increase in the fluorescence of biacetyl in the presence of sensitizer (above that expected from direct excitation of biacetyl) is noted, we may conclude that energy transfer from the singlet state of the sensitizer to the singlet state of biacetyl has occurred.

$$D^* \text{ (singlet)} + Bi_0 \rightarrow Bi^* \text{ (singlet)} + D_0 \qquad (5\text{-}34)$$
$$\downarrow \qquad\qquad\qquad\qquad \downarrow$$
$$D_0 + h\nu \qquad\qquad\qquad Bi_0 + h\nu$$

Sensitizers are chosen so that observation of quenching of sensitizer fluorescence may be made simultaneously with the observation of acceptor fluorescence. Rates of sensitization K_s and quenching K_q may be measured independently and compared to one another. We have seen earlier that

the yield of emission quenched or sensitized may be expressed in kinetic
terms as a Stern-Volmer equation of the form

$$\frac{\phi_0}{\phi} = 1 + K_q[Q] = 1 + K_s[Q] \qquad (5\text{-}35)$$

where $K_s = K_q = \tau k_q$, the product of the specific rate constant k_q for the
transfer process and the actual mean lifetime τ, of the excited donor
under the experimental conditions in the absence of Q. Results of such
experiments [28, 29] are given in Table 5-7.

Table 5-7 *Quenching and sensitization of biacetyl fluorescence at 25° C
in fluid solution* [28, 29]

Donor [a]	K_s [b]	K_q [b]	τ ($\times 10^{-9}$) [c]	R_0 [d]
Diethyl ketone	34	28	3.7	4.1
Cyclopentanone	19	25	3.3	4.0
Phenanthrene	131	128	17	6.3
Naphthalene	175	180	24	—
Benzene	190	190	8.6	—

[a] Concentration of biacetyl 0.01 to 0.05 M in cyclohexane; concentration of donor
variable depending on system.   Excitation provided by 3,200 Å light E_T (Donor) > 60.
[b] Sensitization or quenching constant from a plot of Eq. 5-35.
[c] The lifetime in seconds of the donor fluorescence in aerated cyclohexane solution
in the absence of biacetyl.
[d] Critical-transfer distance in angstroms for singlet-singlet transfer.

In the table R_0 is the experimental critical distance for which the
rate of energy transfer from the sensitizer is equal to the rate of all other
modes of decay of the sensitizer—i.e.,

$$\tau_D k_{et}[A]_{1/2} = 1 \qquad (5\text{-}36)$$

where $\tau_D = (1/\Sigma_i \, k_i)$, $[A]_{1/2}$ is the acceptor concentration for which the
equation is valid, and k_i is the rate constant of processes which deactivate
D^*.   A plot of $1/\tau_D$ versus k_{et} yields the appropriate value of $[A]_{1/2}$. R_0,
the "critical distance" for 50% probability of energy transfer, is then
calculated from Eq. 5-21 discussed above.

The efficiency of the transfer process can be estimated from the value
of $k_{et}\tau_D$ if τ_D is known from independent measurements.   A typical calculation [16] is that for benzene for which the upper limit of τ_D has been
determined to be 2.5 × 10^{-8} sec.   The value of $k_{et}\tau_D = 190$ liter mole^{-1}
for benzene as sensitizer; therefore

$$k_{et} = \frac{190 \text{ liter mole}^{-1}}{2.5 \times 10^{-8} \text{ sec}}$$

or $k_{et} = 7.6 \times 10^9$ liter mole^{-1} sec^{-1}.

This value is close to that predicted for the rate of diffusion in cyclo-hexane, the solvent used in these experiments, by the Debye [3, 33] equation (Eq. 5-13)(η = 0.089 poise)

$$k_{\text{diffusion}} = \frac{8\,RT}{3,000\,\eta} = 7.5 \times 10^9 \text{ liter mole}^{-1} \text{ sec}^{-1}$$

The evidence is fairly conclusive, within the validity of the assumptions, that long-range singlet-singlet energy transfer noted in other cases is absent. This is probably not due to the lack of overlap of the emission spectrum of the sensitizer and the absorption spectrum of biacetyl but rather to the low extinction coefficient of biacetyl absorption which makes the rate of resonance-energy transfer slow compared to the rate of exchange-energy transfer.

Triplet-Triplet Transfer

The sensitization and quenching of biacetyl phosphorescence has proven to be a valuable tool for the detection of triplet-triplet excitation transfer in fluid solution. The sensitization of biacetyl phosphorescence may be used to detect the triplet states of suitable donors, and the quenching of biacetyl phosphorescence may be used to populate the triplet states of suitable acceptors. The lifetimes, quantum yields, and energies of biacetyl fluorescence and phosphorescence are summarized [34] in Table 5-8.

Table 5-8   *Lifetimes and quantum yields of biacetyl emission in various phases* [34]

State	Φ_f	Φ_p	τ_p [a]
Gas	0.002	0.15	1.8×10^{-3}
Dilute Solution	0.01	0.08	1.0×10^{-3}
Rigid Glass	0.005	0.23	2.3×10^{-3}

[a] Phosphorescence lifetime in seconds.

The Stern-Volmer equation (Eq. 5-9) or some variation of it, is used to investigate the *quenching* of biacetyl emission. Table 5-9 summarizes the quenching constants [35-38] for a number of compounds along with their triplet energies E_T. In these studies, the lifetime of phosphorescent biacetyl τ is measured in dilute benzene solutions at 25°. It is found that τ obeys the equation

$$\frac{1}{\tau_q} = \frac{1}{\tau} + k_q[Q] \tag{5-37}$$

where τ is the lifetime of biacetyl phosphorescence in pure benzene, and

Table 5-9   *Quenching constants and E_T values for quenching of biacetyl ($E_T = 56$) phosphorescence [38] in benzene solution at 20° C*

Quencher	E_T	k_{q_f} [a]	k_{q_r} [b]
Phenanthrene [c]	62	2×10^3	—
Naphthalene	61	2×10^6	1×10^{10}
Nitrobenzene [c]	61	1×10^4	—
2-Iodonaphthalene	60	6×10^6	—
1-Chloronaphthalene	59	3×10^7	4×10^9
1-Bromonaphthalene	59	3×10^7	3×10^9
1-Iodonaphthalene	59	3×10^7	—
2,2'-Dinaphthyl	56	3×10^9	1×10^9
Fluoranthene	54	5×10^9	2×10^7
1,2-Benzpyrene	54	6×10^9	5×10^7
Pyrene	49	8×10^9	2×10^4
Anthracene [c]	42	8×10^9	—
Oxygen [c]	23	8×10^9	—

[a] Bimolecular quenching constants for energy transfer from biacetyl triplets to quencher from Eq. 5-10, corrected for reversible energy transfer.

[b] Bimolecular quenching constants for energy transfer from quencher triplets to biacetyl.

[c] Quenching constant uncorrected for reversible energy transfer.

τ_q is the lifetime in the presence of a quencher whose concentration is $[Q]$ and whose quenching rate constant is k_q.

From Table 5-9 it can be seen that the effectiveness of an energy transfer quencher is determined mainly by the position of its lowest triplet level and not by its molecular structure.[38] This result and the fact that biacetyl fluorescence is negligibly affected by those quenchers which have an S_1 state at higher energy than biacetyl, demand that quenching involves only the triplet states of biacetyl and quencher. Furthermore, the strongest quenchers (E_T less than 50 kcal mole^{-1}) have nearly the same value of k_q which in turn is close to that estimated from the Debye equation (Eq. 5-13), which yields $k_q = 1 \times 10^{10}$ liter mole^{-1} sec^{-1} for bimolecular diffusion in benzene solution at 25°.

For quenchers with triplet levels higher than 55 kcal mole^{-1} there is a general trend toward a lowering [38] of k_q with increasing E_T. The scatter of the data observed for quenchers whose triplet energies are close to that of biacetyl may be due to reversible energy transfer. This result is to be expected since at 20° about one molecule in 100 will possess about 3 kcal mole^{-1} excess vibrational energy, so that coupled transitions between donor and acceptor (of slightly greater energy) may occur with reasonable probability. It may also be possible for transfer to be reversed if, during its lifetime, the triplet quencher molecule should encounter a

ground-state biacetyl molecule.   Reversible transfer,[38] for quenchers with
triplet levels slightly below or above that of biacetyl, will be enhanced as
the concentration of biacetyl increases—i.e., k_q will decrease with increasing biacetyl concentration, as has been confirmed experimentally.

We have seen earlier that naphthalene and 1-iodonaphthalene (whose
oscillator strengths for singlet-triplet absorption differ by a factor of 1000)
are equally effective at quenching the phosphorescence of benzophenone
in rigid solution at 77° K (Table 5-6).   In this case the donor possessed
a higher E_T than the quencher.   A similar result was found for the
quenching of biacetyl phosphorescence by naphthalene and iodonaphthalene [38] *when reversible energy transfer is taken into account*.   It can be seen
from Table 5-9 that reversible energy transfer from naphthalene to
biacetyl occurs at a diffusion-controlled rate.   If reverse transfer is
ignored, k_q is 4×10^3 liters mole^{-1} sec^{-1} for energy transfer from biacetyl
to naphthalene—lower than the true rate by three orders of magnitude!
On the other hand, 1- and 2-iodonaphthalene possess such short triplet
lifetimes that reverse transfer is negligible and no correction of k_q is necessary.   These results are consistent with the assumptions (a) that the
exchange mechanism only operates when the partners involved in the
energy transfer process collide, and (b) that factors such as the oscillator
strength of the $S_0 \rightarrow T_1$ transition of the acceptor are not important, even
when the E_T of D^* lies below that of the acceptor.

It should be pointed out that chemical reactions such as hydrogen
abstraction and electron transfer also may efficiently quench biacetyl
triplets.[35-37]   Thus, phenol and aniline are quenchers of biacetyl phosphorescence but triphenylamine and anisole are not.   All of these compounds
have E_T values > 56, which eliminate triplet energy transfer as the
quenching mechanism.

Sensitization of Biacetyl Phosphorescence [29, 32, 37]

We have seen that the fluorescence of biacetyl may be sensitized by
suitable donors.   Observation of sensitization of biacetyl phosphorescence
requires oxygen-free solutions, or the phosphorescence is completely
quenched.   Measurements of solutions containing both sensitizer and
biacetyl show that the latter may be induced to phosphoresce by light
absorbed primarily by the sensitizer.   In the case of benzophenone as
donor the spectrum of sensitized luminescence consists of a high yield of
pure biacetyl phosphorescence, but fluorescence is also found if the
biacetyl is excited directly.[37]   This result is strong evidence for the fact
that

1. benzophenone forms triplets when irradiated in fluid solution at
room temperature;

2. benzophenone can efficiently transfer its triplet energy to the triplet state of biacetyl.

Since no fluorescence at all is observed from benzophenone, the lifetime of the singlet state of benzophenone can be calculated to be less than 10^{-10} sec from a kinetic analysis, as shown in Section 4-4. Some data are given in Table 5-10 for the sensitization of biacetyl phosphorescence.[26]

Table 5-10   *Sensitization of biacetyl phosphorescence* [29]

Donor [a]	K_s [b]	τ_D ($\times 10^{-5}$) [c]
Biphenyl	6×10^5	3.0
Naphthalene	1.5×10^6	7.4
Acetone	8×10^3	0.04
Acetophenone	7.2×10^3	0.04

[a] Donor-concentration variable in hexane solution, biacetyl concentration about 10^{-4} M. Excitation at 3,200 Å E_T (Donor) > 61.
[b] Sensitization constants determined from Eq. 5-35.
[c] Lifetime in seconds of donor triplet in the absence of biacetyl.

None of the sensitizers phosphoresce in fluid solutions, so measurement of donor quenching was not possible. In Table 5-10 the lifetimes were calculated by assuming that sensitization occurs at the diffusion-control rate equal to 2.2×10^{10} liter mole^{-1} sec^{-1} for hexane at 25°. The exchange mechanism for excitation transfer is again operating since the critical-transfer distance for these transfers is close to that expected for collisional diameters.

Energy Transfer in Fluid Solutions
Detected by Flash Photolysis [39, 40]

The failure of the majority of organic compounds to phosphoresce in fluid solution necessitated the indirect detection of triplets (by processes such as sensitization of biacetyl phosphorescence) until the development of the technique of flash photolysis. Since this powerful technique detects triplet states, the lifetimes of these states may be measured directly. Using this method, the results described above were confirmed, and the assumption of diffusion-controlled energy transfer, if the process is over-all exothermic, was vindicated. Typical quenching constants [39, 40] for triplet-triplet transfer are summarized in Table 5-11. The rate constants k_q are calculated from the half-quenching concentration $[Q]_{1/2}$, for which

$$k_q[Q]_{1/2}[D_T] = k_1[D_T] \qquad (5\text{-}38)$$

i.e., the rate of energy transfer to Q equals the rate of unimolecular decay

Table 5-11   *Quenching rate constants by flash photolysis* [39, 40]

Donor [a]	Acceptor [a]	k_q [b]	R_0 [c]
Triphenylene	Naphthalene	1×10^9	0.11
Phenanthrene	1-Bromonaphthalene	1×10^8	0.40
Benzophenone	Naphthalene	1×10^9	0.18
Biacetyl	1,2-Benzanthracene	3×10^9	0.19
Anthracene	Phenanthrene	10^3	—

[a] Donor and acceptor concentrations about 10^{-3} M in hexane. In all cases except the last the triplet energy of the donor is greater than that of the acceptor.
[b] Measured quenching constant in liter mole^{-1} sec^{-1} from Eq. 5-39.
[c] Experimental critical separation distance in angstroms calculated from Eq. 5-19.

of triplets [40] in the absence of Q. From Eq. 5-38 we have

$$k_q = \frac{k_1}{[Q]_{1/2}} \tag{5-39}$$

For example, $[Q]_{1/2}$ for the quenching of triphenylene triplets by naphthalene is 2×10^{-5} mole liter^{-1} and k_1 is 2×10^4 sec^{-1}, both values for hexane solution, so that

$$k_q = \frac{2 \times 10^4 \text{ sec}^{-1}}{2 \times 10^{-5} \text{ mole liter}^{-1}} = 1 \times 10^9 \text{ liter mole}^{-1} \text{ sec}^{-1}$$

It was established that fluorescence of the donors was unaffected by energy transfer under the conditions of these experiments.[40]

These results provide perhaps the most unequivocal proof that quenching of donor triplets occurs at a diffusion-controlled rate if the acceptor triplet level is lower in energy. Again the exchange mechanism is operating for the transfer of triplet energy because transfer occurs at rates which do not exceed those expected or calculated for diffusion-controlled encounters of donor and acceptor. The values of R_0 calculated from Eq. 5-19 are given in Table 5-11. The values for R_0 (theory) are so small that calculation from Eq. 5-19 must not be valid for these systems.

Conclusions from Triplet-Triplet Transfer Experiments in Fluid Solution [16]

The important conclusions derived from studies of triplet-triplet transfer in condensed phases are: (a) if E_T^D, the triplet energy of the donor, is greater than E_T^A, the triplet energy of the acceptor, the rate constant for energy transfer from donor to acceptor equals the rate constant for encounters; (b) if E_T^D is similar or equal to E_T^A, the net rate of energy transfer may be less than the encounter rate because of reversible energy transfer (if A possesses a triplet lifetime greater than about 10^{-6} sec);

(c) if $E_T{}^D$ is less than $E_T{}^A$ by more than several kilocalories per mole, essentially no quenching of donor triplets occurs; (d) there is no evidence for a *decrease* in quenching efficiency as $E_T{}^D - E_T{}^A$ increases; (e) the exchange (collisional) mechanism operates in triplet-triplet energy transfer; (f) triplets are formed in high yield when organic molecules are excited in fluid solution at room temperature; (g) the triplet state of A may be produced *without* the intermediacy of the excited singlet state of A.

Triplet-Triplet Annihilation [41]

Normally, the concentration of excited states is so small that bimolecular reactions involving two excited molecules can be neglected. However, under certain conditions two long-lived triplets D_T may collide with one another in solution and "annihilate" each other simultaneously producing one molecule in the excited singlet state D_{S_1} and the other in a ground state D_{S_0}.

$$D_T + D_T \rightarrow D_{S_1} + D_{S_0} \qquad (5\text{-}40)$$
$$D_{S_1} \rightarrow D_{S_0} + h\nu \qquad (5\text{-}41)$$

The fluorescence emission of D_{S_1} may then be observed, but with a lifetime similar to that of the triplet, because excitation has resided temporarily in D_T. The yield of this "delayed" fluorescence, since it results from a two-photon process, usually depends upon the square of the intensity of the exciting light. This process is clearly different from the thermally activated "delayed" fluorescence which may occur, if the lowest singlet and triplet are so close in energy that thermal activation will occasionally promote triplets up to S_1, from which they fluoresce.

The triplet-triplet annihilation mechanism requires that part of the energy from two separately absorbed photons be transferred to the same molecule. Energy transfer from donor triplets may therefore be used to produce acceptor triplets which, upon annihilation, will produce an excited singlet capable of emitting a photon of higher frequency (greater energy) than the absorbed light. The requirements for such a phenomenon are met if the donor has a S_1 state which lies below that of the acceptor, but whose T_1 state lies above that of the acceptor. The phenanthrene-naphthalene system fulfills this requirement,[41-43] and the energy diagram for this system is shown in Fig. 5-5.

The mechanism of sensitized naphthalene fluorescence is given by the following scheme

$$P_0 \xrightarrow{3,500\text{Å}} P_1 \rightsquigarrow P_3 \qquad (5\text{-}42)$$

$$P_3 + N_0 \longrightarrow N_3 + P_0 \qquad (5\text{-}43)$$

$$2\,N_3 \longrightarrow N_1 + N_0 \qquad (5\text{-}44)$$

$$N_1 \longrightarrow N_0 + h\nu \ (3,250\ \text{Å}) \qquad (5\text{-}45)$$

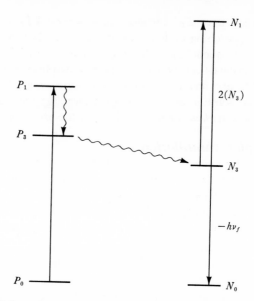

Fig. 5-5   *Energy diagram for the phenanthrene-naphthalene system.*

where P and N refer to phenanthrene and naphthalene, and the sub-
scripts 0, 1, and 3 refer to ground, lowest singlet, and triplet states,
respectively.   The quantum yield for delayed emission is about 1%, but
an excess of about 6 kcal $mole^{-1}$ greater than that of the exciting light
was produced.

Triplet-triplet annihilation is a very efficient process in crystals,[44] solid
solutions,[45] and may also be important in some vapors.[46]   In the latter
phase it has been found that triplet-triplet annihilation completely dominates relatively rapid first-order decay processes and that annihilation
occurs upon every collision of two triplets.[46]

The discovery of bimolecular reactions between two excited states
opens some exciting photochemical possibilities.   The reactions of two
triplet molecules with each other may be quite different from the reaction
of one triplet with a ground state.   It may be possible with properly
chosen systems to effect "cross" triplet reactions of two molecules or
intercept excited singlets with a triplet.   Although development of high-
intensity sources has increased the attractiveness of such studies, to date
very little is known about the photochemistry associated with annihilation.

The annihilation process has been shown to be capable of providing
qualitative information [41-43] about

1. the internal conversions and intersystem crossings of molecules
in solution;

2. the relative positions of triplet levels.

Unfortunately the number of such studies is quite small but will hopefully become larger.

5-5. INTRAMOLECULAR ENERGY TRANSFER

The radiationless processes which convert one electronic state to another in the same molecule may be considered as an example of *intramolecular* energy transfer and, in principle, may be treated theoretically in a manner similar to intermolecular energy transfer. For the sake of convenience we shall consider intramolecular energy transfer of three types:

    1. excitation transfer within a given chromphore;
    2. excitation transfer between two conjugated chromophores;
    3. excitation transfer between two nonconjugated chromophores.

Excitation transfer within a molecular complex was discussed earlier in Section 4-2.

Excitation Transfer within a Chromophore [47]

The carbonyl group serves as an example of type 1. Figure 4-15 is representative of the energy diagram of a molecule such as benzophenone or acetone, in which excitation is localized on the carbonyl group. Absorption of a photon by the molecule to excite the $^1(\pi,\pi^*)$ state is followed by rapid intramolecular excitation transfers before the molecule returns to S_0. As in the case of the intermolecular excitation transfer, only energetically favorable transitions are probable. Thus, the processes

$$^1(\pi,\pi^*) \rightsquigarrow {}^3(\pi,\pi^*)$$

and

$$^1(\pi,\pi^*) \rightsquigarrow {}^1(n,\pi^*)$$

will compete for degradation of $^1(\pi,\pi^*)$. If the latter process occurs, then the two processes

$$^1(n,\pi^*) \rightsquigarrow {}^3(n,\pi^*)$$

$$^1(n,\pi^*) \rightsquigarrow S_0$$

will compete with each other and fluorescence for the dissipation of energy of the lowest excited singlet state. These intramolecular excitation transfers are precisely the internal conversion and intersystem crossing processes discussed in Section 4-3.

Excitation Transfer within a Conjugated Chromophore [47, 51]

An interesting situation arises when one chromophore such as a carbonyl group is conjugated with another chromophore such as a benzene or naphthalene nucleus. If one chromophore can be excited selectively, is the excitation localized on the initially excited group or may it be transferred to the other? From analogy with the intermolecular excitation transfers discussed above we might expect a general rule such as: *The lowest excited states of a molecule possessing two independently absorbing but formally conjugated chromophores is determined by the chromophore moiety possessing the lowest excitation energy.* In other words, the excitation will be passed on from one excited state to another until the lowest S_1 or T_1 states are reached.[47] Lewis and Calvin [61] proposed a similar theory in which they proposed that electronic energy can be transferred within a molecule until it reaches a "loose-bolt" group which efficiently dissipates the energy.

The rule given above can be tested by observation of the nature of the emission spectrum of a molecule which emits from S_1 or T_1. If the fluorescence and phosphorescence can be shown to arise mainly from a particular group, then the extent of excitation transfer between the absorbing and emitting groups can be evaluated. We might expect that if energy transfer is possible because of the weak intermolecular interactions due to the peripheral parts of the electron clouds of different molecules, this process should take place more efficiently between two groups in the same molecule.

As an example, consider intermolecular excitation transfer between triplet levels for a molecule such as 4-phenylbenzophenone.[47] The absorption spectrum of this molecule in ethanol-ether at 77° K is shown in Fig. 5-6. The long wavelength bands are due to an n,π^* excitation. This assignment is made on the basis of

1. the blue shift which the bands suffer upon going to more polar solvents;
2. the vibrational spacing ($1,200$ cm^{-1}) which is expected from carbonyl stretching in a $S_1(n,\pi^*)$ state where excitation is localized on the C$=$O group;
3. the low extinction coefficient of the bands ($\epsilon \sim 100$).

This spectrum should be compared to that of benzophenone which is given in Fig. 4-3

The emission spectrum of 4-phenylbenzophenone [47] is given in Fig. 5-7, along with the emission yields and lifetimes. Although the absorption spectrum of benzophenone and its 4-phenyl derivative look very similar, the emission spectrum of the latter compound is completely differ-

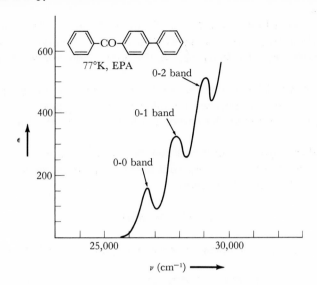

Fig. 5-6   *Absorption spectrum of 4-phenylbenzophenone in ethanol ether at 77° K.*

ent in position, lifetime, and structure from the spectrum of benzophenone and is similar to the spectrum of biphenyl.[47]   The latter compound *must* possess a lowest $T_1(\pi,\pi^*)$ state, so that an intramolecular energy transfer from the $S_1(n,\pi^*)$ state localized on C=O to the $T_1(\pi,\pi^*)$ state localized on the biphenyl radical has occurred.   This process is formally analogous to the intermolecular energy transfer between benzophenone and biphenyl (see Table 5-4).

Let us now make use of Fig. 5-8, which is the energy-level diagram for 4-phenylbenzophenone.   Excitation in the first absorption band produces a $S_1(n,\pi^*)$ state which like benzophenone undergoes efficient intersystem crossing to $T_2(n,\pi^*)$, since no fluorescence is observed from 4-phenylbenzophenone.   This triplet in turn passes by intramolecular excitation transfer to $T_1(\pi,\pi^*)$ of the biphenyl group which then phosphoresces.

Benzophenone does not phosphoresce from a benzene-like triplet because the lowest triplet of benzene is at 85 kcal mole^{-1} and $T_1(n,\pi^*)$ is at 69 kcal mole^{-1}.   On the other hand, the lowest triplet in biphenyl is at 65 kcal mole^{-1}, which makes triplet-triplet excitation transfer energetically favorable.

If we assume that the triplet energies of all states of simple carbonyl compounds are about 70 kcal mole^{-1}, then we predict that attachment of a moiety (radical) whose triplet excitation energy E_T is much greater than 70 kcal mole^{-1} (e.g., alkyl groups and simple aryl groups) will result in a molecule whose lowest S_1 and T_1 are n,π^* states. Attachment of a moiety whose E_T is much lower than 70 kcal mole^{-1} results in intramolecular excitation transfer from the $^3(n,\pi^*)$ state to the triplet of attached group.

As a result of intramolecular triplet-triplet transfer, the properties of the phosphorescence spectrum resemble most clearly that expected from the moiety attached to the carbonyl which possesses the lowest triplet energy.

Another important point to remember in assigning the lowest triplet levels is that the singlet-triplet splittings of n,π^* states are smaller than those of π,π^* states. As a result,

$$\Delta E_{ST}^{\pi,\pi^*} > \Delta E_{ST}^{n,\pi^*}$$

if the $S_1(\pi,\pi^*)$ state is lowest in a molecule, the $T_1(\pi,\pi^*)$ state must be

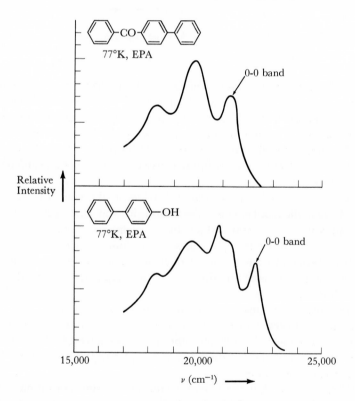

Fig. 5-7   *Total-emission spectrum (pure phosphorescence) of 4-phenylbenzophenone and phosphorescence spectrum of 4-hydroxybiphenyl (lower curve) in ethanol-ether at 77° K ($\phi_p = 0.5$, $\tau_p = 0.1$ sec).*

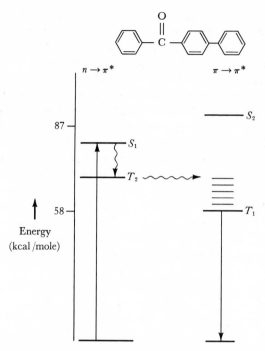

Fig. 5-8   *The electronic states of 4-phenylbenzophenone which participate in intramolecular energy transfer.*

lowest also.   We run into trouble only when the $S_1(n,\pi^*)$ state is lowest, and we need further information before we can make an assignment.

Excitation Transfer between Isolated Chromophores [50, 52, 53]

Intramolecular excitation transfer between two chromophores, which are separated by an "insulating" link, may be considered the special example of intermolecular excitation transfer in which the donor and acceptor are forced to be in the vicinity of each other.[48]   Singlet-singlet intramolecular energy transfer has been demonstrated for the systems 1 a, b, and c in which an anthracene and naphthalene unit are joined by

1   *a*   *n* = 1
    b   *n* = 2
    c   *n* = 3

saturated chains of one, two, and three carbon atoms.[50]   The absorption spectrum of these compounds indicates that there is no complexing interaction between the anthracene and naphthalene units, and the spectrum closely resembles that of an equimolar mixture of 9-methylanthracene and 1-methylnaphthalene. If an equimolar solution of the latter two compounds is irradiated at 2,800 Å, both naphthalene and anthracene fluorescence are observed at 20° C. When solutions of compounds 1 a, b, and c are irradiated under the same conditions, only the *anthracene fluorescence* can be detected, although the naphthalene unit absorbs most of the exciting light. The mechanism of sensitized anthracene fluorescence must be singlet-singlet *intramolecular* energy transfer, which is many times faster than the intermolecular excitation transfer between an equimolar solution of 1-methylnaphthalene and 9-methylanthracene of the same concentration.

Both singlet-singlet and triplet-triplet transfer have been demonstrated [52, 54] for the systems 2 a, b, and c. The absorption spectra of compounds 2 a, b, and c are virtually superimposable upon that of an equimolar solution of 1-methylnaphthalene and 4-methylbenzophenone,

so that two independent absorbing systems are indicated. At 77° K the only emission detected from an equimolar $(5 \times 10^{-3} \ M)$ solution of 1-methylnaphthalene and 4-methylbenzophenone under excitation with 3,660 Å light (absorbed only by the ketone) is that of 4-methylbenzophenone. Triplet-triplet transfer, it should be recalled, occurs by an exchange mechanism which requires high concentrations (about 0.5 M) in solid solution for efficient transfer. If compounds 2 a, b, or c are irradiated under identical conditions, the only emission detected is that of pure phosphorescence of the 1-methylnaphthalene moiety, even though the benzophenone moiety absorbs all of the exciting light. Singlet transfer from the benzophenone moiety to the naphthalene moiety is unlikely because S_1 of the ketone lies about 15 kcal mole^{-1} lower than S_1 of the hydrocarbon. Conversely, singlet transfer is energetically possible from the naphthalene unit to the benzophenone unit if 3,130 Å light (absorbed mainly by the naphthalene group) is employed. In fact, singlet-singlet transfer does occur from the naphthalene unit to the benzophenone group, but the latter then undergoes intersystem crossing to the triplet *which then transfers energy back to the hydrocarbon triplet!* This type of excitation transfer tag game may be followed by consideration of Fig. 5-9. It is interesting that while totally efficient triplet excitation transfer from the benzophenone groups to the naphthalene groups occurs, the transfer of singlet excitation from the naphthalene to benzophenone

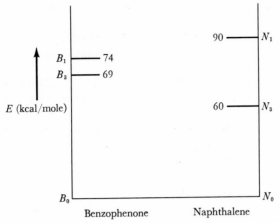

Fig. 5-9   *Energy diagram for the benzophenone and naphthalene moieties of compounds 2 a, b, and c.*

group is only 90% efficient in 2 a, 75% efficient in 2 b, and 85% efficient in 2 c. The reason for the inefficiency is probably related to the fact that the exchange mechanism operates for singlet transfer, as a result of benzophenone's low intensity singlet absorption spectrum, and the collisional transfer must compete with the rapid naphthalene fluorescence. It is not clear what part the conformations of compounds 2 a, b, and c play, if any, in the energy transfer process.

Intramolecular Energy Transfer in Chelates
The excitation of the organic ligand of a rare-earth metal chelate results in the emission from the metal ion if the lowest triplet of the ligand lies above the lowest triplet of the metal ion.[55]   If no metal-ion triplet lies below that of the ligand triplet, emission from the ligand is observed. It is possible to find triplet-energy quenchers, with triplet levels in between those of the ligand and the ion, which quench the excited ligand competitively with the metal ion.   Thus, the mechanism of metal-ion excitation is the transfer of triplet excitation from the ligand.[56]

5-6. ENERGY TRANSFER AND ORGANIC PHOTOCHEMISTRY

An elegant method of measuring the fraction of excited singlet molecules which reach the lowest triplet state in fluid solids has been employed by Lamola and Hammond.[54]   Under conditions such that

1. all donor triplets are quenched,
2. the quencher undergoes a measurable photochemical reaction,

the intersystem crossing yield, Φ_{ST} may be defined as

$$\Phi_{ST} = \frac{\text{number of molecules forming triplets}}{\text{number of photons producing singlets}}$$

The donor and acceptor are chosen so that triplet-triplet transfer is energetically favorable but singlet-singlet transfer is not. Under these conditions, if the donor singlets can be selectively excited in the presence of a relatively high concentration of acceptor molecules, than all donor triplets will be quenched. Thus a chemical method for "counting" triplets is available if conditions 1 and 2 are met.

Chemical Spectroscopy [54]

By choosing as a standard donor, a compound for which $\Phi_{ST}{}^{SD}$ is unity, then

$$\frac{\Phi_{ST}{}^{D}}{\Phi_{ST}{}^{SD}} = \frac{\Phi_r{}^{D}}{\Phi_r{}^{SD}} = \Phi_{ST}{}^{D} \qquad (5\text{-}46)$$

where $\Phi_{ST}{}^{D}$ is the triplet yield of the unknown donor and $\Phi_r{}^{D}$ and $\Phi_r{}^{SD}$ are the quantum yields for some triplet reaction of the quencher. Under conditions of *equal absorption* of light by a solution of an unknown donor and a separate solution of a standard, $\Phi_{ST}{}^{D}$ can be quite simply calculated from the ratio of the extent of the photochemical reaction of the acceptor produced for the two cases.

Consider the following example. A benzene solution contains a sufficient concentration of benzophenone to absorb all incident radiation from a monochromatic source. The solution also contains a sufficient concentration of some quencher, such that *all benzophenone triplets which are formed will be quenched.* Since $\Phi_{ST}{}^{SD} = 1$ for benzophenone, if energy transfer occurs with unit efficiency $[E_T$ (acceptor) $< E_T$ (benzophenone)], then the number of acceptor triplets produced equals the number of photons absorbed by the benzophenone. Suppose the triplet acceptor dimerizes [65] (for example, cyclohexadiene) with unit efficiency. Then each photon absorbed results in the formation of one molecule of dimer. In order to measure $\Phi_{ST}{}^{D}$ for an unknown donor, we must again choose conditions such that the unknown absorbs all of the incident radiation and all donor triplets are quenched by the standard acceptor (e.g., cyclohexadiene). The two samples (one solution containing benzophenone and the second containing the unknown) are then irradiated under comparable conditions, such that each solution absorbs equal quantities of light. In order to estimate the intersystem crossing yield for the unknown, we must "count" the number of percentage or the diene dimers produced by each sensitizer. Vapor-phase chromatography is a convenient method of measuring the concentration and (from knowledge of the volume of solution) the number or percentage of diene dimer produced. If the benzophenone produces 20% dimerization while the unknown produces 10% dimerization under these conditions, then we may calculate $\Phi_{ST}{}^D$ of the unknown from Eq. 5-46

$$\Phi_{ST}{}^D = \tfrac{10}{20} = 0.5$$

In other words, one-half of the excited singlets of the unknown cross to the triplet state. If benzophenone is chosen as the standard donor, then the intersystem crossing yields in Table 5-12 are found. It should

Table 5-12   *Intersystem crossing efficiencies determined by chemical quenching* [54]

Compound [a]	Φ_{ST}	Compound [a]	Φ_{ST}
Naphthalene	0.39	1-Fluoronaphthalene	0.63
Naphthalene-d_8	0.38	1-Naphthol	0.27
Triphenylene	0.95	Quinoline	0.16 [b]
Phenanthrene	0.76	Quinoline	0.32 [c]
Chrysene	0.67	Acetophenone	0.99
1,2,5,6-Dibenzanthrene	0.89	Benzophenone	(1.00) [d]
Fluorene	0.31	Michler's ketone	1.01
Benzene	0.24	2-Acetonaphthone	0.84
Diphenylamine	0.38	Fluorenone	0.93
Triphenylamine	0.88	Benzil	0.87
Carbazole	0.36	Anthraquinone	0.87

[a] Benzene solution, 25°.
[b] Moist benzene.
[c] Dry benzene.
[d] Assumed equal to 1.0.

be pointed out that these values *assume* that all donor triplets are quenched; if this is not so, $\Phi_{ST}{}^D$ is too low. These results prophesy the importance of the triplet state in organic photoreactions. An important application of chemical spectroscopy is that the rate of radiationless processes can be calculated (without assumptions) from known emission data.

Sensitized Reactions in Organic Photochemistry

A large body of evidence is rapidly accumulating which indicates that irradiation of organic compounds in solution yield triplets in fairly high yield. The high rate of exothermic energy transfer processes and the relatively long lifetime of triplets make photosensitized reactions involving triplets quite attractive.

Table 5-13   *Triplet energies of organic compounds* [51-60]

Compound	E_T (kcal mole^{-1})	Compound	E_T (kcal mole^{-1})
Benzene	85	Michler's ketone	61
Phenol	82	Naphthalene	61
Benzoic acid	78	4-Acetylbiphenyl	61
Benzonitrile	77	Nitrobenzene	60
Aniline	77	2-Acetonaphthone	59
Xanthone	74	Acridene yellow	58
Acetophenone	74	1-Naphthylphenylketone	57
Diisopropylketone	74	Chrysene	57
Diphenylsulfide	74	1-Acetonaphthone	56
Diphenylamine	72	1-Naphthaldehyde	56
Benzaldehyde	72	Biacetyl	55
Diphenylselenium	72	Coronene	55
Carbazole	70	Benzil	54
Triphenylamine	70	Fluorenone	53
Hexachlorobenzene	70	1,2,5,6-Dibenzanthracene	52
4,4-Diphenylcyclo-hexadienone	69	Fluorescine (acid)	51
1,2-Dibenzoylbenzene	69	trans-4-Nitrostilbene	50
Thiophene	69	Pyrene	49
Benzophenone	69	Pentaphene	48
1,4-Diacetylbenzene	68	1,2-Benzanthracene	47
Fluorene	68	11,12-Trimethylene-tetraphene	46
Triphenylene	67	1,12-Benzperylene	46
4-Cyanobenzophenone	66	Phenazine	44
Biphenyl	65	Eosin	43
Thioxanthone	65	Anthracene	42
Phenylglyoxal	63	3,4-Benzpyrene	42
Anthraquinone	62	Thiobenzophenone	40
Quinoline	62	Crystal violet	39
Phenanthrene	62	Naphthacene	29
Flavone	62	Oxygen	23 [a]

[a] Lowest triplet-singlet transition. Recall that oxygen is a triplet ground-state molecule.

Before running a photosensitized reaction the following questions should be asked:

1. What are the absorption spectra of the donor and acceptor?
2. What are the E_T's of the donor and acceptor?
3. What type of triplet yield from S_1 occurs in the sensitizer?
4. What are the known reactions of the T_1 state of the sensitizer and donor?
5. Are the products likely to absorb light or be triplet quenchers?

Knowledge of the absorption spectrum is critical because ideally the sensitizer should absorb most or all of the exciting light.   If the acceptor absorbs too strongly in the same regions as the donor, direct photo-reactions of the acceptor may dominate.

Knowledge of the triplet levels of donor and acceptor is crucial since energy transfer occurs at the diffusion-controlled rate from the donor to acceptor only if E_T (donor) $>$ E_T (acceptor). These values are available from phosphorescence spectra, perturbed absorption spectra and sensitized reactions.[65]

We should seek sensitizers which produce high yields of triplets for maximum efficiency. Data such as Φ_p/Φ_f, Φ_{ST} and value of k_{ST} are important for this estimation (see Table 4-13).

Finally, we should consider the various reactions of triplets such as hydrogen abstraction and addition which will guide our choice of solvent and other reaction conditions. For example, benzene nicely fulfills these requirements.

In general, carbonyl compounds nicely fulfill all the requirements listed above—i.e., high E_T, long wavelength absorption, and high yield of triplets.

A list of triplet energies [51-60] available from the literature is given above in Table 5-13. Photosensitization usually refers to *triplet* energy transfer from a sensitizer to an acceptor unless specified otherwise.

PROBLEMS

1. If a compound Q quenches biacetyl triplets at a diffusion-controlled rate, what concentration of Q is required to quench 99% of the biacetyl phosphorescence ($\Phi_p = 0.25$, $k_p = 10^3$ sec^{-1})?

2. Will the following compounds act as sensitizers or quenchers of biacetyl (a) fluorescence and (b) phosphorescence? 1. Benzene, 2. quinoline, 3. 9,10-dibromoanthracene, 4. fluorenone.

3. Quinoline at 77° K shows $\Phi_p/\Phi_f = 100$ in hydrocarbon solvents and $\Phi_p/\Phi_f = 0.1$ in alcoholic solvents. Assume that no chemical reaction occurs under these conditions and draw two state diagrams to rationalize this solvent effect.

4. Predict the energy of the lowest S_1 and T_1 states and whether they are π,π^* or n,π^* states for the following molecules.

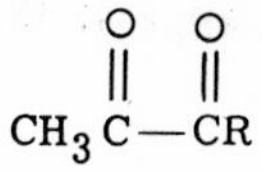

$$CH_3 C-CR \quad \text{where} \quad R = CH_3,\ C_6H_5,\ C_{10}H_7,\ C_{14}H_9$$

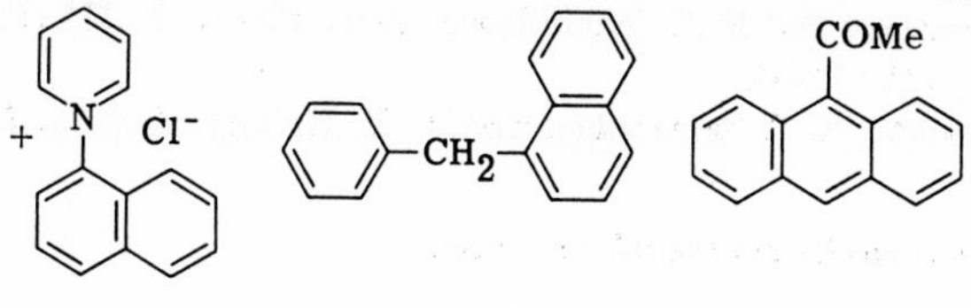

5. How would you construct a molecule possessing the following properties:

1. nonfluorescent and nonphosphorescent,
2. strongly fluorescent and nonphosphorescent,
3. nonfluorescent and strongly phosphorescent,
4. moderately fluorescent and phosphorescent

Indicate a specific example and show how you would substitute groups on the molecule or change the environment to achieve the properties listed above.

6. The unimolecular decay constant k_1 for triphenylene triplets in hexane solution is 2×10^4 sec^{-1}. The half-quenching concentration of naphthalene required to quench triphenylene triplets is 2×10^{-5} M. What is k_q for this system?

7. Which of the following compounds will quench benzophenone triplets at a diffusion-controlled rate? 1. CH_2=CH—CH=CH_2, 2. benzene, 3. anthracene, 4. 2-acetonaphthone, or 5. acetophenone.

8. Which of the two compounds 1. butadiene $(E_T = 60)$ or 2. cis-stilbene $(E_T = 63)$ do you expect to be the better quencher of benzophenone triplets $(E_T = 69)$?

9. Do you expect benzil $[E_T = 56, T_1(n,\pi^*)]$ or naphthalene $[E_T = 60, T_1(\pi,\pi^*)]$ to be a better sensitizer of biacetyl $(E_T = 54)$ phosphorescence?

REFERENCES*

1. E. J. Bowen, Quart. Revs., 1, 1 (1947); ibid., 4, 236 (1950).
2. A. W. Noyes, Jr. and P. A. Leighton, Photochemistry of Gases (New York: Reinhold, 1941).
3. P. J. Debye, Trans. Electrochem. Soc., 82, 265 (1942).
4. T. Forster, Disc. Faraday Soc., 27, 1 (1959); Radiation Research, Supplement 2, 326 (1960).
5. D. L. Dexter, J. Chem. Phys., 21, 836 (1953).
6. T. Forster, Z. Electrochem., 64, 157 (1960); Naturwiss., 33, 166 (1946); Ann. Phys., 2, 55 (1948); Fluorezenz Organische Verbindungen (Gottingen: Vandenhoech and Ruprech, 1951).
7. J. Perrin, Comp. rend. Acad. Sci. Paris, 184, 1097 (1927).
8. F. Perrin, Ann. Chem. Phys., 17, 283 (1932).
9. W. Ware, J. Am. Chem. Soc., 83, 4374 (1961); E. J. Bowen and R. Livingston, J. Am. Chem. Soc., 76, 6300 (1954).
10. E. J. Bowen and B. Brockelhurst, Trans. Faraday Soc., 49, 1131 (1953); ibid., 51, 774 (1955).
11. R. G. Bennett, J. Chem. Phys., 41, 3037 (1964).
12. V. L. Ermolaev and E. B. Sveshnikova, Soviet Physics, 8, 373 (1963); Opt. and Spect., 17, 321 (1964).
13. R. G. Bennett, R. P. Schwenker, and R. E. Kellogg, J. Chem. Phys., 41, 3040 (1964).

* See Addendum for additional references.

14. R. E. Kellogg and R. G. Bennett, *J. Chem. Phys.*, **41**, 3042 (1964).
15. E. H. Gilmore, G. E. Gibson, and D. S. McClure, *J. Chem. Phys.*, **20**, 829 (1952); *ibid.*, **23**, 399 (1955).
16. For a review of the work in rigid media see V. L. Ermolaev, *Soviet Physics, Uspekhi*, **80**, 333 (1963).
17. A. Terenin and V. Ermolaev, *Trans. Faraday Soc.*, **52**, 1042 (1956); *Bull. Soc. Acad. Sci., U.S.S.R.*, Phys. Ser., **20**, 471 (1956).
18. J. B. Farmer, C. L. Gardner, and C. A. McDowell, *J. Chem. Phys.*, **34**, 1058 (1961).
19. V. L. Ermolaev, *Bull. Acad. Sci. U.S.S.R.*, Phys., **20**, 471 (1956).
20. M. A. El-Sayed, *J. Chem. Phys.*, **40**, 3443 (1964).
21. V. L. Ermolaev, *Soviet Physics, Uspekhi*, **80**, 333 (1963).
22. A. N. Terenin and V. L. Ermolaev, *Bull. Acad. Sci. U.S.S.R.*, **26**, 21 (1962):
23. V. L. Ermolaev, *Opt. and Spect.*, **13**, 49 (1962);
24. V. L. Ermolaev, *Soviet Physics, Doklady*, **6**, 600 (1962).
25. M. R. Wright, R. P. Frosch, and G. W. Robinson, *J. Chem. Phys.*, **33**, 934 (1960).
26. V. L. Ermolaev, *Opt. and Spec.*, **6**, 417 (1959).
27. J. T. Dubois and B. Stevens in *Luminescence of Organic and Inorganic Materials* (New York: Wiley, 1962), p. 115.
28. J. T. Dubois and M. Cox, *J. Chem. Phys.*, **38**, 2536 (1962).
29. J. T. Dubois and F. Wilkinson, *ibid.*, **38**, 2541 (1963); *ibid.*, **39**, 377 (1963).
30. B. Stevens and J. T. Dubois, *Trans. Faraday Soc.*, **59**, 2813 (1963).
31. J. T. Dubois and R. L. Van Hemert, *J. Chem. Phys.*, **40**, 923 (1964).
32. S. Lipsky, *ibid.*, **38**, 2786 (1963).
33. R. M. Noyes, *J. Am. Chem. Soc.*, **86**, 4529 (1964).
34. J. T. Dubois and F. Wilkinson, *J. Chem. Phys.*, **39**, 899 (1963).
35. H. L. J. Backstron and K. Sandros, *J. Chem. Phys.*, **23**, 2197 (1955).
36. H. L. J. Backstrom and K. Sandros, *Acta. Chem. Scand.*, **12**, 3 (1958).
37. H. L. J. Backstrom and K. Sandros, *ibid.*, **14**, 48 (1960).
38. K. Sandros and H. L. J. Backstrom, *ibid.*, **16**, 958 (1962); *ibid.*, 2355 (1964).
39. G. Porter and F. Wilkinson, in *Luminescence of Organic and Inorganic Materials* (New York: Wiley, 1962), p. 132.
40. G. Porter and F. Wilkinson, *Proc. Royal Soc.*, **A264**, 1 (1961).
41. C. A. Parker, in *Advances in Photochemistry*, Vol. II, ed. W. A. Noyes, Jr., G. S. Hammond, and J. N. Pitts, Jr. (New York: Interscience, 1964), p. 305.
42. C. A. Parker and C. G. Hatchard, *Proc. Chem. Soc.*, 386 (1962).
43. C. A. Parker, *Proc. Chem. Soc.*, **A276**, 125 (1963).
44. G. C. Nieman and G. W. Robinson, *J. Chem. Phys.*, **37**, 2150 (1962); *ibid.*, **38**, 1326 (1963).
45. R. E. Kellogg, *J. Chem. Phys.*, **41**, 3046 (1964).
46. G. Porter and P. West, *Proc. Royal Soc.*, **A279**, 302 (1964).
47. V. L. Ermolaev and A. N. Terenin, *Soviet Physics, Uspekhi*, **3**, 423 (1960); *J. Chim. Phys.*, **55**, 698 (1958).
48. For other examples not mentioned in the text see G. Weber and F. W. J. Teale, *Trans. Faraday Soc.*, **54**, 640 (1958); *Nature*, **180**, 1409 (1957).
49. R. Bersohn and I. Isenburg, *J. Chem. Phys.*, **40**, 3175 (1964).

50. O. Schnepp and M. Levy, *J. Am. Chem. Soc.*, **84**, 172 (1962).

51. D. N. Shigorin, *et al.*, *Proc. Natl. Acad. Sci.*, *U.S.S.R.*, *Phy. Chem.*, **137**, 371 (1961).

52. P. A. Leermakers, G. W. Byers, A. A. Lamola, and G. S. Hammond, *J. Am. Chem. Soc.*, **85**, 2670 (1963).

53. S. Shifrin, *Biochem. Biophys. Acta*, **81**, 205 (1964).

54. A. A. Lamola, Ph. D. Thesis (Pasadena: California Institute of Technology, 1965).

55. G. A. Crosby, R. E. Whan, and R. M. Alire, *J. Chem. Phys.*, **34**, 743 (1961).

56. M. L. Bhaumik and M. A. El-Sayed, *J. Phys. Chem.*, **68**, 275 (1965).

57. G. N. Lewis and M. Kasha, *J. Am. Chem. Soc.*, **66**, 2100 (1944).

58. D. S. McClure, *J. Chem. Phys.*, **17**, 905 (1949).

59. E. Clar and M. Zander, *Ber.*, **89**, 749 (1958).

60. W. G. Herkstroeter, A. A. Lamola, and G. S. Hammond, *J. Am. Chem. Soc.*, **86**, 4537 (1964).

61. G. N. Lewis and M. Calvin, *Chem. Revs.*, **25**, 273 (1939).

62. R. V. Nauman, Ph. D. Thesis (Berkeley: University of California, 1947).

63. D. R. Arnold, *Abstr. 149th Meeting ACS*, Detroit, April, 1965, p. 50P.

64. L. S. Forster and D. Dudley, *J. Phys. Chem.*, **66**, 838 (1962).

65. D. Valentine, N. J. Turro, and G. S. Hammond, *J. Am. Chem. Soc.*, **86**, 5202 (1964).

chapter
six

Photoreduction and Related Reactions

6-1. INTRODUCTION

The rapid surge of interest in organic photochemistry since about 1960 has received impetus from several sources:[1]

1. an increasing realization of the synthetic utility of photoreactions;

2. the rapidly expanding use of spectroscopic techniques and concepts which yield important information concerning electronically excited molecules;

3. the highly energetic but selective nature of the act of absorption;

4. the fascinating relationship between photochemical behavior and the rates and nature of processes which interconvert electronic states and dissipate excitation energy.

Spectroscopy and Photochemistry [1]

The concepts and applications of spectroscopy are of the utmost importance for organic photochemistry. Chemical techniques such as energy transfer are also capable of yielding photochemical information which is not available from spectroscopic techniques. In spite of these remarkable advances, in general, knowledge of the structure of electronically excited states is still relatively underdeveloped. Attempts to apply quantum mechanics to photochemical problems, while of great theoretical interest, have received relatively little attention, but this is probably a situation subject to change.[2]

137

Electronically Excited States [1]

Spectroscopic data, if available, allow the construction of a state-energy diagram, which provides some insight into the nature of the lowest electronically excited states. The following questions should be asked as we consider specific photoreactions:

1. What is the detailed fate of the electronic excitation provided by absorption of a photon of visible or ultraviolet light?
2. What are the energies, structures, and lifetimes of the various electronic states?
3. How does knowledge of questions 1 and 2 above allow comprehension, prediction, and generalization of the chemical properties of the excited states?

The deactivation of electronically excited states is extremely rapid in comparison to the rates of conventional "dark" reactions. Photoreactions must therefore utilize the large excess of energy possessed by the excited molecule to follow reaction paths of low activation energy—i.e., photochemical reactions must be very rapid. The emission rates from S_1 and T_1 fix the time scale of photoreactions in the sense that most photoreactions originate from one of these states. The rates of fluorescence range from 10^6 to 10^9 sec^{-1}, so that a photoreaction involving S_1 must have a comparable or greater rate in order to be significant. The much slower rate of phosphorescence (10^3 to 10^{-1} sec^{-1}) allows relatively inefficient reactions to occur from T_1. In addition, T_1 is invariably of the lowest energy among the electronically excited states and usually possesses a "biradical" character as a result of the Pauli principle which tends to keep spin-unpaired electrons away from one another.

These considerations should not cause the immediate dismissal of S_1 as a candidate for photoreactions because the higher energy (compared to T_1) of this state may speed up the rate of reaction. A "hot" ground state produced by radiationless conversion from S_1 or T_1 to a high vibrational level of S_0 may also be important. Also, it will not be surprising if on rare occasions S_2 or T_2 are the states from which photoreaction occurs. One of the most important and intriguing problems of theoretical organic photochemistry is the development of methods for the determination of which excited states are involved in photochemical reactions.

Role of the Triplet State [1, 5]

Several lines of evidence force the conclusion that the excited state responsible for the photochemistry of carbonyl compounds in solution is usually the triplet state. For example, we have seen earlier that carbonyl compounds:

1. exhibit high yields of phosphorescence relative to fluorescence, indicating efficient intersystem crossing from S_1 to T_1;
2. transfer triplet excitation efficiently to suitable donors in fluid solution;
3. possess triplets which may be detected directly by flash photolysis in fluid solution.

The intersystem crossing rate constant k_{ST} for benzophenone and other carbonyl compounds has been found to be about 10^{10} sec^{-1}, indicating a lifetime of S_1 which is less than 10^{-10} sec. Clearly, any reaction of S_1 for carbonyl compounds will have to occur extremely rapidly if it is to compete with intersystem crossing.

6-2. PHOTOREDUCTION OF CARBONYL COMPOUNDS

The photochemistry of carbonyl compounds has received a great deal of attention. Simple alkyl and aryl ketones and aldehydes show a weak longest wavelength absorption [2, 3] ($\epsilon_{max} \sim 20$–100) between 2,800 and 3,500 Å corresponding to an n-π^* transition—i.e., S_1 is (n,π^*). At shorter wavelengths an intense π-π^* transition ($\epsilon_{max} \sim 1,000$–$3,000$) occurs—i.e., S_2 is (π,π^*). Conjugation of a delocalizing group such as naphthalene or a strongly electron-releasing group with the carbonyl usually causes the intense π,π^* transition to move to longer wavelengths and "bury" the relatively feeble n,π^* absorption band (which does not shift very much) so that the latter is undetectable.

The emission spectra of nearly all carbonyl compounds [3, 4, 5] possess a high Φ_p/Φ_f ratio (50 to ∞). The alkyl carbonyl compounds and simple alkyl-aryl ketones have similar triplet-state energies and lifetimes ($E_T \sim 75$–65, $\tau_p \sim 10^{-2}$ sec). Furthermore, the phosphorescence emission vibrational structure of these compounds suggests that excitation is localized on the C$=$O group in T_1. Thus, for these compounds T_1 is (n,π^*). Extensive conjugation with the carbonyl causes the similarity of the emission spectra to disappear, and the emission characteristics of the attached group become dominant in the spectrum (see Section 5-5).

Mechanisms of Photoreduction of Aromatic Ketones [6, 18]

Electronically excited carbonyl compounds have been long known to be voracious hydrogen-atom abstractors. The time-honored formation of benzpinacol by irradiation of benzophenone in alcoholic solution has received a great deal of mechanistic study and serves as a bulwark for the interpretation of the photoreactions of aromatic ketones.[6-14] The photoreduction of benzophenone [7] by benzene solutions of benzhydrol at 25° C may be represented by the following scheme†:

$$\text{Rate}$$

$$(C_6H_5)_2C{=}O \xrightarrow{h\nu} (C_6H_5)_2C{=}O^* \qquad\qquad aI \qquad (6\text{-}1)$$
$$B B^*$$

$$(C_6H_5)_2C{=}O^* + (C_6H_5)_2CHOH \rightarrow (C_6H_5)_2\overset{\bullet}{C}OH \quad k_r[B^*][BH_2] \quad (6\text{-}2)$$

$$(C_6H_5)_2C{=}O^* \rightsquigarrow (C_6H_5)_2C{=}O \qquad\qquad k_d[B^*] \qquad (6\text{-}3)$$

$$(C_6H_5)_2C{=}O^* + Q \rightarrow (C_6H_5)_2C{=}O + Q^* \qquad k_q[B^*][Q] \quad (6\text{-}4)$$

$$2(C_6H_5)_2\overset{\bullet}{C}OH \rightarrow \underset{\underset{OH}{|}}{(C_6H_5)_2C}{\text{----}}\underset{\underset{OH}{|}}{C(C_6H_5)_2} \qquad k_c[BH]^2 \quad (6\text{-}5)$$

where a is the efficiency of conversion of initially excited benzophenone singlets to the chemically active state, I is the rate of absorption of light by benzophenone in einsteins/liter, and Q is an added quencher. The following rate law is predicted by this scheme [6-8]

$$\frac{1}{\phi_B} = \frac{1}{a} + \frac{k_d}{ak_r[BH_2]} + \frac{k_q[Q]}{ak_r[BH_2]} \qquad (6\text{-}6)$$

where ϕ_B is the quantum yield for benzophenone disappearance.

If quenchers are rigorously excluded, then Eq. 6-6 becomes

$$\frac{1}{\phi_B} = \frac{1}{a} + \frac{k_d}{ak_r[BH_2]} \qquad (6\text{-}7)$$

A plot of $1/\phi_B$ versus $1/[BH_2]$ is linear [7] and possesses an intercept of 1 and a slope of 0.033 (a redetermined value [8]) as shown in Fig. 6-1. Therefore, we have $a = 1$ and $k_d/k_r = 0.033$. If quenchers are now added to the systems and the concentration of BH_2 is kept constant, a plot of $1/\phi_B$ versus $[Q]$ will lead to a value of k_q/k_r. Again, such a plot is found to be linear for a number of quenchers, and the value of k_q/k_r is about 400 for quenchers such as naphthalene and oxygen.[7]

Replacement of benzhydrol with benzhydrol-α-d_1 (BHD) demonstrates that the photoreduction is not diffusion controlled.[7] A linear relationship between $1/\phi_B$ and $1/[BHD]$ is found and the intercept of this plot is still unity, but k_d/k_r is now equal to 0.13 (see Fig. 6-1). The rate of deuterium abstraction is therefore *slower* than that of hydrogen abstraction, provided that deuterium substitution does not effect k_d.

† In the following sections, unless specified, all reactions are conducted in fluid solution at 20 to 25° employing wavelengths of light greater than 3,000 Å for excitation. The solvent, if not mentioned in the text, will appear under the equation arrow. The E_T values will always be given in kcal/mole.

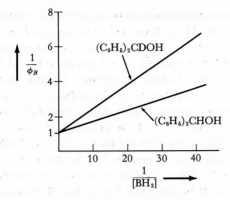

Fig. 6-1   *Photoreduction of benzophenone by benzhydrol.*[7]

It is most probable that the triplet state T_1 of benzophenone is the chemically active species B* in this photoreduction, as can be seen by the following kinetic argument and the data given in Fig. 6-1. The rate constant for deactivation of S_1 must be at least 10^{10} sec^{-1}, the minimum rate constant for intersystem crossing (Table 4-13). The quantum yield *expected* for photoreduction by S_1 is given by

$$\phi_B{}^{S_1} = \frac{k_r{}^{S_1}[S_1][BH_2]}{k_r{}^{S_1}[S_1][BH_2] + k_{ST}[S_1]} \tag{6-8}$$

i.e., the rate of abstraction divided by the rate of absorption of light. The latter rate equals the rate of formation of S_1, which in turn equals the rate of disappearance of S_1 (the sum of the two rates in the denominator of (Eq. 6-8), ignoring other processes which appear to be unimportant). We may assume that $k_r{}^{S_1}$ is *less* than 10^8 liter mole^{-1} sec^{-1}, since quenching is more than 100 times faster than abstraction (k_q/k_r) and the *maximum* rate constant for quenching of B* in benzene is calculated to be 10^{10} liter mole^{-1} sec^{-1} (the rate constant for diffusion in benzene at 25° from Eq. 5-13).

Substituting these estimated numbers in Eq. 6-8, we have, for $[BH_2] = 0.1\ M$

$$\phi_B{}^{S_1} = \frac{10^8[0.1]}{10^8[0.1] + 10^{10}} = 10^{-3} \tag{6-9}$$

From Fig. 6-1, we see that ϕ_B is close to unity when $[BH_2] = 0.1\ M$. Therefore, S_1 cannot be the chemically active species B* in the photoreduction of benzophenone by benzhydrol.

Elimination of S_1 leaves two likely candidates for the all-important chemically active species: T_1 and $S_0{}^*$, a "hot" ground state. Since the rate constant of vibrational deactivation of S_0^* to a thermally equilibrated ground state S_0 is probably as rapid as it is for electronically excited states (10^{13} to 10^{11} sec^{-1}), then we are driven to the conclusion that a long-lived triplet—i.e. T_1—is the chemically active species in this photoreaction.

Flash-photolysis experiments completely confirm this conclusion.[9] The triplet state of benzophenone has been detected, and the rate constants for deactivation, hydrogen abstraction, and triplet quenching have been measured directly. The data achieved by the indirect kinetic approach and by flash photolysis are summarized in Table 6-1 and can be seen to be in excellent agreement.[7, 9] It should be noted that the estimation of the diffusion control rate constant as calculated from Eq. 5-13 is about 10 times higher than the measured maximum quenching rate constant.

Table 6-1 *Rate constants for the photoreduction of benzophenone by benzhydrol [7, 9]*

Rate Constant	I^a	II^b
k_q (liter mole^{-1} sec^{-1})	1×10^9	1×10^9
k_r (liter mole^{-1} sec^{-1})	2.5×10^6	2×10^6
k_d (sec^{-1})	1.5×10^5	1×10^5

[a] Rate constants by photochemical kinetic analysis assuming $k_q = 1 \times 10^9$ liter mole^{-1} sec^{-1}.
[b] Rate constants measured directly by flash photolysis.

The ketyl radical $(C_6H_5)_2\overset{\bullet}{C}OH$ appears to be formed in these reactions *even in pure benzene.*[9, 11] The rate constant of abstraction of a hydrogen atom from benzene [9] has been calculated to be 10^3 mole liter^{-1} sec^{-1}. It has not been established conclusively, however, whether, in fact abstraction of an electron or addition to the benzene ring are also occurring. It will not be surprising if electron abstraction, followed by *proton* transfer occurs in certain systems.

Photoreduction of Benzophenone in Various Solvents [7, 12]

The quantum yields for disappearance of benzophenone in various hydrogen-donating solvents are summarized [12] in Table 6-2. Three classes of behavior of benzophenone triplets can be distinguished from these data:

1. In some solvents (water or benzene) Φ_B is nearly zero, presumably because the high activation energy for hydrogen-atom abstraction prohibits photoreduction.

2. In some solvents (ethanol or hexane) Φ_B varies linearly with concentration of benzophenone and tends toward a limiting value of 1.

Table 6-2 *Quantum yields of benzophenone disappearance in various solvents* [12]

Solvent	Φ_B [a]	$[(C_6H_5)_2C{=}O]$ [b]
Water	0.02	10^{-4}
Benzene	0.05	10^{-2}
Hexane	0.67	10^{-2}
Toluene	0.45	10^{-2}
Isopropyl alcohol	0.80 to 2.0	10^{-5}–10^{-1}
Ethanol	1.0	10^{-4}–10^{-1}

[a] Quantum yield for benzophenone disappearance.
[b] Concentration of benzophenone in mole liter^{-1}.

3. In isopropanol Φ_B depends on the benzophenone concentration and tends toward a limiting value of 2.

The variation of Φ_B with concentration depends on the thermal reactions of the radicals R· formed from the solvent R—H. If R· can react selectively with an unexcited benzophenone molecule to produce a ketyl radical and a stable molecule, the over-all yield of benzophenone disappearance will tend toward 2 instead of 1, as shown for isopropyl alcohol below.

$$(C_6H_5)_2C{=}O^* + (CH_3)_2\overset{H}{\underset{|}{C}}OH \rightarrow (C_6H_5)_2\overset{\bullet}{C}OH + (CH_3)_2\overset{\bullet}{C}OH$$

$$(6\text{-}10)$$

$$(CH_3)_2\overset{\bullet}{C}OH + (C_6H_5)_2C{=}O \rightarrow (CH_3)_2C{=}O + (C_6H_5)_2\overset{\bullet}{C}OH \quad (6\text{-}11)$$

The net result is that two molecules of benzophenone disappear per photon absorbed.

In the case of toluene or hexane as solvent, abstraction of a second hydrogen from a benzyl or hexyl radical is not probable. In ethanol, a reaction sequence similar to that for benzophenone and benzhydrol is followed.

Table 6-3 summarizes the values of k_d and k_r from a flash-photolysis study of photoreduction in the presence of naphthalene as a diffusion-controlled quencher of benzophenone triplets.[11–13]

Summary of the Results for Benzophenone Photoreduction

The data presented above compel the following conclusions:

1. The $T_1(n,\pi^*)$ state is the chemically active state in the photoreduction of benzophenone.

Table 6-3   *Rate constants for the photoreduction of benzophenone in isopropyl alcohol and toluene* [11–13]

Rate Constant	Isopropyl Alcohol [a]	Toluene [b]
k_q (liter mole^{-1} sec^{-1})	3.2×10^9	1.3×10^{10}
k_d (sec^{-1})	1.5×10^7	—
k_r (liter mole^{-1} sec^{-1})	1.3×10^6	1.1×10^6

[a] Rate constants based on assumption of $k_q = 3.2 \times 10^9$ liter mole^{-1} sec^{-1}.
[b] Rate constants based on assumption of $k_q = 1.3 \times 10^{10}$ liter mole^{-1} sec^{-1}.

2. The quenching of benzophenone's $T_1(n,\pi^*)$ state is diffusion controlled if quenchers such as naphthalene (E_T quencher less than 69) are employed.

3. The maximum rate of hydrogen abstraction is about 100 times slower than the rate of diffusion-controlled quenching for the systems studied.

6-3. PHOTOREDUCTION OF SUBSTITUTED BENZOPHENONES

The quantum yield Φ_B for the disappearance of a number of substituted benzophenones [13, 14] in isopropyl alcohol at 25° C are summarized in Table 6-4. It is seen that for this standard hydrogen donor, a wide

Table 6-4   *Quantum yields for photoreduction of various ketones in isopropyl alcohol* [13, 14]

Ketone	Φ_B [a]
Benzophenone	2.0
4,4′-Dimethoxybenzophenone	2.0
2-*tert*-Butylbenzophenone	0.5
4-Methylbenzophenone	0.5
4-Phenylbenzophenone	0.2
2-Methylbenzophenone	0.05
2-Ethylbenzophenone	0.02
4-Hydroxybenzophenone	0.02
2,4-Dihydroxybenzophenone	0.005
4,4′-tetra-Methyldiaminobenzophenone	~0
4-Aminobenzophenone	~0
3-Nitrobenzophenone	~0
Fluorenone	~0

[a] Limiting value for ketone disappearance.

variation in reactivity exists for the various ketones. The question immediately arises as to the cause of this variation. It may be assumed that
by analogy with benzophenone, all the aromatic ketones which efficiently photoreduce possess a reactive $T_1(n,\pi^*)$ state.

Mechanisms for the Suppression of Photoreduction

The failure of certain benzophenone derivatives and related compounds to undergo efficient photoreduction in alcoholic solution may
stem from a number of causes. Consider the following general mechanism for photoreduction (emission is not an important deactivation path
in fluid solution for excited ketones, in general).

$$
\begin{array}{lll}
 & & \text{Rate} \\
h\nu + B_0 \longrightarrow B_1 & \qquad & I \\
B_1 \rightsquigarrow B_3 & & k_{ST}[B_1] \\
B_1 \rightsquigarrow B_0 & & k_s[B_1] \\
RH + B_1 \longrightarrow \cdot BH + R\cdot & & k_r{}^s[B_1][RH] \\
B_3 \rightsquigarrow B_0 & & k_t[B_3] \\
RH + B_3 \longrightarrow \cdot BH + R\cdot & & k_r{}^t[B_3][RH]
\end{array}
$$

The quantum yield for photoreduction of singlets is equal to the ratio
of the rate of reaction of singlet B_1 with RH to the sum of the rates of all
processes which deactivate B_1 (i.e., at the steady state, the rate of absorption of light = rate of formation of B_1 = rate of disappearance of B_1).

$$
\Phi_{B_1} = \frac{k_r{}^s[B_1][RH]}{k_s[B_1] + k_{ST}[B_1] + k_r{}^s[B_1][RH]}
$$

or

$$
\Phi_{B_1} = \frac{k_r{}^s[RH]}{k_s + k_{ST} + k_r{}^s[RH]}
$$

Since $k_r{}^s \leq 10^9$ liter mole^{-1} sec^{-1} (Table 6-1) for a diffusion-controlled
reaction, if $[RH] = 0.1\ M$ and $k_{ST} = 10^{10}$ (k_s will in general be small
compared to k_{ST} except in special cases discussed below), then

$$
\Phi_{B_1} \leq \frac{10^9[0.1]}{10^{10} + 10^9[0.1]} = 10^{-2}
$$

For triplets the quantum yield of photoreduction is given by

$$
\Phi_{B_3} = \frac{k_r{}^t[B_3][RH]}{k_t[B_3] + k_r{}^t[B_3][RH]}\ \Phi_{ST}
$$

where Φ_{ST} is the quantum yield for triplet formation (see Section 5-6).

For aromatic ketones, $\Phi_{ST} = 1$, in general, so that

$$\Phi_{B_3} = \frac{k_r{}^t[RH]}{k_t + k_r{}^t[RH]}$$

Let us assume that $k_r{}^t = 10^6$ liter mole^{-1} sec^{-1} (three orders of magnitude *less* than the diffusion-controlled rate), $[RH] = 0.1\ M$, and $k_t = 10^5$ sec^{-1} (these values are close to the actual measured rate constants for the photoreduction of benzophenone by benzhydrol or isopropyl alcohol given in Tables 6-1 and 6-3), then

$$\Phi_{B_3} = \frac{10^6[0.1]}{10^5 + 10^6[0.1]} = 0.5$$

These simple calculations emphasize the importance of the lifetime of excited states in controlling the relative efficiencies of B_1 and B_3 in bimolecular reactions. Although in the above hypothetical example the triplet B_3 is *1000 times less reactive* than B_1 (probably a gross overestimation of the reactivity of this state), the triplet photoreduces nearly two orders of magnitude more efficiently, as measured by the *net* quantum yield.

We are now in a position to point out the factors which will lead to suppression of photoreduction. The short lifetime of B_1 militates against its participation in efficient photoreduction, except, perhaps, in the case where RH is the solvent. (The photoreduction of duroquinone is an apparent exception.[24]) Thus, we expect that efficient photoreduction will in general involve B_3. The failure of a carbonyl compound B to photoreduce under standard conditions (e.g., conditions under which benzophenone abstracts hydrogen atoms with unit efficiency) may result from (1) lack of formation of B_3 ($k_s > k_{ST}$), which necessitates the involvement of B_1 if abstraction is to occur at all; (2) lack of reactivity of B_3 (assumed to be formed efficiently from B_1), which implies that $k_r{}^t$ is small compared to k_t (which in turn for our hypothetical case is comparable to benzophenone); this effect may be due to the nature of the lowest triplet state of B_3 or to the strength and nucleophilicity of the hydrogen atom to be abstracted; (3) Rapid rate of destruction of B_3 compared to the rate of encounters of B_3 with RH (i.e., k_t may be abnormally large, adventitious quenchers may be present, specific side reactions may occur, etc.); (4) reversibility of hydrogen abstraction, e.g.

$$B_3 + RH \rightarrow \cdot BH + R\cdot$$
$$R + \cdot BH \rightarrow RH + B_0$$

The latter mechanism implies a high *primary* quantum yield but low *net* or *overall* quantum yield for photoreduction.

We shall see that the study of a number of substituted benzophenones has allowed, in certain cases, a decision to be made as to which of the above mechanisms is operating under a given set of conditions. Other mechanisms, in addition to those specifically listed above (e.g., suppression of photoreduction due to molecular aggregation), may apply in special cases.

2-Alkyl Benzophenones

The long wavelength portion of the absorption spectra of 2-methyl-benzophenone (1a) and 2-tert-butyl benzophenone (2) are quite similar to benzophenone itself; therefore each compound possesses a $S_1(n,\pi^*)$ state. Although their emission spectra have not been reported, they are not expected to differ greatly from benzophenone—i.e., both compounds 1 and 2 should possess $T_1(n,\pi^*)$ states. It may therefore be unsettling that 1 does not photoreduce in isopropyl solution, while 2 does and nearly as efficiently as benzophenone.[15] Clearly, steric effects are working the wrong way to explain the relative reactivities of 1 and 2. Compound 1, however, is capable of forming a six-membered transition state for internal hydrogen abstraction while 2 cannot. There are ample examples in organic photochemistry in which a six-member transition state is favored over a five- or seven-membered one.[25]

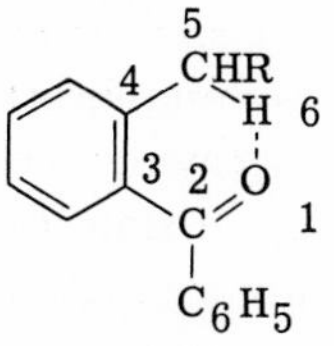

1 a   R = H
  b   R = C_6H_5 2

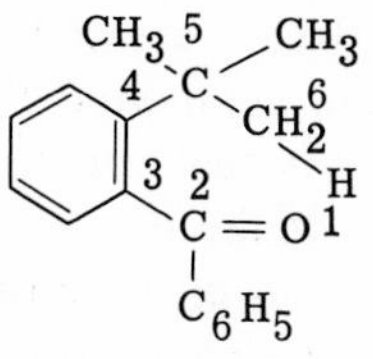

If compound 1b is irradiated in CH_3OD, no photoreduction occurs, but deuterium is introduced on the benzylic carbon.[15, 16] This exchange presumably occurs via the photoenol (3) according to the sequence given in Eq. 6-12.

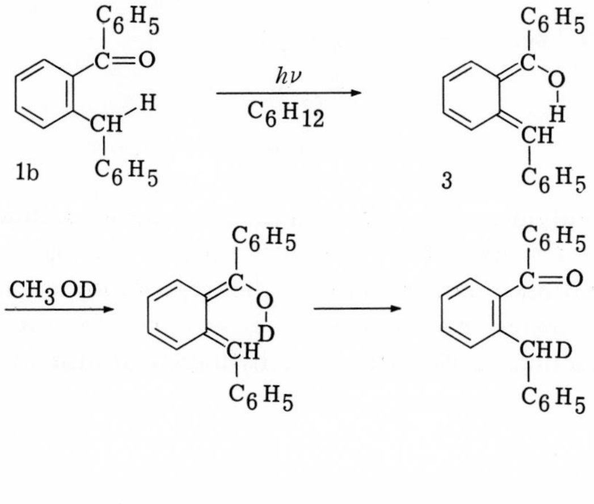

(6-12)

The photoenol (3) was trapped by addition to dimethyl acetylene dicar-
boxylate and the Diels-Adler adduct (4) was formed in good yield (Eq.
6-13).

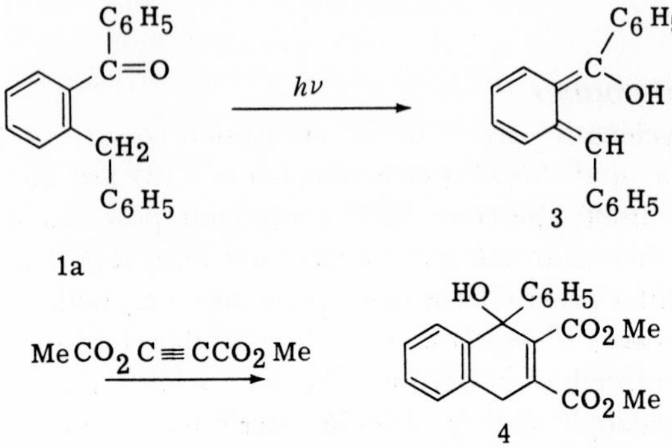

(6-13)

Flash-photolysis studies of this system [16] determined the $T_1(n,\pi^*)$ state
as the chemically active state in the intramolecular hydrogen abstraction.
A transient possessing a unimolecular decay rate of 2×10^3 sec^{-1} was
detected and assigned to the $T_1(n,\pi^*)$ state of 1b on the basis of the similarity of its spectrum to that of benzophenone.   The spectrum of a second
transient with a decay rate of 10^{-1} sec^{-1} was also detected and assigned
to the enol 3.   For compound 1b it was further established that the fast-
decaying transient is converted into the slow-decaying one.   Finally, the
direct conversion of the initially excited $S_1(n,\pi^*)$ state to 3 is excluded
because the spectrum of 3 is not produced immediately after the flash,
but appears at a rate equal to that of the disappearance of the transient
assigned to the $T_1(n,\pi^*)$ state.

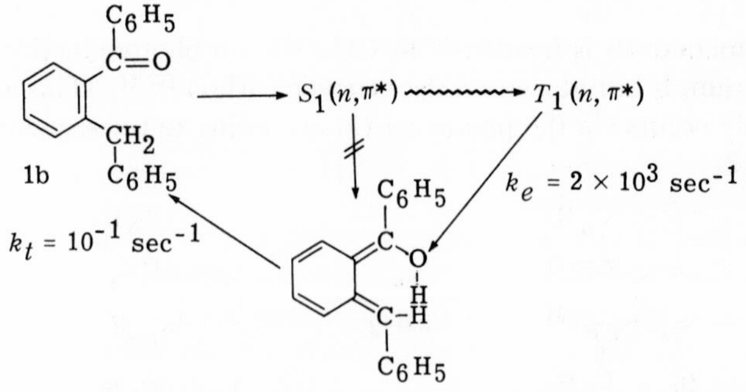

    Since 2-*tert*-butylbenzophenone exhibits normal photoreductive prop-
erties, the low reactivity of other 2-alkyl-substituted benzophenones is not
due to steric hindrance of intermolecular hydrogen abstraction.   Apparently, a six-membered transition state is required for intramolecular
hydrogen abstraction to compete with hydrogen abstraction from the

solvent. Such chemical isomerizations (Eq. 6-12) to yield short-lived, high energy intermediates may be an important path for "cooling" off excess electronic energy.[14]

The earlier argument that photochemical enolization suppresses the intermolecular photoreduction of 1b in isopropyl alcohol seems quite reasonable and straightforward. However, a closer scrutiny of the data shows that the reported rate constant of decay of the $T_1(n,\pi^*)$ state of 1b ($k_t = 10^3$ sec^{-1}) is disconcertingly low. For example, the rate constant for decay of benzophenone triplets (which do not have an internal enolization process available) under comparable conditions (Table 6-1) is 10^5 sec^{-1}. It is not easy to simultaneously rationalize, therefore, both the low rate of decay of the triplet assigned to 1b and photoenolization as the mechanism for suppression of photoreduction of 1b in isopropyl alcohol, as can be seen from the following discussion.

Recall that the rate constant for hydrogen abstraction from isopropyl alcohol by benzophenone triplets is about 10^6 liter mole^{-1} sec^{-1} (Table 6-3). Since 2-*tert*-butylbenzophenone undergoes smooth photoreduction in isopropyl alcohol (Table 6-4), there is no obvious reason why the rate of abstraction of hydrogen atoms from the same solvent by triplets of 1b should not have a rate constant comparable to that of benzophenone triplets. One may calculate (see Addendum, Problem 6-9) that, in order to explain the low quantum yield of photoreduction of 1b (assuming $k_t = 10^3$ sec^{-1}) in isopropyl alcohol, the rate constant for hydrogen abstraction from isopropyl alcohol by triplets of 1b *must be lower than the rate constant for hydrogen atom abstraction by the triplets of benzophenone by at least six powers of ten.*

This conclusion seems somewhat improbable, so that we must either reassign the transient from 1b which precedes the enol (3) or explain the abnormally low rate constant for hydrogen abstraction by triplets of 1b. The resolution of this dilemma must await further experiments.

Photoreduction of 2- and 4- Hydroxy- and Aminobenzophenones

The effect of strong electron-donating 2- or 4-substituents on the quantum yield of photoreduction of substituted benzophenones is striking (Table 6-5). It is tempting to correlate these effects with the properties and shifts of excited states as indicated by the absorption and emission spectra of these compounds. Such a correlation must explain the following facts.

1. The 2-hydroxy- and aminobenzophenones do not luminesce at 77° K in rigid media.

2. The 4-substituted benzophenones phosphoresce strongly at low temperatures in rigid media.

3. Substitution of -N(CH$_3$)$_2$, -NH$_2$, and -OH in the 2- or 4-position of benzophenone suppresses photoreduction in isopropyl alcohol, but 4-OCH$_3$ has no effect (even though the spectra of the 4-OH and the 4-OCH$_3$ benzophenones are nearly identical and the lowest triplet is clearly n, π^*).

4. The $^1(\pi,\pi^*)$ band of benzophenone is located at 2500 Å, and an absorption of similar intensity and position exists for the 2- and 4-amino-substituted benzophenones. Thus, the $^1(\pi,\pi^*)$ states of the latter compounds do not seem to be shifted greatly relative to benzophenone (and presumably the corresponding triplets will not be shifted greatly either).

The lack of luminescence from 2-amino- and 2-hydroxybenzophenone indicates that some radiationless process (or processes) efficiently dissi-

$$\text{[structure: } o\text{-hydroxybenzophenone] } \xrightarrow{h\nu} \text{[enol tautomer structure]}$$

pates the excitation energy provided by absorption of a photon. Since the molecule is stable to photolysis, k_s or k_t must be enhanced (compared to benzophenone) relative to k_{ST} or k_p, respectively. The analogy to photoenolization (recall the difficulties mentioned earlier) of 2-alkyl-benzophenones, suggests that intramolecular hydrogen abstraction dominates intermolecular hydrogen abstraction from solvent. Thus, k_s or k_t may really describe a rapid, reversible photoreaction in these cases. It should be recalled that *bond stretching* alone (Section 4-3) is sufficient to enhance the rates of radiationless conversions.

Porter [21] has proposed that the lack of reactivity of benzophenones possessing strongly electron-releasing substituents (e.g., hydroxyl or amino groups) in alcoholic solvents results from the intercession of an *intramolecular* charge-transfer (C-T) state. This state is supposedly responsible for a large solvent shift which occurs for the longest wavelength band in molecules like 4-aminobenzophenone in alcoholic solvents. The charge-transfer state presumably becomes the lowest energy singlet

$$\text{[structure: 4-aminobenzophenone]} \xrightarrow{h\nu} \text{[charge-transfer structure]}$$

or triplet state in isopropyl alcohol. Since an electron is donated from the electron-releasing group *to the carbonyl group* (an intramolecular electron abstraction) in the C-T state, the reactivity of the excited molecule is far less than that of an n,π^* state. On the other hand, in cyclohexane no particular stabilization of the C-T state occurs, and the n,π^* states remain lowest in energy.   As a result, 4-amino- and 4-hydroxybenzophenone are reactive in hydrogen abstraction in cyclohexane but unreactive in iso-propyl alcohol, as is shown in Table 6-5.   In cyclohexane the reactive

Table 6-5   *Reactivity toward photoreduction in isopropyl alcohol and cyclohexane* [21]

Compound	Φ_{IP} [a]	Φ_{CX} [b]
Benzophenone	1.0	0.5
4-Methoxybenzophenone	1.0	0.5
4-Hydroxybenzophenone	0.02	0.9
4-Aminobenzophenone	0.00	0.2
4-Dimethylaminobenzophenone	0.00	0.6

[a] Quantum yield for disappearance of ketone in isopropyl alcohol.
[b] Quantum yield for disappearance of ketone in cyclohexane.

n-π^* triplet state is the lowest excited level, but in isopropanol not only is the n,π^* excitation energy raised but the energy of the charge-transfer state is lowered by solvation so that this *unreactive state* becomes the triplet of lowest energy.[22]   This is a remarkable example of a difference in photochemical reactivity in two solvents which result from shifting of a C-T and n,π^* states.

Although 2-aminobenzophenone is inert to photoreduction in iso-propyl alcohol, the addition of 0.5 M HCl causes the molecule to become very reactive toward photoreduction.   The effect of acid is complex for the following reasons.

1. The n,π^* states become lowest in energy in the presence of acid (contrary to the usual effect of acid on the relative energies of n,π^* and π,π^* state because in this case the "charge-transfer" state is con-siderably raised in energy).

2. The strength of the N—H bond is greatly increased.

3. The free electrons on nitrogen are no longer available (thereby obstructing electron abstraction).   Each of these effects may con-tribute to a certain extent.

The photoreduction of 4-dimethylaminobenzophenone in isopropyl alcohol proceeds readily if HCl is added.   The long wavelength absorp-tion of 4-dimethylaminobenzophenone is an intense charge-transfer absorption (λ_{max} 3,500 Å, log ϵ 4.33).   This band is shifted to shorter wavelengths when HCl is added to the solutions and the n,π^* band, which is not as drastically affected, becomes the longest wavelength band in the spectrum (λ_{max} 3,400 Å, log ϵ 2.18).   Thus, the lack of reactivity of 4-dimethylaminobenzophenone in isopropyl alcohol is attributed to the fact that the lowest triplet, like the lowest singlet under these conditions, is a charge-transfer state. The latter is similar to the π,π^* state in its reactivity toward hydrogen abstraction. In acid solution the charge-transfer transition is raised in energy because the acid "ties up" the electrons (on nitrogen) which participate in the "charge transfer."

Finally, consider the anomalous case of 4-hydroxybenzophenone, which has a lowest n,π^* triplet state, but fails to photoreduce efficiently ($\Phi_B = 0.02$) in isopropyl alcohol. In this case, apparently, the much higher pK of the excited states (see Section 4-6) causes proton ejection from the 4-OH group in the excited singlet and triplet states, so that the excited molecule must react in the unprotonated form. Clearly, the 4-O$^-$ benzophenone triplet should be very unreactive toward photoreduction, because O$^-$ is such a strong electron-donating substituent. On the other hand, in cyclohexane, the unprotonated form is not stabilized by the nonpolar solvent, and the equilibrium concentration of protonated triplets in the $^3(n,\pi^*)$ state increases, and the quantum yield of photoreduction rises markedly ($\Phi_B = 0.9$).

The Photoreduction of 2-Acetonaphthone and 1-Naphthaldehyde [10, 19, 20]

2-Acetonaphthone ($E_T = 59$) and 1-naphthaldehyde ($E_T = 57$) fail to undergo photoreduction reactions with alcohols.[18] However, both compounds are smoothly photoreduced in the presence of the much better hydrogen donor, tributyl tin hydride.[19, 20] Photochemical kinetic studies similar to those described above for benzophenone indicate that the triplet (π,π^*) state is the chemically active species in both cases. If the rate of quenching by "good" quenchers, i.e., quenchers whose E_T is less than 57 (E_T of the naphthyl compounds), is assumed to be diffusion controlled, the rate constants [9, 10, 19, 20] summarized in Table 6-6 are obtained.

The absorption spectra of 1-naphthaldehyde and 2-acetonaphthone both show a relatively intense maximum around 3,200 Å, indicating a π-π^* absorption under which presumably the low intensity n-π^* absorption is hidden. The phosphorescence spectra of these compounds resembles

Table 6-6 *Rate constants for the photoreduction of 1-naphthaldehyde and 2-acetonaphthone with tributyl tin hydride* [19, 20]

Rate Constants	1-Naphthaldehyde I[a]	II[b]	2-Acetonaphthone I[a]	II[b]
k_q (liter mole^{-1} sec^{-1})	1×10^9	1×10^9	1×10^9	1×10^9
k_r (liter mole^{-1} sec^{-1})	5×10^5	5×10^5	1×10^6	9×10^5
k_d (sec^{-1})	3×10^5	3×10^5	1.5×10^5	2×10^5

[a] Rate constants based on the assumption of $k_q = 1 \times 10^9$ liter mole^{-1} sec^{-1}.
[b] Rate constants measured directly by flash photolysis.

that of naphthalene more than that of benzophenone in that they have a long lifetime ($\tau_p \sim 0.1$ sec), show none of the vibrational structure expected for carbonyl localized excitation, and possess triplet energies in the range of 50 to 57 kcal (see Section 5-5). On the other hand, the triplet energies of the good photoreducers such as the alkyl phenyl ketones and simple benzophenones are grouped together close between 69 and 74 kcal mole^{-1}. These compounds also possess "carbonyl-like" vibrational structure in their phosphorescence spectra and similar short phosphorescence lifetimes (10^{-2} to 10^{-3} sec), i.e., they possess $T_1(n,\pi^*)$ states.

The failure of 1-naphthaldehyde and 2-acetonaphthone to photoreduce may be related therefore to differences in both electronic structures and energies of their triplet states which reflect different chemical reactivities from the triplet state of, for example, benzophenone.

The similarities in the absorptive and emissive properties of the "good" photoreducers make it clear that both of their lowest singlet and triplet states are $S_1(n,\pi^*)$ and $T_1(n,\pi^*)$, respectively. Thus, because of the localization of excitation on the carbonyl portion of the molecule they are potent hydrogen abstractors. The "poor" photoreducers possess a C-T or $T_1(\pi,\pi^*)$ triplet, which, because of its greater delocalization, loses some hydrogen abstracting power.

The explanation of suppression of photoreduction can be given in terms of the relative energies and reactivities of n,π^* and π,π^* triplet states. An n-π^* excitation results in a decrease of negative charge at the oxygen atom of the carbonyl group, whereas π-π^* excitation causes an electronic shift toward the oxygen of the carbonyl and results in an increased negative charge on oxygen. Thus, hydrogen and electron abstraction should occur more readily from a (n,π^*) state than a (π,π^*) state. Conjugation with a naphthalene nucleus or a strong electron-releasing group with a carbonyl reduces the positive character of the carbonyl oxygen and lowers the energy of the π-π^* transition to a larger extent than the n-π^* transition, so that the π,π^* states lie lowest (see Section 5-5) and photoreduction is suppressed.

The free radical character of the n,π^* triplet state is shown by the work of Walling and Gibian [23] and Padwa [23] who have pointed out that benzophenone and tert-butoxy radicals possess similar reactivities in competitive hydrogen-abstraction reactions. These results imply that the n,π triplet, like the tert-butoxy radical, is an electrophilic species. Indeed, the triplet shows a greater selectivity and sensitivity toward electron availability in the hydrogen donor. In addition, the energetics of triplet-hydrogen abstraction are similar to that of alkoxy radical reactions.[23]

Summary

The combination of photochemical and spectroscopic techniques provides a powerful means to illuminate the mechanism of photoreduction of carbonyl compounds. The spectroscopic methods were capable of detecting the carbonyl triplet directly, measuring its rate of decay and providing absolute rate constants for hydrogen abstraction (flash photolysis); in addition, the electronic nature and energy of the (lowest) triplet level was revealed (phosphorescence), and a correlation between this spectroscopic information and chemical reactivity was found. As a result of these studies the electronic structure of the triplet state of carbonyl compounds is revealed. This approach to photochemical problems should be quite fruitful, and, although relatively few of the known photochemical reactions have been studied from this point of view, the development of new spectroscopic techniques and realization of their place in the solution of photochemical problems is resulting in a wider acceptance of the combined photochemical-spectroscopic method.

6-4. INTRAMOLECULAR PHOTOREDUCTION OF CARBONYL COMPOUNDS

A six-membered transition state favors intramolecular hydrogen abstraction over intermolecular reaction with solvent. Photoelimination and cyclization reactions may also result from intramolecular abstraction.[25]

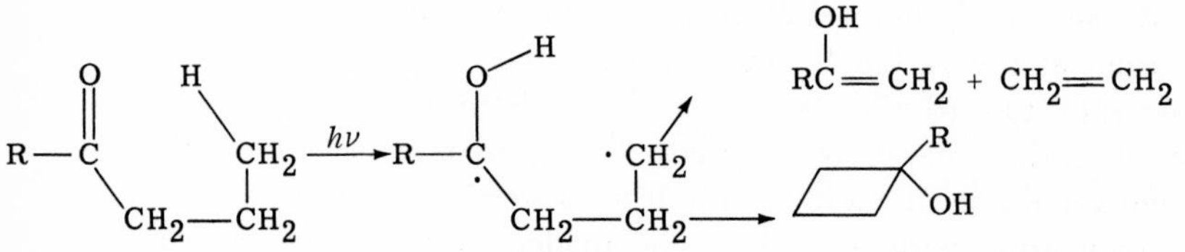

$$RC = CH_2 + CH_2 = CH_2 \quad (6\text{-}14)$$

$$\qquad\qquad\qquad (6\text{-}15)$$

The "Type II" Cleavage [25]

In the case of simple alkyl ketones and aldehydes, benzophenone does not appear to sensitize the "type II" (Eq. 6-14) elimination, but does yield "free radical" products associated with direct irradiation of the compound. This has been interpreted to mean that the triplet state of simple carbonyl compounds decomposes to free radicals, while the excited singlet state produces the "type II" process.[26] However, these results are not compelling, and conflicting results which indicate that reactions 6-14 and 6-15 do involve the triplet state have appeared.[27]

In contrast to results discussed above, a number of butyrophenone-ring-substituted derivatives have been found to undergo the "type II" elimination by the way of the lowest triplet.[28] The quantum yields for the elimination are sensitive to the ring substituent, as is shown by the data in Table 6-7. The effect is similar to that observed in the *inter-*

Table 6-7   *Quantum yields of ethylene formation in the photolysis of butyrophenone derivatives in benzene solution at room temperature* [28]

Compound	$\Phi_{CH_2=CH_2}$
Butyrophenone	0.40
4-Methylbutyrophenone	0.39
4-Aminobutyrophenone	0.00
4-Hydroxybutyrophenone	0.00
2-Hydroxybutyrophenone	0.00

molecular photoreduction of ring-substituted benzophenones, in which the reactive state was a lowest $T_1(n,\pi^*)$. The absorption spectra of these compounds indicate that only butyrophenone and 4-methylbutyrophenone possess lowest $S_1(n,\pi^*)$ states while for the other derivatives in Table 6-7, the $^1(\pi,\pi^*)$ state merges with the $^1(n,\pi^*)$ state, and it is difficult to decide which state lies at the lowest energy. The triplet levels probably follow the same energetic order so that the unreactive ketones possess lowest $T_1(\pi,\pi^*)$ states. These experiments should be corroborated by triplet-quenching experiments as have those mentioned above for simple alkyl ketones.[27]

The enol of acetone has been detected as a discrete intermediate in the vapor-phase photolysis of 2-pentanone.[29] The enol was found to disappear at the same rate at which acetone appeared. The results lend strong support to the hypothesis that enols are involved in the analogous type II reaction of other ketones.

Cyclobutanol Formation [32]

Photochemical cyclobutanol formation is apparently *stereospecific*, although conflicting reports have appeared.[30, 31] The following ketone was found to undergo cyclobutanol formation (in addition to a number of other reactions) with retention of optical activity, indicating that either cyclization is a concerted process or that any biradical intermediate cyclized faster than it rotates about the C—C bond (Eq. 6-16). This latter interpretation is not consistent with other results involving biradical intermediates (see Section 8-3).

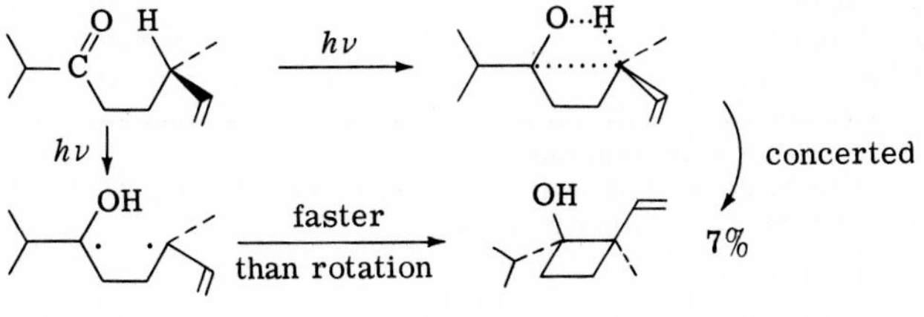

It is interesting to note that the intramolecular enesynthesis (Eq. 6-17) which accompanies this reaction also proceeds in a stereospecific manner.[31, 32]

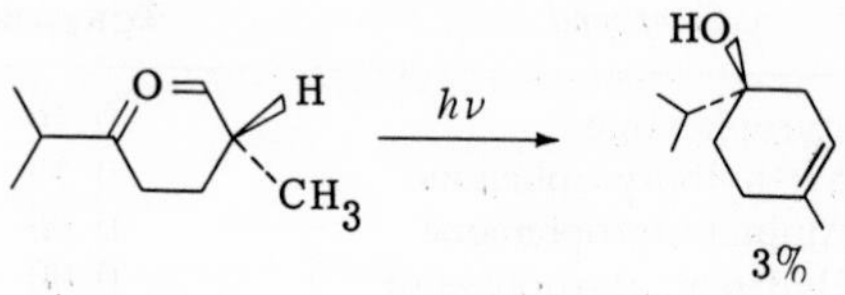

$$hv \qquad\qquad\qquad\qquad (6\text{-}17)$$

3%

It is important to establish exactly what conditions favor cyclobutanol formation over type II cleavage (or *vice-versa*) for a given molecule. No systematic studies of this nature have been reported to date, unfortunately.

Photochemistry of α-Dicarbonyl Compounds [18, 33–40]

α-Dicarbonyl compounds are quite reactive hydrogen abstractors. The lowest energy transition for these molecules is usually $n\text{-}\pi^*$. Removal of electron density from the oxygen atoms towards the central carbon atoms is expected to occur as a result of $n\text{-}\pi^*$ excitation (and also for $\pi\text{-}\pi^*$ excitation).[33]

Backstrom and Sandros [34] have measured the rate constants of (presumed) hydrogen-abstraction reactions of biacetyl. Some typical data are given in Table 6-8. These reactivities are somewhat peculiar in several cases and perhaps an electron-abstraction or addition reaction

Table 6-8   *Quenching of biacetyl phosphorescence by hydrogen donors* [34, 35]

Quencher	E_T [a]	k_q (*liter mole^{-1} sec^{-1}*)
Diphenylamine	72	7×10^9
Hydroquinone	—	5×10^9
Aniline	77	2×10^9
Resorcinol	—	3×10^8
Phenol	82	9×10^7
Cyclohexene	—	1×10^5
Triphenylamine	70	4×10^4
(Tetrachloroethylene) [b]	—	3×10^4
4-Chlorobenzaldehyde	70	2×10^4
Benzylalcohol	82	7×10^3
Isopropanol	—	3×10^3
Methanol	—	3×10^2

[a] Triplet energy in kcal mole^{-1}.
[b] Energy transfer and hydrogen abstraction are not possible here, but perhaps a cycloaddition is occurring.

rather than a hydrogen abstraction is occurring. The authors simply measured the quenching of biacetyl phosphorescence by the solvents given in Table 6-8, but product studies were not made.

The emission of α-dicarbonyl compounds has not been studied in detail, but for biacetyl and benzil and their simple derivatives the triplet state is usually the one which emits.[35] Although T_1 is probably n,π^* for these compounds, E_T is usually about 56 to 54 kcal mole^{-1}. In spite of the relatively low excitation energy, α-dicarbonyl compounds are quite reactive in photoreduction reactions, both intra- and intermolecular. This result is due, in part at least, to the relatively long lifetime of α-carbonyl triplets.

Pyruvic acid [$T_1(n,\pi^*)$, $E_T = 65$ kcal mole^{-1}] undergoes a remarkable reaction to form acetoin (5) when it is irradiated in aqueous solution.[36]

$$CH_3COCO_2H \xrightarrow[\text{H}_2\text{O}]{h\nu} CH_3COCHOHCH_3 \qquad (6\text{-}18)$$
$$4 \phantom{\xrightarrow[\text{H}_2\text{O}]{h\nu}} 5$$

A hydroxycarbene (presumably in a triplet state) has been proposed as an intermediate in this reaction. Attempts to intercept the intermediate with typical carbene traps have been unsuccessful. In addition, the reaction does not proceed in other solvents, but competing reactions such as *intermolecular* photoreduction and acetaldehyde formation become the important modes of photochemical decomposition. The same intermediate has been invoked in the γ-ray decomposition of 2-pentanone.[37] Pyruvic acid esters and related compounds undergo unimolecular decomposition which apparently involve "back-biting" intramolecular abstraction.[36]

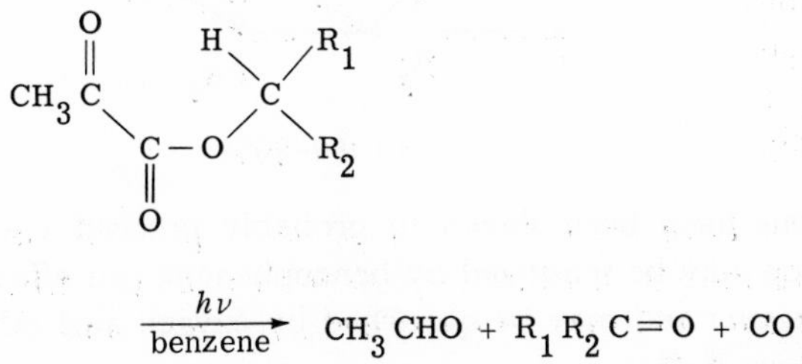

$$(6\text{-}19)$$

$$\xrightarrow[\text{benzene}]{h\nu} CH_3CHO + R_1R_2C{=}O + CO$$

A pronounced temperature effect is noted for the photolysis of phenylglyoxalates in alcoholic solutions.[38] At room temperature the reaction is mainly intermolecular photoreduction (as it is for pyruvic esters [41] in alcohols). At 80° C *intramolecular* photoreduction to form the hydroxyketene (7) predominates. The isolated product is the ketene-alcohol adduct (8), an ester of mandelic acid.

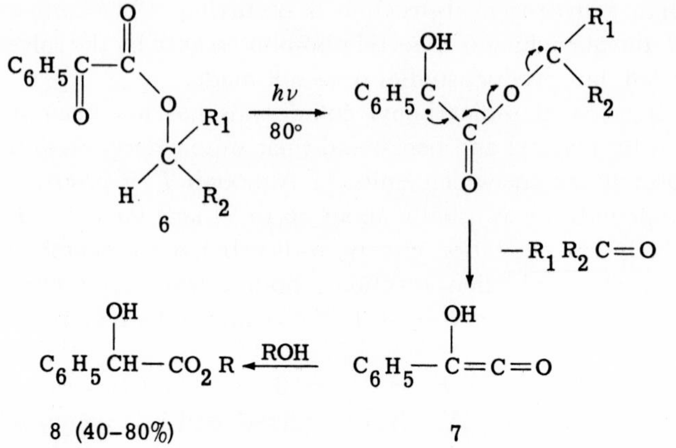

(6-20)

A final example illustrates the variety of photochemistry found for α-dicarbonyl compounds.[39] Derivatives of biacetyl undergo efficient intramolecular hydrogen abstraction followed by *cyclization* to form 1-keto-cyclobutanols (10):

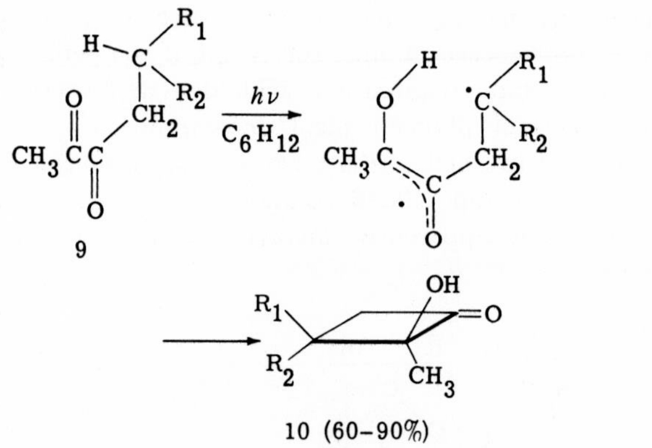

(6-21)

These reactions have been shown to probably proceed via the triplet state since they may be sensitized by benzophenone (an efficient triplet-transferring agent) and may be quenched by oxygen and other efficient triplet quenchers.[39, 40]

Summary

The variety of the photoreactions of α-carbonyl compounds and their sensitivity to changes in reaction conditions and substrate structure make these systems worthy of further systematic studies. All of the evidence to date indicates that the triplet state of these compounds is the chemically active state and that hydrogen abstraction (occasionally accompanied by cyclization or fragmentation) is the important mode of reaction. Intriguing questions remain to be answered:

1. What are the factors which dictate whether inter- or intramolecular hydrogen abstraction dominates?

2. What determines whether fragmentation or cyclization of intermediates (biradicals?) occurs?

3. Why do five-membered transition states occasionally become important for such compounds?

PROBLEMS*

1. Construct energy diagrams for the following molecules in isopropyl alcohol: 2-methylbenzophenone, Michler's ketone, 2-hydroxybenzophenone, and 1-naphthaldehyde. How do these diagrams rationalize the activity of these compounds in the photoreduction of isopropyl alcohol? Use the following information:

Compound	Φ_p (sec)	E_T (kcal mole^{-1})	S_1
1. 2-Methylbenzophenone	10^{-3}	69	n,π^*
2. 2-Hydroxybenzophenone	?	?	π,π^*
3. Michler's ketone	0.1	61	π,π^*
4. 1-Naphthaldehyde	0.1	59	π,π^*

2. Using the steady-state approximation for triplets derive the equation

$$\frac{1}{\Phi_B} = \frac{1}{a} + \frac{k_d}{ak_r} \frac{1}{[(C_6H_5)_2CHOH]}$$

for the mechanism given in Eqs. 6-1 through 6-5 assuming $[Q] = 0$. Hint

$$\Phi_B \equiv -\left[\frac{\dfrac{d[(C_6H_5)_2C{=}O]}{dt}}{I} \right]$$

3. Suggest mechanisms for the following reactions:

1. $2 \ CH_3COCO_2H \xrightarrow[H_2O]{h\nu} CH_3COCHOHCH_3 + CO_2$

2. $CH_3COCO_2CH_2CH_3 \xrightarrow[C_6H_6]{h\nu} 2 \ CH_3CHO + CO$

3. $C_6H_5COCH_2CH_2CH_3 \xrightarrow{h\nu} C_6H_5COCH_3 + CH_2{=}CH_2$

4. $CH_3COCH_2CH_2CH_2CH{=}CH_2 \xrightarrow{h\nu}$

---

* See Addendum for additional problems.

4. Which of the following ketones do you expect to undergo type II cleavage and why?

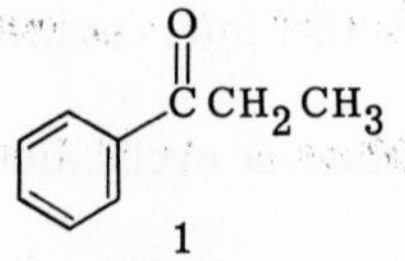

5. Do you expect the following compounds to undergo efficient photoreduction? Why?

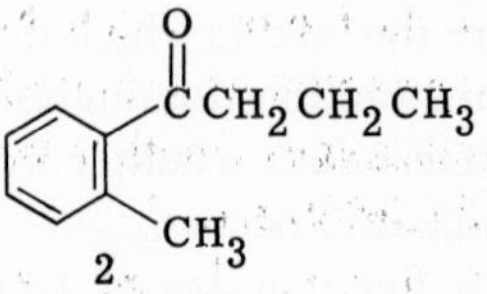

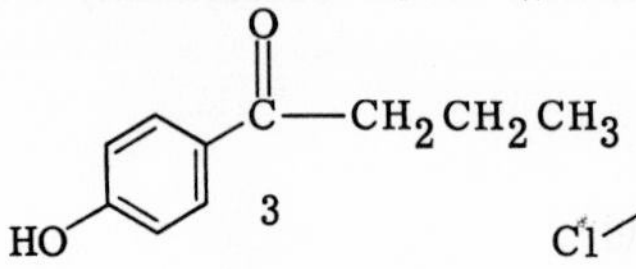

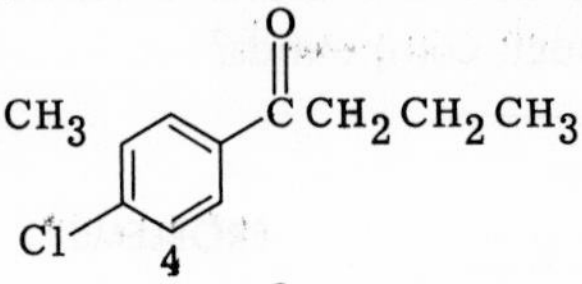

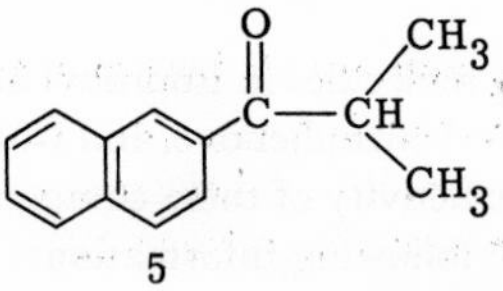

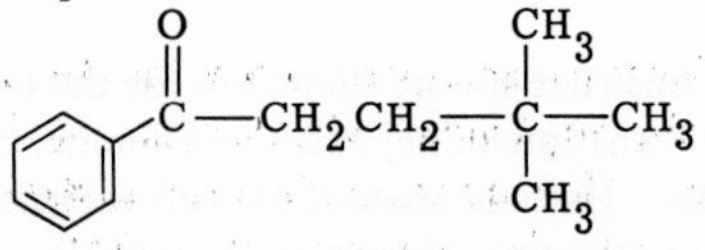

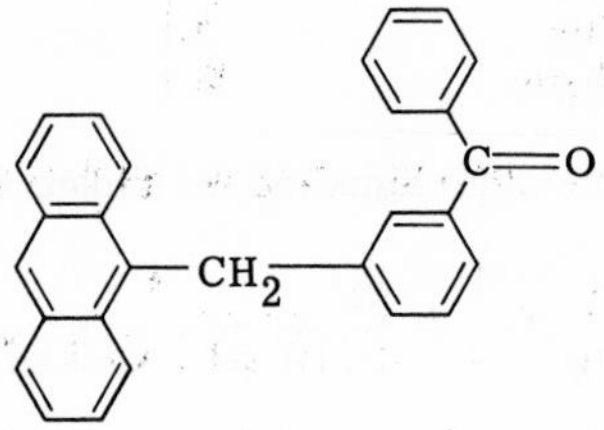

REFERENCES*

1. See the general references at the end of Chapter 1.
2. H. L. McMurry and R. S. Mulliken, *Proc. Natl. Acad. Sci., U.S.A.*, **26**, 312 (1940); H. L. McMurry, *J. Chem. Phys.*, **9**, 231, 241 (1941).
3. J. W. Sidman, *Chem. Rev.*, **58**, 689 (1958).
4. M. Kasha, *Disc. Faraday Soc.*, **9**, 14 (1950).
5. M. Kasha, in *Light and Life*, ed. W. D. McElroy and B. Glass (Baltimore, Md.: Johns Hopkins Press, 1961), p. 31.
6. J. N. Pitts, Jr., *et al.*, *J. Am. Chem. Soc.*, **81**, 1068 (1959).
7. W. M. Moore, G. S. Hammond, and R. P. Foss, *J. Am. Chem. Soc.*, **83**, 2789 (1961); G. S. Hammond, W. P. Baker, and W. M. Moore, *ibid.*, **83**, 2795 (1961).
8. W. M. Moore and M. Ketchum, *ibid.*, **84**, 1368 (1962).
9. J. A. Bell and H. Linschitz, *J. Am. Chem. Soc.*, **85**, 528 (1963).

* See Addendum for additional references.

10. W. A. Bryce and C. H. J. Wells, *Canad. J. Chem.*, **41**, 2722 (1963).

11. G. Porter and F. Wilkinson, *Trans. Faraday Soc.*, **57**, 1686 (1961).

12. A. Beckett and G. Porter, *Trans. Faraday Soc.*, **59**, 2039 (1963).

13. A. Beckett and G. Porter, *ibid.*, **59**, 2051 (1963); J. N. Pitts, Jr., H. W. Johnson, and T. Kuwana, *J. Phys. Chem.*, **66**, 2471 (1962).

14. Photochemical intramolecular hydrogen abstractions followed by a rapid thermal reversal are well known in phototropic systems: R. Dessauer and J. Paris, in *Advances in Photochemistry*, ed. W. A. Noyes, Jr., G. S. Hammond, and J. N. Pitts, Jr. (vol. I, New York: Interscience, 1963), p. 275; R. D. Luck and H. Sand, *Angew. Chem.* (Internat. Eng. Ed.), **3**, 570 (1964).

15. N. C. Yang and C. Rivas, *J. Am. Chem. Soc.*, **83**, 2213 (1961).

16. E. F. Zwicker, L. I. Grossweiner, and N. C. Yang, *ibid.*, **85**, 2671 (1963).

17. S. G. Cohen and M. N. Siddiqui, *J. Am. Chem. Soc.*, **86**, 5047 (1964).

18. C. R. Masson, V. Boekelheide, and W. A. Noyes, Jr., in *Technique of Organic Chemistry*, ed. A. Weissberger, (vol. II, New York: Interscience, 1956), p. 257.

19. G. S. Hammond and P. A. Leermakers, *J. Am. Chem. Soc.*, **84**, 207 (1962).

20. G. S. Hammond and P. A. Leermakers, *J. Phys. Chem.* , **66**, 1148 (1962).

21. G. Porter and P. Suppan, *Proc. Chem. Soc.*, 191 (1964).

22. G. Porter and P. Suppan, *Pure Appl. Chem.*, **9**, 499 (1964).

23. C. Walling and M. Gibian, *J. Am. Chem. Soc.*, **86**, 3902 (1964); A. Padwa, *Tetrahedron Letters*, 3465 (1964).

24. N. K. Bridge and G. Porter, *Proc. Royal Soc.*, **A244**, 259, 276 (1958).

25. J. N. Pitts, Jr., *J. Chem. Ed.*, **34**, 112 (1957).

26. P. Borrell, *J. Am. Chem. Soc.*, **86**, 3156 (1964).

27. P. Ausloos and R. E. Rebbert, *ibid.*, **86**, 4512 (1964).

28. J. N. Pitts, Jr., *et al.*, *Photochem. and Photobiol.*, **4**, 323 (1965).

29. G. R. McMillan, J. G. Calvert, and J. N. Pitts, Jr., *J. Am. Chem. Soc.*, **86**, 3602 (1964).

30. I. Orban, K. Schnaffner, and O. Jeger, *ibid.*, **85**, 3033 (1963).

31. K. H. Schulte-Elte and G. Ohloff, *Tetrahedron Letters*, 1143 (1964).

32. N. C. Yang, A. Morduchowitz, and D.-D. H. Yang, *J. Am. Chem. Soc.*, **85**, 1017 (1963).

33. J. W. Sidman and D. S. McClure, *J. Am. Chem. Soc.*, **77**, 6461 (1955).

34. H. L. J. Backstrom and K. Sandros, *Acta Chem. Scand.*, **12**, 3, 823 (1958).

35. H. L. J. Backstrom and K. Sandros, *ibid.*, **14**, 48 (1960).

36. P. A. Leermakers and G. F. Vesley, *J. Am. Chem. Soc.*, **85**, 3776 (1963); *ibid.*, **86**, 1768 (1964).

37. J. N. Pitts, Jr. and A. D. Osborn, *J. Am. Chem. Soc.*, **83**, 3011 (1961).

38. E. S. Huyser and D. C. Neckers, *J. Org. Chem.*, **29**, 276 (1964).

39. W. H. Urry, D. J. Trecker, and D. A. Winey, *Tetrahedron Letters*, 609 (1962).

40. W. H. Urry and D. J. Trecker, *J. Am. Chem. Soc.*, **84**, 118 (1962).

Photochemical Rearrangements and Isomerizations

7-1. PHOTOCHEMICAL TRANSFORMATION OF DIENONES AND RELATED COMPOUNDS

The photochemical transformations of dienones represent some of the most intriguing and remarkable photochemical rearrangements.[1, 2, 8] The mechanisms of these rearrangements have been compared to analogous ground-state reactions,[1] perhaps a hazardous venture. The structure-reactivity relationships of an excited state need not be parallel to those of the ground state. A species containing over 50 kcal mole^{-1} of excess electronic energy (over that of the ground state) is capable of exploring reaction paths which are inaccessible to the ground state. Furthermore, our knowledge of excited states is considerably less developed than our knowledge of the ground state. Simple-minded pictures which are engendered by molecular orbital (MO) theory, while helpful from a pictorial standpoint, may be wholly inadequate for application to some or many photochemical transformations.[2]

Rearrangement of 4,4-Diphenylcyclohexadienone

Although it is difficult to obtain accurate descriptions of the structures of the excited states of molecules, some reasonable descriptions of the mechanistic paths of photoreactions are possible which allow an organic chemist to rationalize the paths of known modes of photochemial transformations and, hopefully, to predict or anticipate modes for unstudied systems.[2, 8]

An example of a detailed study is the work which has been done on 4,4-diphenylcyclohexadienone (1). Irradiation of this compound in

162

aqueous dioxane yields the bicyclic ketone (2), which then undergoes further photochemical rearrangement to form the products [1] shown in Eq. 7-2.

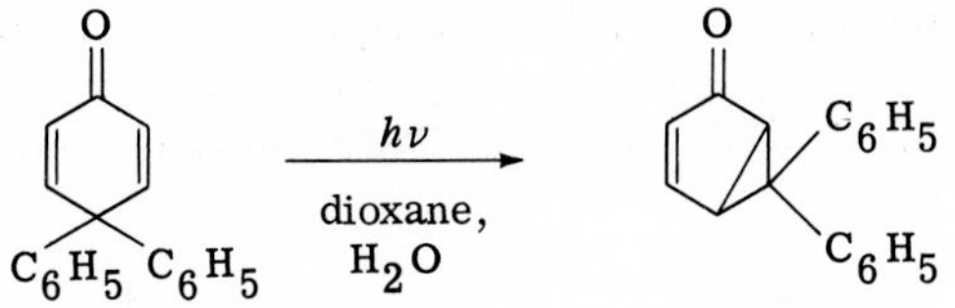

(7-1)

1

2 (10%)

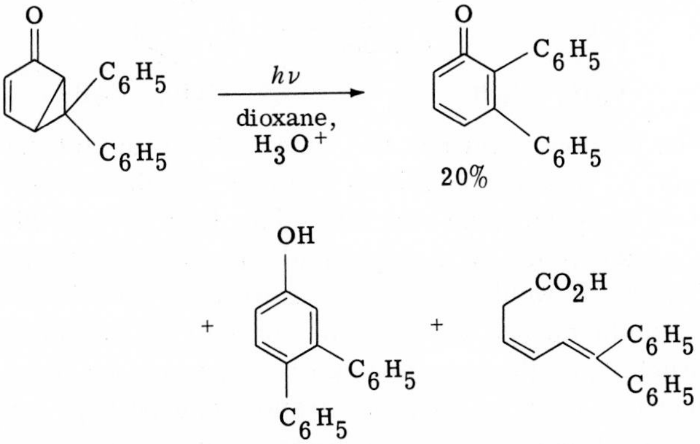

(7-2)

trace   40%

The dienone (1) has a lowest $S_1(n,\pi^*)$ state [4] at 73 kcal mole^{-1} and a $T_1(n,\pi^*)$ state at 69 kcal mole^{-1}. The *postulated* sequence of steps which convert (1) to (2) is [2]

1. n-π^* excitation to the $S_1(n,\pi^*)$ state;
2. deactivation to the chemically active excited state (which may be either S_1 or T_1);
3. formation of new bonds *in the excited state;*
4. π^*-n electronic demotion which produces a ground-state species;
5. reaction of the latter in a manner consistent with established organic chemical reactivity-structure relationships.

Let us now apply this sequence to compound 1. The transition to S_1 may be represented by

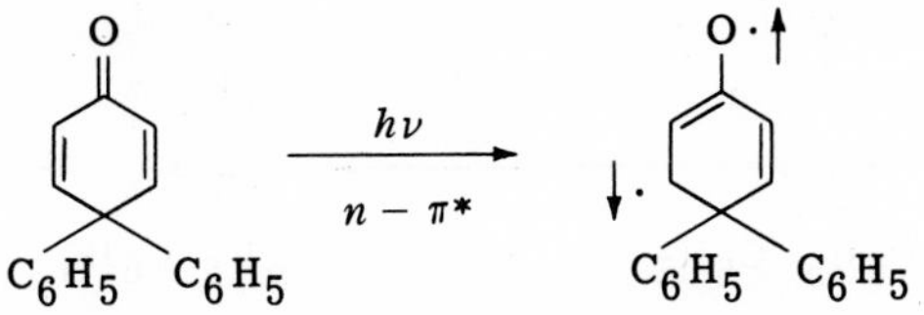

(7-3)

in which only one valence structure is shown. The evidence that the

$S_1(n,\pi^*)$ state is the initially excited level is derived from the absorption spectrum of compound 1 which shows a low extinction, long wavelength absorption band with a 0-0 component at 3,920 Å (73 kcal mole^{-1}).

Acetophenone ($E_T = 74$), a known triplet excitation donor,[3] sensitizes the conversion of 1 to 2, so that *it may be assumed* [4] that the *direct* photoreaction occurs by way of $T_1(n,\pi^*)$. This intersystem crossing step may be represented by

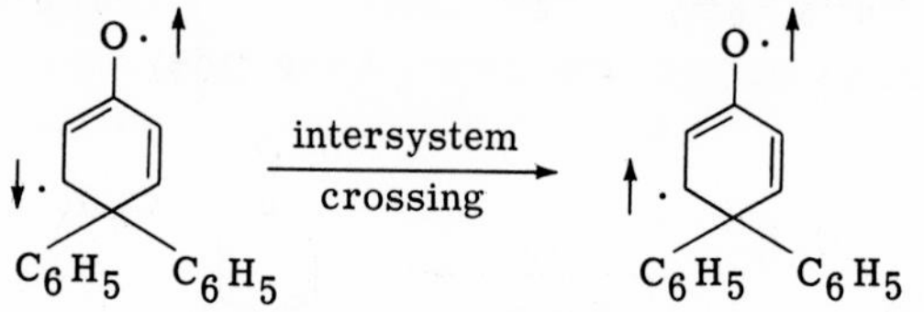

$$(7\text{-}4)$$

It should be possible to quench this state and thus inhibit the formation of compound 2. However, addition of 0.1 M naphthalene ($E_T = 61$ kcal mole^{-1}) fails to quench the reaction. This lack of quenching may be construed as the result of a very rapid rate of unimolecular reaction from $T_1(n,\pi^*)$. It would be interesting to see if 1-methylnaphthalene, as solvent, could quench this reaction, because as solvent (10 M) the rate of quenching by the 1-methylnaphthalene would be about 100 times greater than it is for a 0.1 M concentration, and perhaps would be fast enough to compete with the rapid intramolecular rearrangement of the dienone.

The excited state $T_1(n,\pi^*)$ is now capable of forming a new bond which will help to form the observed product:

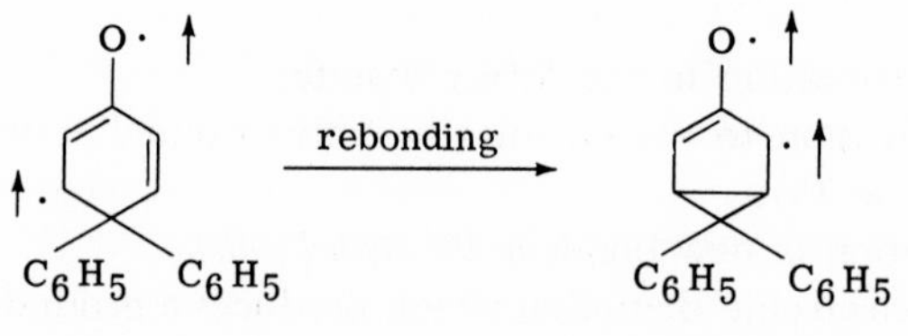

$$(7\text{-}5)$$

The next step is an internal conversion to the ground state by deactivation of the π^* electron into the original n orbital. This step is also an intersystem crossing step from a postulated zwitterion intermediate as shown in Eq. 7-6.

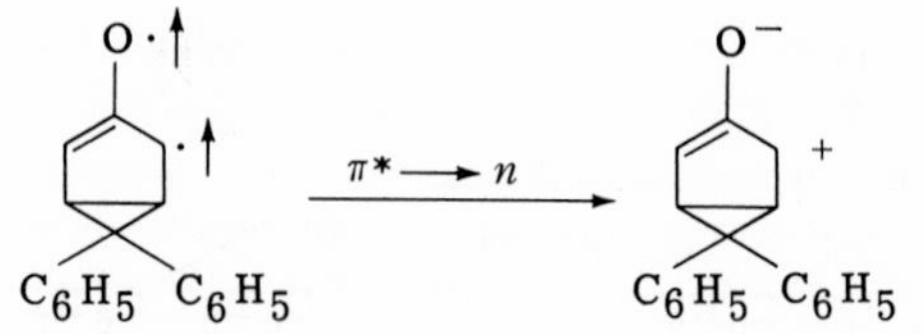

$$(7\text{-}6)$$

It has been proposed [4] that the zwitterion is a true intermediate, possibly detectable by some spectroscopic or other physical method. This species, whatever its chemical pedigree, will have a short lifetime because it lacks the maximum number of possible covalent bonds and possesses a separation of charges. One should point out the limitations of formulae which depict electrons as dots moving from atom to atom and remember that the *interconversion of states* takes into account all nuclear movements and electronic energies.

The zwitterion may now be considered to proceed to the product in a conventional organic sequence. Thus, the rearrangement of the zwitterion to the final product is analogous to the cyclopropylcarbinyl rearrangements.[2]

$$(7\text{-}7)$$

Such a sequence serves as a *useful device* to assist in the correlation of the multifarious reactions of dienones.[2, 8] However, several alternate views have been presented to explain reactions such as the rearrangement of compound 1 to 2. One may simply note empirically that such rearrangements are typical of a polar state, such as the zwitterion depicted above, and assume that excitation leads to such a state, without concerning oneself with the details leading to its formation.[8]

Theoretical MO calculations[4] (to be taken *cum grano salis*) indicate that n, π^* states may undergo reactions characteristic of electron-deficient systems as a direct result of the electronic distributions of n and π^* orbitals.[4] This result is shown in Fig. 7-1. Note that Eq. 7-3 implies an *increase* in the electron density of the ring electron system since an electron presumably localized on oxygen is donated to the π-electron system of the ring. Finally, as was pointed out earlier, a species which possesses 50 to 70 kcal mole^{-1} of excess electronic energy need not explore the same reaction paths which are followed by ground-state structures. In other words, the excited states of dienones have sufficient excess energy *that reactions characteristic of ground-state molecules may provide no suitable criteria for the prediction of chemical reactivity in photochemical reactions*. It may be useful to reiterate at this point that the classification of electronically excited states in terms of the electronic configuration which is believed to make the major contribution to that state (Section 2-2) is only an approximation. There is mounting evidence that the localization of n orbitals and σ orbitals may not be valid. Thus, one must be careful when making arguments based on zero order quantum mechanical calculations, because more refined calculations may reverse or substan-

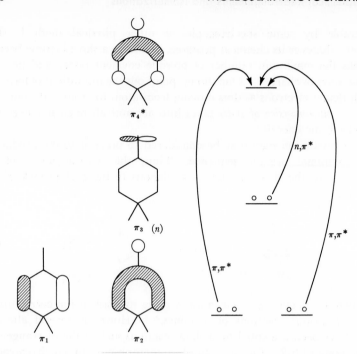

Fig. 7-1   *Molecular orbitals of cyclohexadienone calculated by the simple first-order method.   (The molecular orbitals are superimposed on the molecular skeleton.   The shaded area indicates a positive wave function as one looks down on the plane of the molecule; the open areas represent negative wave functions; straight lines indicate zero electron-density contribution from the given orbital.)*

tially alter the conclusions which are made on the basis of such simple calculations.

Photochemical Rearrangements of Santonin [2, 8]

The isolation and characterization of the sundry products formed from the photolysis of santonin (3) in various media, has received considerable attention.[5]   The occasional isolation of new intermediates [6, 7] deters premature speculation concerning the mechanisms of the various photorearrangements of santonin.   Benzophenone $(E_T = 69)$ sensitizes the photorearrangement [6] of compound 3 to 4 but Michler's ketone $(E_T = 61)$ does not (Eq. 7-8).

$$\xrightarrow[\text{dioxane}]{h\nu}$$

(7-8)

3   4

1,3-Pentadiene, an excellent quencher of triplets [3] possessing E_T greater than 60 kcal mole^{-1}, is found to inhibit this reaction, but the diene was not simultaneously isomerized [6] (a peculiar result). The high energy and short radiative lifetime of santonin's lowest triplet ($E_T = 68$) indicates that T_1 is a n,π^* state.

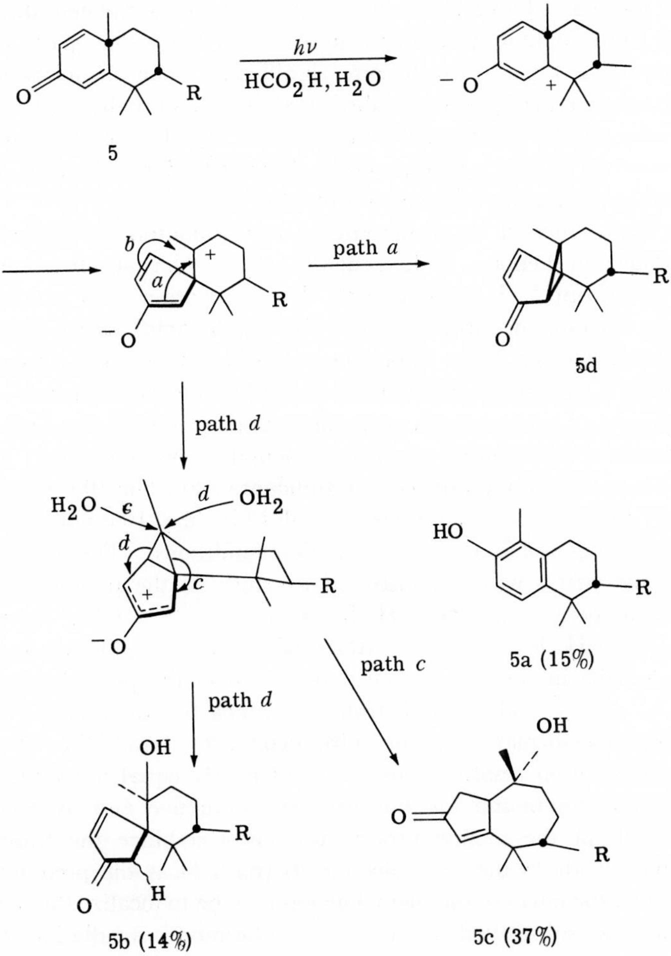

(7-9)

The photochemistry of a large number of 1,4-dien-3-ones such as santonin has been studied and will not be mentioned here. Much of this work has lacked mechanistic study, but recent work [8, 9] seems to be reversing this situation.

For example, Kropp [9] has made a number of elegant studies of the effect of substituents and solvent on the course of the photorearrangements of 1,4-dien-3-ones. He has been able to separate, in certain cases, electronic and steric effects by constructing appropriate model compounds for which only one of these effects would dominate. Thus, irradiation of the 1,4-dien-3-one (5) results in formation the three products (5b) (isolated as its dehydration derivative), (5c) and (5d). If the gem-dimethyl group is absent, similar amounts of products corresponding to (5c) and (5b) are formed. This result indicates that the role of the gem-dimethyl group is steric in that it hinders side attack of the water (path d) and allows path c in Eq. (7-9) to become significant. The phenol 5a is also a significant product because unsubstituted dienones usually give m-cresol type products. In this case, the intermediate which leads to formation of the m-cresol product is apparently difficult to form because of the unfavorable steric effect of the gem-dimethyl group.

The importance of electronic effects on the photorearrangements of cross-conjugated dienones of the general formula 6 has also been demonstrated by Kropp.[9] It is postulated that irradiation of 6 produces a zwitterion 7 (resonance forms 7a and 7b) which rapidly rearranges to a second mesomeric ion 7c (or its protonated form in acid media, as shown). Compounds 8, 9, and 10 are produced (in addition to some phenols) when 6 is irradiated in acidic media, with compounds 8 and 9 being formed in larger amounts. In neutral media, compound 10 predominates. Compounds 8 and 9 are not produced in significant yield when 10 is irradiated separately in acidic solution, thereby establishing that 10 is not converted to the mesomeric ion 7c under the reaction conditions. The importance of electronic effects was demonstrated by study of the photorearrangements of compounds 6a ($R_1 = H$, $R_2 = H$), 6b ($R_1 = CH_3$, $R_2 = H$), and 6c ($R_1 = H$, $R_2 = CH_3$). Attack of water on the back side of 7c (path a) results in the stereospecific formation of the perhydroazulene-alcohol 8. On the other hand, frontside attack by water on 7c results in stereospecific formation of the spiro-alcohol 9. Irradiation of 6a in acetic acid solution results in formation of nearly equal amounts of 8a and 9a. For compound 6b, however, the inductive and hyperconjugative effects of the methyl group apparently stabilize the transition state, which leads to the spiro-alcohol 9b (path b) as the predominant product (i.e., the effect of the methyl group may be to localize the positive charge at the substituted position). Furthermore, irradiation of 6c under comparable conditions results in formation of the perhydroazulene 8c as the predominant product. Thus, it appears that the predominant product formed from the cyclopropylcarbinyl intermediate 7c in each case is the one in which the methyl group is located on the newly formed double bond. Although electronic arguments alone can explain the changing relative yields of compounds 8 and 9 as one changes

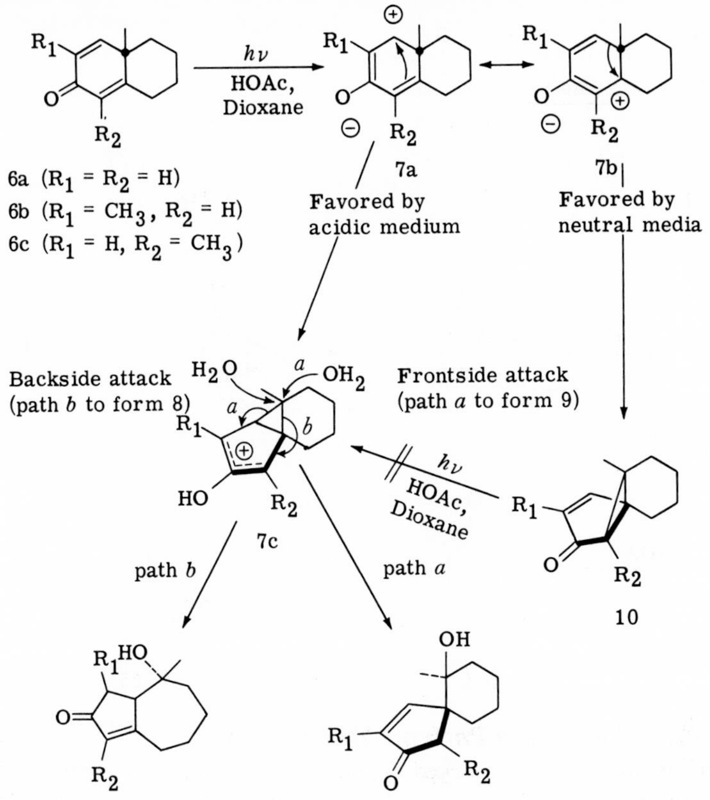

R_1 $\xrightarrow[\text{Dioxane}]{\substack{h\nu \\ \text{HOAc,}}}$ R_1 $\longleftrightarrow$ R_1

O O O

R_2 $\ominus$ R_2 $\ominus$ R_2

6a ($R_1 = R_2 = H$)   7a   7b|

6b ($R_1 = CH_3$, $R_2 = H$)   Favored by   Favored by

6c ($R_1 = H$, $R_2 = CH_3$)   acidic medium   neutral media

Backside attack H_2O a OH_2 Frontside attack

(path b to form 8) a (path a to form 9)

R_1 b

$\oplus$ $\xrightarrow[\text{Dioxane}]{\substack{h\nu \\ \text{HOAc,}}}$ R_1 (7-10)

HO R_2

7c O R_2

path b path a 10

R_1 HO OH

O R_1

R_2 O R_2

	Yield		Yield
8a ($R_1 = H$, $R_2 = H$)	19%	9a ($R_1 = H$, $R_2 = H$)	16%
8b ($R_1 = CH_3$, $R_2 = H$)	0	9b ($R_1 = CH_3$, $R_2 = H$)	51%
8c ($R_1 = H$, $R_2 = CH_3$)	50%	9c ($R_1 = H$, $R_2 = CH_3$)	0

R_1 and R_2, it is possible that in the case of 6b ($R_1 = CH_3$, $R_2 = H$) steric effects also contribute by shielding the water as it attacks from the back side (path a) or by releasing a greater amount of strain in the transition state by proceeding by path b rather than path a.[9]

Photoreactions of Cyclic Enones [8, 13]

Simple cyclic enones such as compound 11, undergo rearrangements formally similar to those of dienones, showing that the rebonding step of the detailed mechanism presented above is not required and that rearrangement cannot be uniquely dependent upon the presence of two double bonds.[10] The following example indicates a possible mechanism for the conversion of compound 11 into the observed products.

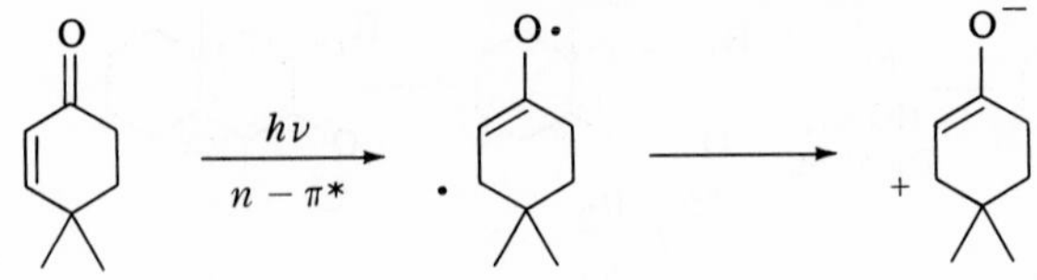

$$(7\text{-}11)$$

60%

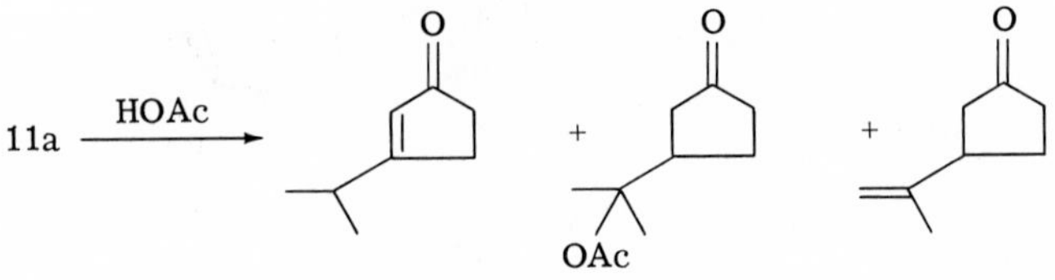

10%   40%   25%

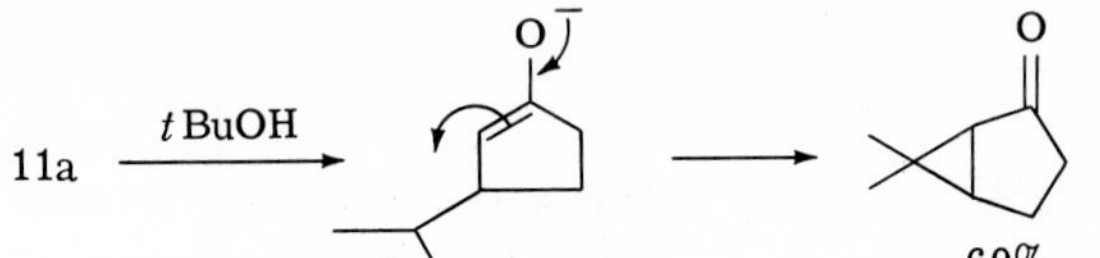

Dependence of Reaction Path on Multiplicity [11]

An interesting case of a marked dependence of a reaction path of an enedione (dibenzoylethylene, 12) on multiplicity has been noted.[11] Irradiation of 12 in alcoholic solution leads to the formation of one to one adducts (13). The *cis* isomer is the reactive one in this reaction, since the *trans* isomer is unreactive toward addition but undergoes isomerization to the *cis* compound under irradiation (Eq. 7-12).

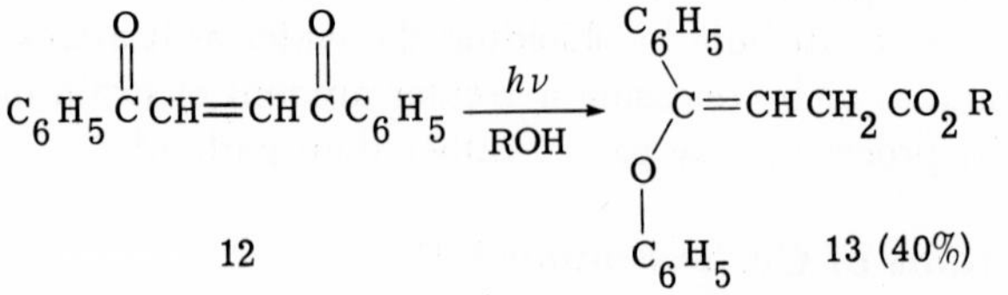

$$C_6H_5 \overset{O}{\underset{||}{C}} CH{=}CH \overset{O}{\underset{||}{C}} C_6H_5 \xrightarrow[ROH]{h\nu} \underset{\underset{C_6H_5}{|}}{\overset{C_6H_5}{\underset{O}{|}}} C{=}CH\,CH_2\,CO_2\,R \qquad (7\text{-}12)$$

12   13 (40%)

The reaction takes a completely different course in the presence of triplet photosensitizers such as benzophonone.

$$C_6H_5 \overset{O}{\underset{||}{C}} CH{=}CH \overset{O}{\underset{||}{C}} C_6H_5 \xrightarrow[ROH,\,h\nu]{(C_6H_5)_2\,C{=}O} C_6H_5 \overset{O}{\underset{||}{C}} CH_2\,CH_2 \overset{O}{\underset{||}{C}} C_6H_5 \quad (7\text{-}13)$$

12   13a

Benzophenone is an efficient triplet energy-transferring agent. The difference in reaction course shown in Eqs. 7-12 and 7-13 can be rationalized if the former is assumed to proceed via a singlet state and the latter via a triplet state. The rearrangement shown in Eq. 7-12 must be a very efficient reaction of the $S_1(n,\pi^*)$ state of compound 12, *before intersystem crossing*. Equation 7-13 indicates that the $T_1(n,\pi^*)$ triplet of 12 $(E_T < 69)$ is involved since this state has been shown to be very reactive in photoreductions.

Thus, the detailed paths of the photoreaction of 12 may be summarized [11] as follows:

Direct

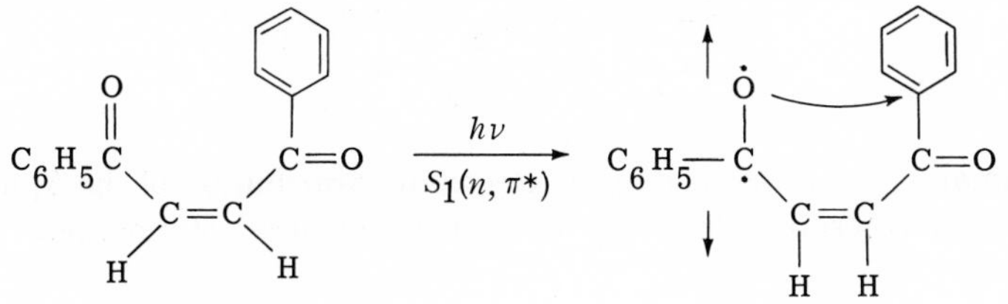

12 $S_1(n, \pi^*)$

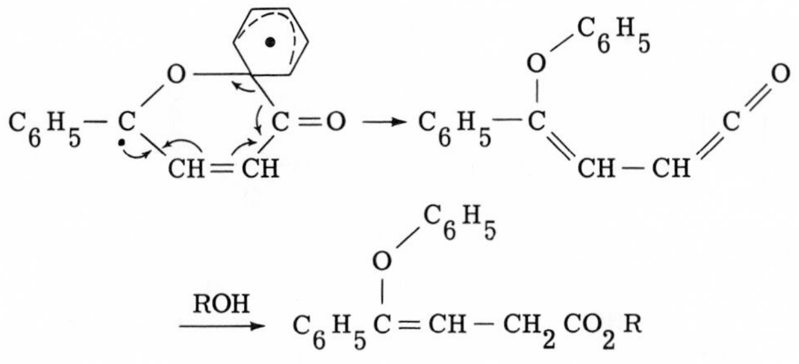

$$C_6 H_5 C = CH - CH_2 CO_2 R$$

13

Sensitized

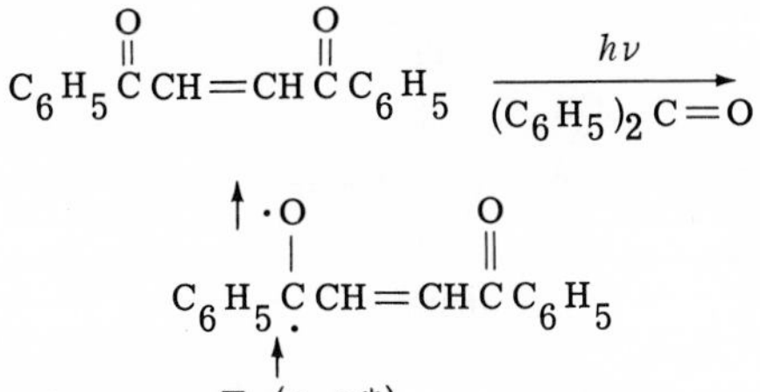

$T_1(n, \pi^*)$

by energy transfer

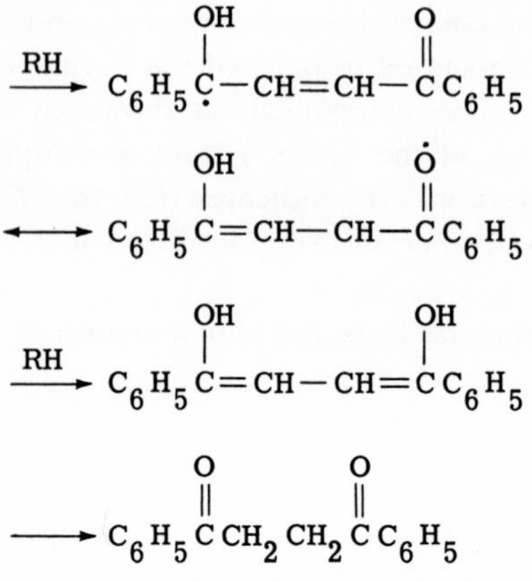

$$\xrightarrow{RH} \ C_6H_5\overset{OH}{\underset{\cdot}{C}}-CH=CH-\overset{O}{\overset{\|}{C}}C_6H_5$$

$$\longleftarrow \ C_6H_5\overset{OH}{\underset{\cdot}{C}}=CH-CH-\overset{\overset{\cdot}{O}}{\overset{\|}{C}}C_6H_5$$

$$\xrightarrow{RH} \ C_6H_5\overset{OH}{\underset{\cdot}{C}}=CH-CH=\overset{OH}{\underset{\cdot}{C}}C_6H_5$$

$$\longrightarrow \ C_6H_5\overset{O}{\overset{\|}{C}}CH_2\,CH_2\overset{O}{\overset{\|}{C}}C_6H_5$$

13a

Presumably, the difference in the electronic distribution of the S_1 and T_1 state of 12 is responsible for the two separate courses of reaction.

Epoxyketones [8, 12]

Dimethylacrylophenone (14) undergoes photorearrangement [12] to compound 15. A possible mechanism of this reaction is given by Eq. 7-14.

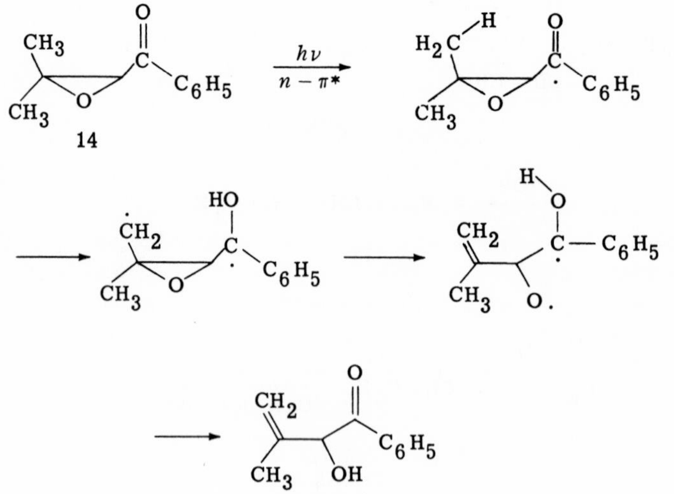

(7-14)

15 (64%)

The indone epoxide (16) undergoes an interesting valence isomerization to the red compound (17) upon irradiation:[13, 14]

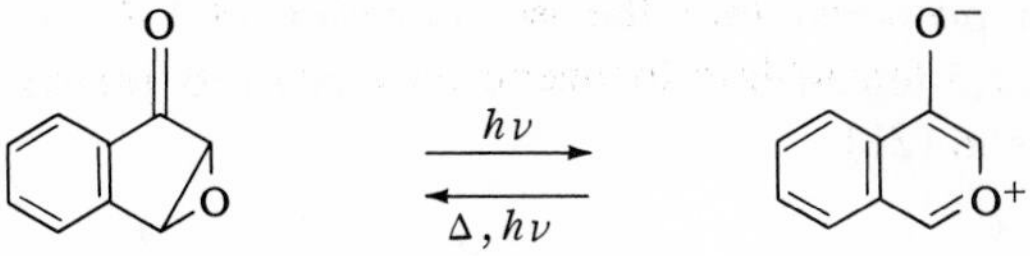

$$16 \ (90\%) \qquad benzene \qquad 17 \ (10\%) \tag{7-15}$$

The reaction may be reversed thermally or photochemically. Benzophenone $(E_T = 69)$ photosensitizes the conversion of compound 16 to 17 while other lower energy (potential) sensitizers $(E_T < 68)$ produce complete oxidative bleaching of 17.

7-2. VALENCE ISOMERIZATIONS

One of the more general photochemical reactions [8] of dienes and trienes is that of *valence isomerization*—i.e., an isomerization in which electron reshuffling occurs and nuclei move to make or break new π and σ bonds. Such reactions have been long known and are important in the vitamin D series.[8] Norbornadiene, formally a 1,4-cyclohexadiene, and its derivatives are ring closed to quadricyclene (18) and its derivatives by direct or triplet sensitized photolysis.[15, 16]

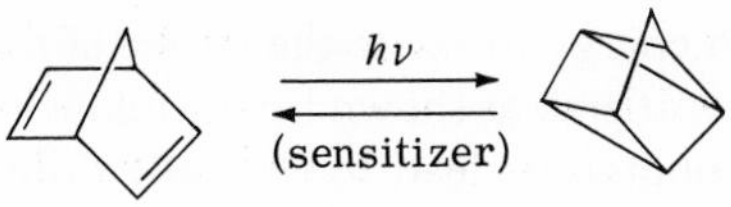

$$isopentane \quad 18 \ (90\%) \tag{7-16}$$

The reaction may be reversed thermally or photochemically. Cyclohexadiene-1,3 and its derivatives may either ring close or ring open.[8] The parent compound ring opens in dilute solution,[17] while the derivative (19) ring closes [18] and provides a splendid route to "Dewar" benzene, bicyclo-(2.2.0)-hexa-2,5-diene, (20). 1,2,5-Tri-*t*-butylbenzene isomerizes directly to 1,2,5-tri-*t*-butylbicyclo-(2.2.0)-hexa-2,5-diene.[19, 20]

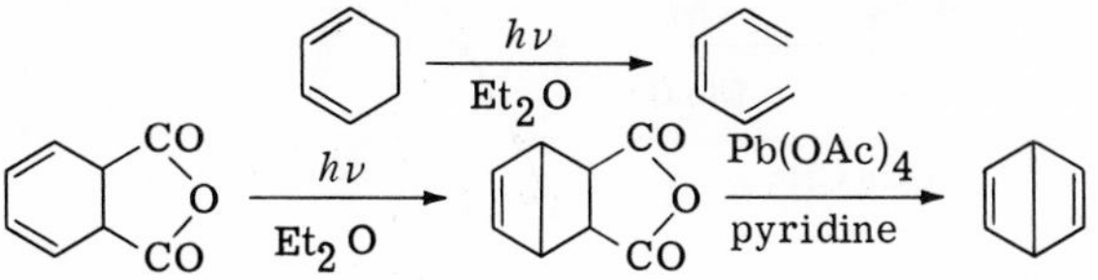

$$\tag{7-17}$$

$$\tag{7-18}$$

19   20 (20%)

It has been proposed that the isomerization of 1,2,4,5-tetra-t-butyl-benzene to 1,2,3,5-tetra-t-butylbenzene may proceed through the "Lau-denberg" benzene (21).

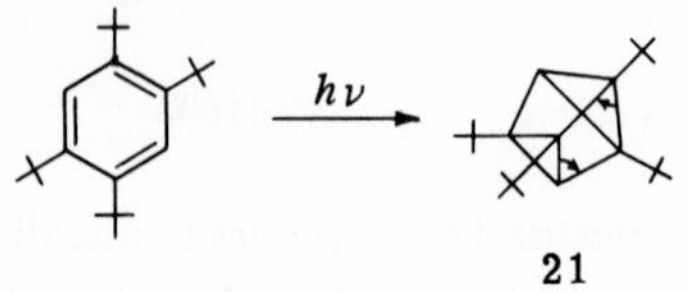

$$(7\text{-}19)$$

21

Butadiene and its derivatives also undergo photocyclization to cyclo-butenes if steric restrictions are not too severe.[21, 22]   The parent compound also forms bicyclobutane in low yield.[22]

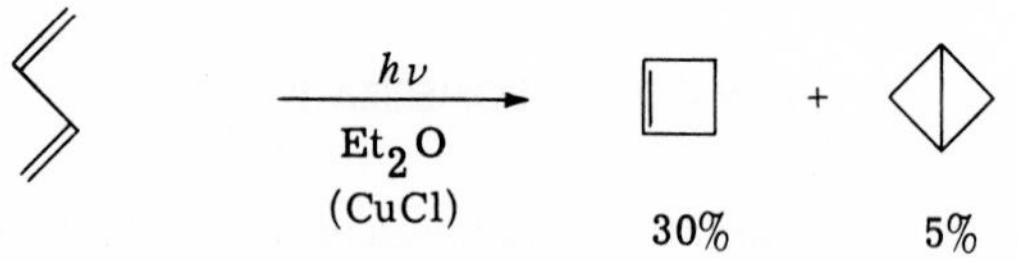

$$(7\text{-}20)$$

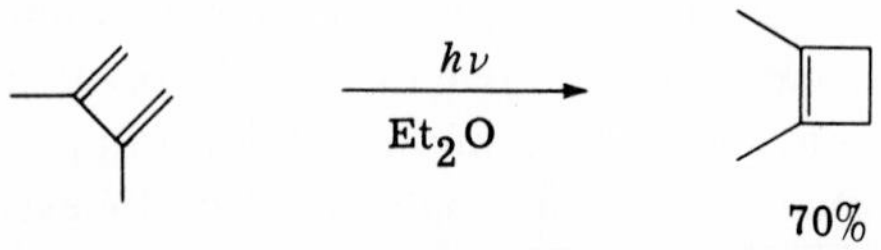

30%   5%

$$(7\text{-}21)$$

70%

Diazomethane has been reported as a photosensitizer for the ring closure of certain cyclohexadienes.[23]   It is difficult to understand the mechanism of this sensitization since diazomethane probably has insuffi-cient triplet excitation energy to excite the triplet of the diene.   However, the reaction is truly sensitized, as shown by the following example in which direct and sensitized photolyses lead to radically different results.

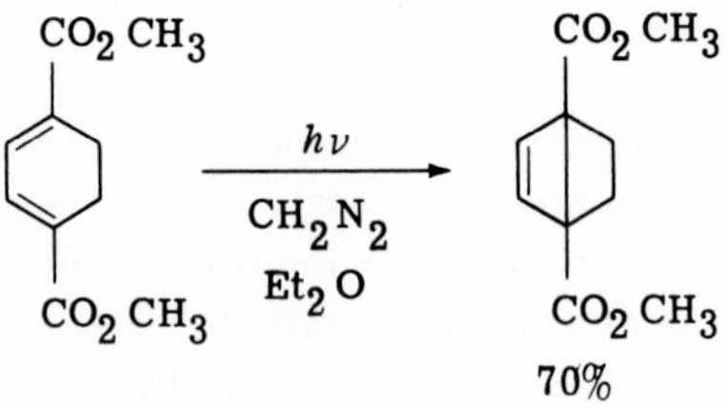

$$(7\text{-}22)$$

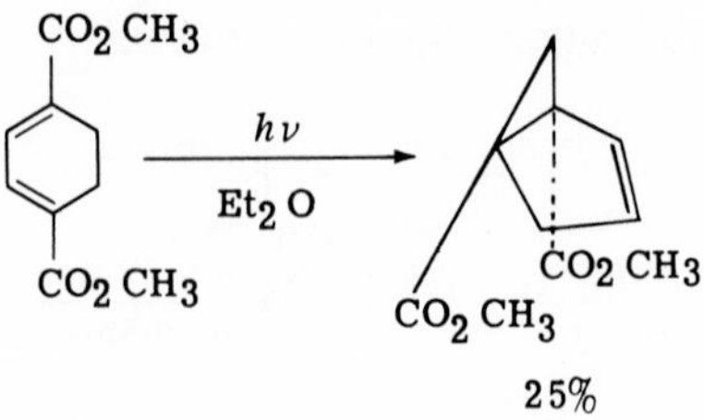

70%

$$(7\text{-}23)$$

25%

Note added in proof.   Equation 7-22 has been shown, in fact, to be incorrect.   See *Ber.*, **98**, 2201 (1965).

The irradiation of concentrated solutions of dienes in the presence of photosensitizers leads mainly to dimerization [15, 24] (*vide infra*, Section 8-3).

1,5-Dienes undergo a remarkable cross-bonding reaction in the vapor phase (mercury sensitized) and solution.[25, 27]

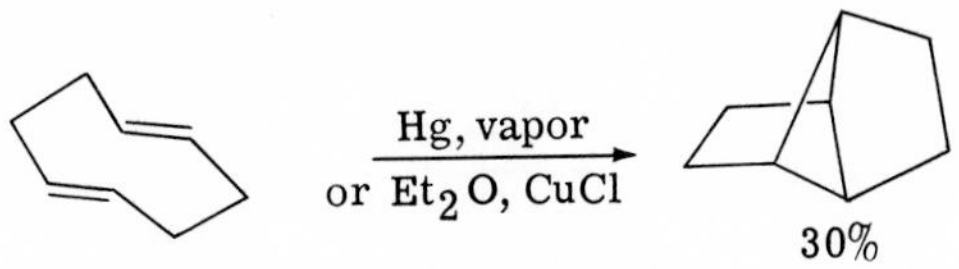

$$\text{(7-24)}$$

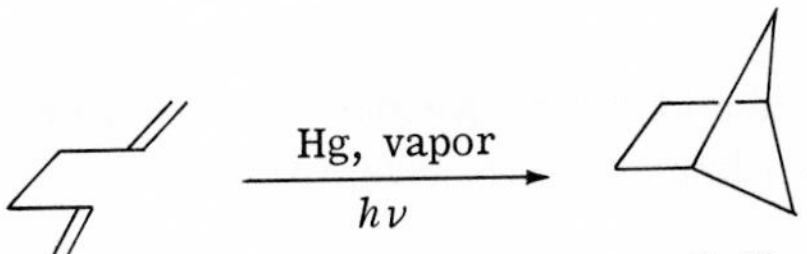

30%

$$\text{(7-25)}$$

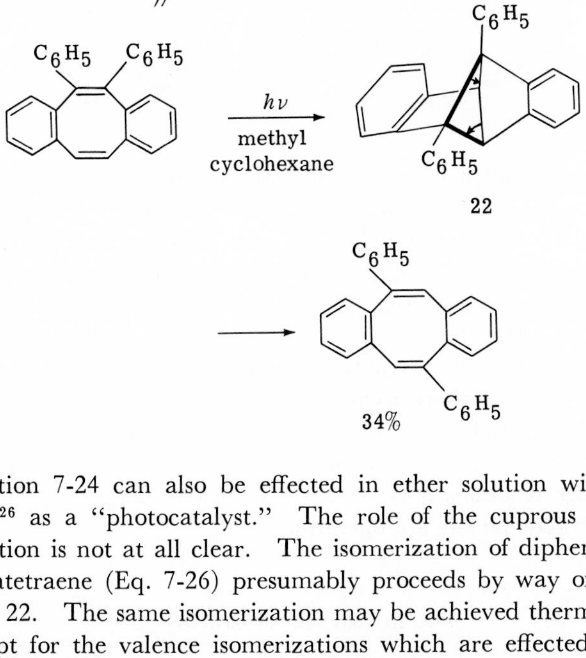

22

$$\text{(7-26)}$$

34%

Reaction 7-24 can also be effected in ether solution with cuprous chloride [26] as a "photocatalyst." The role of the cuprous chloride in this reaction is not at all clear. The isomerization of diphenyldibenzo-cyclooctatetraene (Eq. 7-26) presumably proceeds by way of the inter-mediate, 22. The same isomerization may be achieved thermally.

Except for the valence isomerizations which are effected by triplet sensitizers, nothing much is known about the mechanism of these reac-tions. Emission spectroscopic data are scant for olefins since they are nonluminescent.[29]

Stereochemical Course of Photochemical Valence Isomerization

Woodward and Hoffman [29] have proposed that the steric course of photochemical valence isomerizations involving bond formation between the termini of a linear conjugated system is determined by the symmetry of the lowest π^* orbital, in particular by the symmetry of the π^* wave function at the terminal carbon atoms. For example, the photochemical isomerization [17] of *trans, cis, trans*-2,4,6-octatriene leads to *trans*-5,6-dimethyl-cyclohexadiene-1,3 (Eq. 7-27) (a photoequilibrium exists

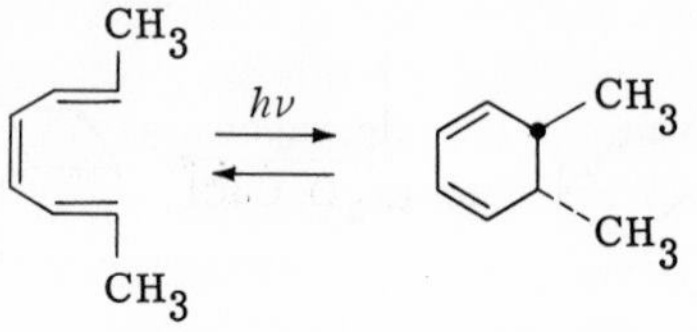

$$(7\text{-}27)$$

between the open and closed forms). The symmetry of the π^* orbital at C_1 and C_6 in a linear triene system is shown below.

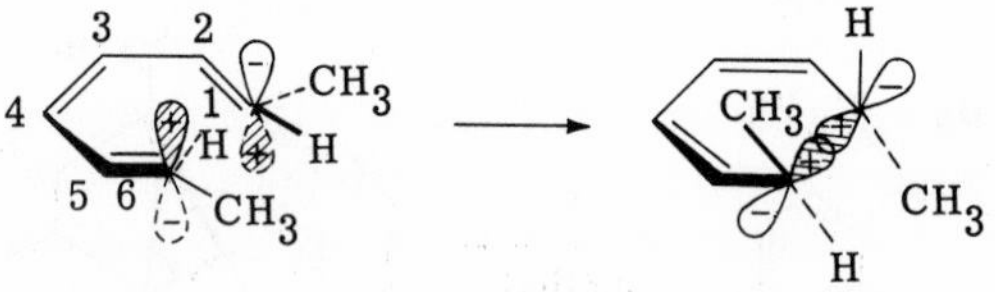

If it is assumed that a bonding interaction between the carbon termini must involve overlap between the same sign portions of the MO located on the termini, then the methyl on C_6 must rotate *up* and the methyl on C_1 must rotate *down* so that the wave function tends to increase bond density (like signs) between C_1 and C_6. The $+$ lobe on C_1 must move up to bond with the $+$ lobe on C_6 (which simultaneously moves down). This hypothesis correctly predicts the course of photochemical triene ring closures in a number of other cases [29] and may be modified to rationalize the course of a number of stereospecific thermal diene and triene ring openings and closures.[29] This simple rule, of course, does not predict whether other reactions may occur and must be modified when strain or other energetic factors are operating.

7-3. cis-trans ISOMERIZATION

Absorption of a photon by a compound containing an olefinic link often results in *cis-trans* geometrical isomerization. In many simple systems the *trans* isomer absorbs light of longer wavelength more intensely than the *cis* isomer; consequently, if long wavelength light is employed a photostationary condition is reached in which the *cis* isomer predominates (i.e., the *trans* isomer is "pumped" back to the *cis* more rapidly than the reverse process).[30] This result merely reflects the difference in the extinction coefficients of the two isomers, if the quantum yields for inconversions of the isomers are similar.[31]

Excited States of Ethylene [30, 34]

Theoretical calculations indicate that the equilibrium configuration of triplet ethylene should have its p_z atomic orbitals in the perpendicular configuration.[32]   The simple MO picture of an electronic transition in ethylene is that of an electron jump from the highest filled bonding π orbital into the lowest unfilled π^* orbital.   MO theory does not differentiate between the singlet and triplet states which result from such a transition, but refined calculations indicate that the destabilizing effect of the π^* electron outweighs the bonding energy of the electron left in the π orbital.   As a result, the ground-state nuclear configuration, in which the two p_z orbitals are parallel and form a π bond, is no longer the most stable configuration.   Twisting the molecule 90° about the C_1-C_2 axis minimizes the overlap between the π and π^* orbitals, and the *perpendicular* configuration is the most stable for the π,π^* configuration.   If one plots the potential-energy curves for twisting of ethylene as a function the angle between the π and π^* orbitals, the result is shown in Fig. 7-2.   It is apparent that the triplet state is actually the *ground state* for the 90° twisted configuration.

It is tempting to assign nonplanar configurations to triplet states of all compounds, but there is no compelling evidence to support such conclusions.

We see that at least two paths are possible for thermal isomerization of an ethylene-like molecule whose energy versus angle of twist profile resembles that in Fig. 7-2.   A low energy path requiring intersystem crossing at points a and b may prevail, or the molecule may remain in the

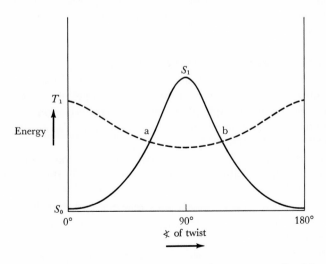

Fig. 7-2   *Potential curve for twisting of ethylene* [32] *(S_0 ground state, T_1 triplet state).*

singlet state for which the activation energy for isomerization is correspondingly higher.

Photochemical isomerization starts from energies above S_1 and T_1 and either may serve as the site of isomerization. Conversion from either of these states may produce a "hot" ground state [33] in which isomerization is possible (see Section 7-4).

Direct Photochemical cis-trans Isomerization [30, 33, 35, 37]

Only typical examples of recent mechanistic investigations of photochemically induced *cis-trans* isomerizations will be discussed.[34]

Isomerization of 4,4'-disubstituted stilbenes and stilbene itself have received considerable attention.[35] Competing formation of phenanthrenes, formation of colored intermediates, and chemical effects of oxygen were not recognized in some studies and vitiate these early results.[34] Careful quantitative study of these compounds indicates that the quantum yields for the *trans* → *cis* process for stilbenes possessing a large dipole moment in the excited state are dramatically solvent and temperature dependent, whereas the *cis* → *trans* quantum yield is generally insensitive to these factors.[35] These results have been interpreted as meaning that there is an energy barrier between S_1 of the *trans* system and another state, probably T_1, in which rotation can occur. The solvent effect is attributed to the selective stabilization of the very polar *trans* S_1 state by polar solvents, while the *cis* S_1 state is rapidly converted into a freely rotating state with little or no activation energy.

Similar results have been found for the isomerization of azobenzenes, for which the quantum yield for the *trans* → *cis* process decreases sharply with decreasing temperature while the yield for the *cis* → *trans* process is relatively constant.[36]

Photosensitized cis-trans Isomerizations [34, 37-40]

Photosensitized isomerization involving triplet sensitizers can circumvent complications which may occur due to competing reactions in the S_1 state. For example, the photosensitized isomerization of stilbene is *not* accompanied by phenanthrene formation which is initiated in the S_1 state [34-36] (see Section 9-2).

Many examples of photosensitized *cis-trans* isomerizations have appeared recently. 2-Butene may be isomerized in the gas phase by various sensitizers.[37] It has been shown that energy transfer occurs upon every collision if the transfer is exothermic and that deactivation of excited triplet butene-2 molecules produces *cis* and *trans* isomers with equal probability.

Several solution-phase sensitized isomerizations have been studied in some detail and have led to a considerable increase in our understanding

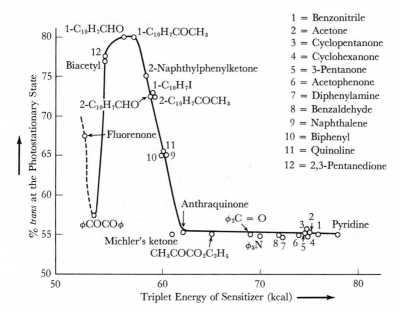

Fig. 7-3   *Photosensitized isomerization of the piperylenes.*[40]

of triplet-energy transfer in solution.   For example, both stilbene and 1,3-pentadiene are isomerized to photostationary mixtures by various sensitizers.[38-40]   A most remarkable feature of these results is that the *ratio of* cis *to* trans *isomers depends on the sensitizer employed.*   The results for the photosensitized isomerization of 1,3-pentadiene are shown in Fig. 7-3 as a plot of the percent of *trans* in the photostationary mixture versus the triplet energy of the sensitizer.   The rates of conversion of *trans* to *cis* and *cis* to *trans* isomers are equal at the photostationary state.

It was found that dibenzalacetone, acetopyrene, and benzanthrone, sensitizers whose triplet states are less than 53 kcal mole^{-1} above their ground states, are extremely inefficient as sensitizers, in marked contrast to the high efficiency exhibited by other carbonyl compounds.   Sensitizers whose triplet-excitation energies are above 60 kcal mole^{-1} give the same results (a *cis-trans* mixture containing 55% of the *trans* isomer), while sensitizers whose triplet excitation energies are below 60 kcal mole^{-1} give a variety of results (photostationary *cis-trans* mixtures varying from 65 to 80% *trans*).

The postulates which most easily accommodate these results are that

1. All of the sensitizers whose E_T is greater than 60 kcal mole^{-1} transfer triplet energy to either *cis-* or *trans-*1,3-pentadiene on every collision, so that the composition of the photostationary mixtures is

dependent only on the unimolecular decay processes of the pentadiene triplets.

2. If the energy of the sensitizer is less than 60 kcal mole^{-1}, transfer to trans-1,3-pentadiene becomes measurably inefficient, and the photostationary mixture becomes richer in trans.

3. A point is reached at which transfer to both isomers becomes somewhat inefficient and energetics are not the controlling factor in the transfer step.

4. Sensitizers with E_T less than 53 kcal mole^{-1} are inefficient at exciting either isomer because they possess insufficient excitation energy to transfer efficiently to either the cis or trans isomer.

The following simple mechanism properly predicts the behavior of sensitized cis-trans isomerizations for which energetics are the controlling factor, where B is the sensitizer,

$$\begin{array}{ll} & Rate \\ B \xrightarrow{h\nu} B^* & I \\ B^* \to B & k_d B^* \\ cP + B^* \to T & k_{qc} B^*[cP] \\ tP + B^* \to T & k_{qt} B^*[tP] \\ T \to cP & k_1 T \\ T \to tP & k_2 T \end{array}$$

cP is cis-1,3-pentadiene, tP is trans-1,3-pentadiene, and T is triplet 1,3-pentadiene (assuming the same triplet is produced by excitation transfer to either the cis or trans isomer).

At the photostationary state the following relationship holds:[34]

$$\frac{[cis]_{\text{pss}}}{[trans]_{\text{pss}}} = \frac{k_{qt}}{k_{qc}} \times \frac{k_1}{k_2}$$

where the subscript pss indicates the photostationary state concentrations. For high-energy sensitizers $k_{qt}/k_{qc} \sim 1$—i.e., transfer occurs at the diffusion-controlled rate to each isomer, and the equation simplifies to

$$\frac{(cis)_{\text{s}}}{(trans)_{\text{s}}} = \frac{k_1}{k_2} \tag{7-28}$$

i.e., the composition of the isomer mixture depends only on the rate of decay of triplet 1,3-pentadiene to cis- or trans-1,3-pentadiene (presumably a molecular constant).

When transfer to trans-1,3-pentadiene becomes inefficient $k_{qc} > k_{qt}$ and the relative yield of trans isomer in the photostationary mixture increases.

Considerably more complicated kinetic schemes are required to describe the behavior of systems for which energetics is *not* the main controlling factor.[34, 36, 39, 40]

Uses of cis-trans Isomerization [34, 40]

Compilation of data such as that shown in Fig. 7-3 allows the estimation of the E_T of sensitizers. This may be important if no other method is available for measurement of this quantity. Direct photochemical reactions may be studied by including isomerizable ethylenes in the photolysis mixture. If quenching of the photoreaction and *cis-trans* isomerization occurs concurrently, presumptive evidence for a triplet intermediate in the direct photolysis is available. Dienes are especially suited for such studies because of their large S_1-T_1 energy split which puts S_1 at close to 125 kcal mole^{-1} (in the far ultraviolet) and T_1 at about 55 to 60 kcal mole^{-1}, which is lower than the E_T of many other organic molecules.

It is interesting to note that 2-hydroxybenzophenone is a particularly inefficient sensitizer,[38] but 2-methoxybenzophenone is quite efficient [38] (for 1,3-pentadiene isomerization). This result correlates with the known inertness of 2-hydroxybenzophenones in photoreduction (Section 6–3) and implies that the triplet of these compounds is too short-lived to be quenched or is not formed.

Photosensitized cis-trans Isomerization of the Stilbenes [34, 40]

The photosensitized *cis-trans* isomerization of the stilbenes shows many remarkable facets.[39, 40] As a result of an exhaustive study of this system, Saltiel and Hammond demonstrated that several novel and unexpected reactions complicated photosensitized stilbene isomerization:

1. Low-energy sensitizers ($E_T < 50$) were capable of reversibly transferring energy back and forth with the *trans* stilbene triplet, but the *cis* triplet was always formed irreversibly.

2. Certain low-energy sensitizers ($E_T < 57$) are capable of transferring energy to *cis*-stilbene ($E_T = 57$) with moderate efficiency.

3. The *cis* triplet rapidly converts to the *trans* triplet which then decays to either *cis*- or *trans*-stilbene.

A plot of E_T (sensitizer) versus the *cis/trans* stilbene ratio at the photostationary state is shown in Fig. 7-4. This curve appears to be more complex than the corresponding 1,3-pentadiene curve shown in Fig. 7-3. Thus, there are minima at 50 and 57 kcal mole.$^{-1}$ However, each point which falls far off the dotted line (which makes the stilbene and 1,3-pentadiene curves more similar) in Fig. 7-4 is a 1,4-quinone, which may be behaving in an unexpected fashion. Originally, the minima were

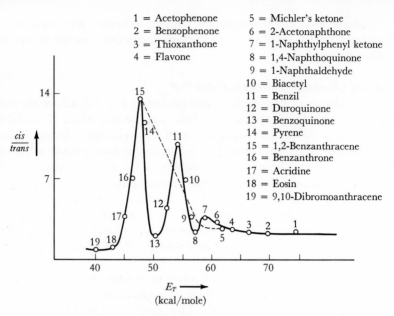

Fig. 7-4　　*Photosensitized isomerization of the stilbenes.*[40]

explained by assuming an exact matching of the vertical excitation energy (a) of the *cis*-stilbene with that of the sensitizer (minimum at 57 kcal mole^{-1}) and (b) of the *trans*-stilbene with that of the sensitizer (minimum at 47 kcal mole^{-1}). A number of other nonquinone sensitizers have now been shown to fall on the dotted line, which leaves as an open question the reason for the peculiarity of quinones as sensitizers for stilbene isomerization.

"Nonvertical" Excitation Transfer From Low-energy Sensitizers [34, 36, 42]

Certain energy acceptors are capable of quenching sensitizer triplets which possess insufficient energy to promote the quencher to its spectroscopic triplet state—i.e., E_T(acceptor) $>$ E_T(donor). Such transfers are usually of lower efficiency than those in which the triplet energy of the donor exceeds that of the acceptor by several kilocalories. Such an effect may be explained (in part) by *reversible* energy transfer from the excited acceptor *back to the donor* (see Section 5-4). However, such transfers occur with moderate efficiency even when the donor (spectroscopic) triplet lies 5 to 10 kcal mole^{-1} (or more) below that of the acceptor. Saltiel and Hammond [42] propose that these transfers (in which the donor's (spectroscopic) triplet is lower than that of the acceptor, but which occur with moderate efficiency), be termed "nonvertical" transitions because the Franck-Condon restrictions do not obtain for these systems.

As an example of a "nonvertical" excitation transfer, consider the conversion of *cis*-stilbene ($E_T = 57$) to the trans-*stilbene triplet* by a sensitizer possessing *less* than 57 kcal mole^{-1} triplet excitation energy. A possible energy profile as a function of angle of twist around the C=C is given in Fig. 7-5. The wavy arrow indicates the "nonvertical" excitation of the *trans* triplet and the straight line indicates the "vertical" excitation of the *cis* triplet. The sensitizer in its triplet state may be pictured as colliding many times with the acceptor during its lifetime (which may be considerable since vertical transfer is improbable). The donor and acceptor may be considered to be a "complex" during their existence as colliding partners. The donor may then "scan" the possible energy states of the acceptor until it interacts strongly with one and a "coupled, nonvertical" transfer occurs.

An extreme case of "nonvertical" transfer involves σ bonds as energy acceptors. Thus, quadricyclene may be converted to norbornadiene by lower ($E_T < 53$) energy sensitizers, although it is difficult to conceive of a (spectroscopic) triplet of this saturated molecule at such a low energy.[44] Indeed, the reverse process does not proceed as efficiently in the presence of low-energy ($E_T < 55$) photosensitizers, and a photostationary mixture which is rich in norbornadiene results. On the other hand, high-energy sensitizers *transfer excitation selectively to form the spectroscopic norbornadiene triplet*, and a photostationary mixture which is nearly pure quadricyclene results.

The process of "nonvertical" excitation offers great potential for organic photochemistry since it promises to be extremely selective.

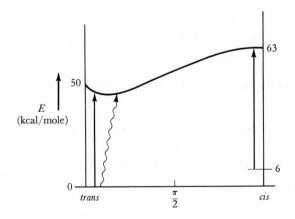

Fig. 7-5   *Possible potential-energy curve as a function of angle of twist for the stilbenes.*[40]

Schenck Mechanism of Excitation Transfer [45]

It should be pointed out that low-energy triplet sensitizers *may* excite acceptors possessing higher excitation energies by mechanisms other than nonvertical energy transfer. Since these compounds have very low ($E_T < 55$) triplet energies, they usually have low-lying singlet states also. Such a situation is ideal for complex formation which is enhanced by low-lying excited states in the donor or acceptor. Complexes may occur between the ground-state donor or acceptor or between an *excited* donor and ground-state acceptor. In the extreme case, the donor may form a bond with the acceptor resulting in a short-lived biradical.

$$\bullet \; Sens^* \bullet + A \rightarrow \bullet \; Sens - A \; \bullet$$

The latter mechanism has been long espoused by Schenck,[45] who proposes that nearly all energy transfer occurs by the addition-elimination mechanism in which the excited sensitizer (which is represented by a biradical structure, • Sens •) adds to the acceptor A, forming the intermediate biradical, • Sens − A •. This intermediate may react with another molecule to yield products or collapse to yield unexcited sensitizer and excited acceptor

$$\bullet \; Sens - A \bullet + B \rightarrow Sens + AB$$
$$\bullet \; Sens - A \bullet \rightarrow Sens + A^*$$
$$A^* + B \rightarrow AB$$

As an example of the Schenck mechanism, consider the photosensitized oxidation of olefins, which proceeds as shown in Eq. 7-29 to produce hydroperoxides.[45]

$$\underset{\underset{CH_3}{|}}{\overset{\overset{CH_3}{|}}{C}} = \underset{\underset{CH_3}{|}}{\overset{\overset{CH_3}{|}}{C}} \quad \xrightarrow[\text{sens.,O}_2]{h\nu} \quad CH_3 - \overset{\overset{O}{\overset{|}{\underset{CH_3}{|}}}}{C} - \overset{OH}{\underset{\underset{CH_3}{}}{C}} \diagdown CH_2 \qquad (7\text{-}29)$$

The first step is the excitation of the sensitizer which causes the formation of a biradical—e.g.,

$$(C_6H_5)_2 C = O \quad \xrightarrow{h\nu} \quad (C_6H_5)_2\overset{\bullet}{C} - \overset{\bullet}{O}$$

The excited sensitizer then adds to a suitable acceptor to form a donor-acceptor biradical:

$$(C_6H_5)_2 \; \overset{\bullet}{C} - \overset{\bullet}{O} \; + \; O_2 \quad \longrightarrow (C_6H_5)_2 C \diagup{\overset{O\,\bullet}{}} \diagdown{\underset{O - O\,\bullet}{}}$$

This biradical then attacks the substrate in a cyclic fashion to produce the observed product:

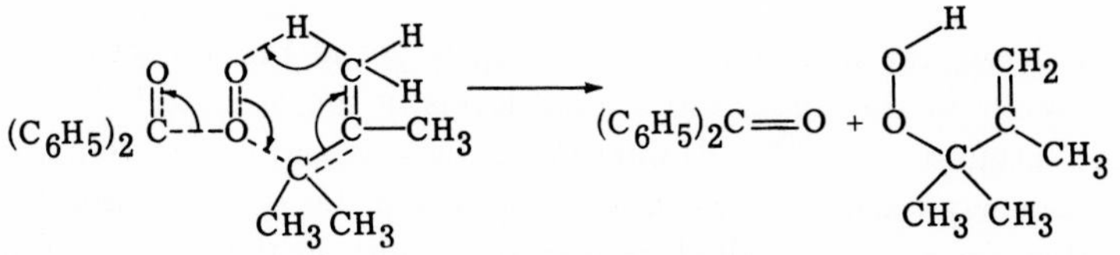

Schenck argues that the large selectivity displayed by such oxidations (see Eqs. 7-30 and 7-31) indicates a large steric requirement of the attacking species, which, therefore, indicates a sensitizer oxygen adduct.[45]

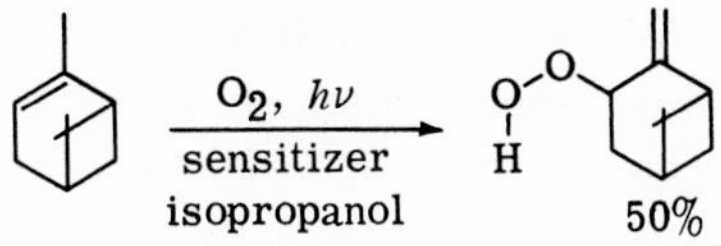

$$(7\text{-}30)$$

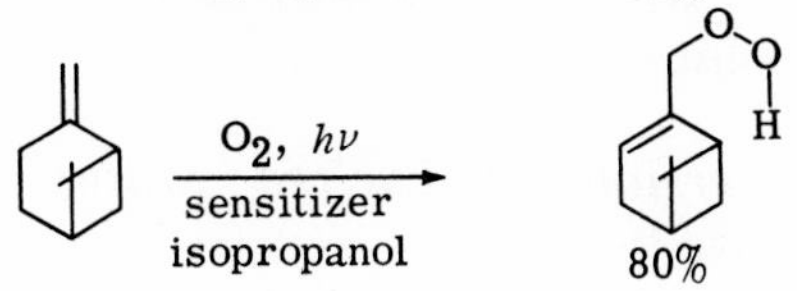

$$(7\text{-}31)$$

On the other hand, Foote[46] and Corey[47] have recently shown that these oxidation reactions (as well as photosensitized cyclic peroxide formation with diene) *can* proceed via singlet oxygen. These results indicate that the alternative energy transfer of triplet excitation from the sensitizer to triplet (ground-state) oxygen may produce oxygen *singlets* which are selective in their reactions with dienes and mono-olefins.

A remarkable sensitizer effect has been noted for the sensitized oxidations[43] of the enol (23):

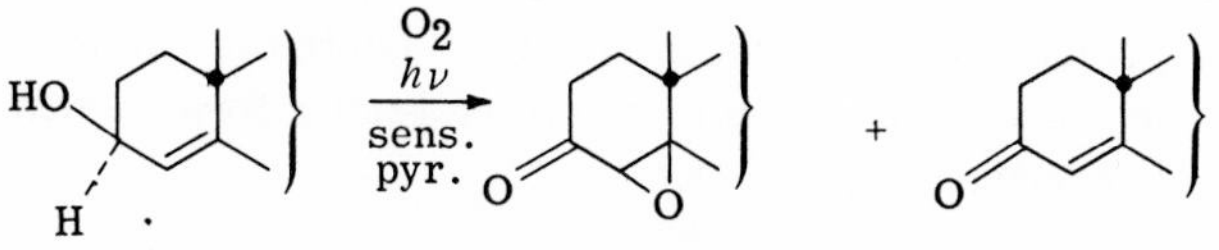

$$(7\text{-}32)$$

The variation of the ratio of the two products 24a and 24b was found to be correlated with the *fluorescence maximum* of the sensitizer. Since the fluorescence maximum is of no fundamental significance (as is the 0—0 band, for instance), it is not clear where the basic cause of this result lies. These results might also be an artifact of the specific reaction of sensitizer with one of the products. It would be of interest to:

1. determine the 0—0 bands of fluorescence and phosphorescence for these sensitizers used, and

2. employ a series of sensitizers which are known to transfer triplet excitation exclusively.

7-4.   "HOT" GROUND–STATE REACTIONS

We have not mentioned any examples yet of photoreactions which might occur in the upper vibrational levels of the S_0 state,[48, 49]—i.e., in a "hot" ground state S_0^*.   If internal conversion and intersystem crossing occur isoenergetically, as we have supposed to be the case (see Section 4-3), then for a system which is absorbing light, in the absence of photo-reaction or electronic-energy transfer, *every excited molecule which does not emit light* winds up in a "hot" ground state.   In solution vibrational quenching occurs so rapidly that only the fastest possible photoreactions can occur from S_0^*.   We expect, however, that certain *unimolecular* reactions, such as *cis-trans* isomerization or structural rearrangements, may have a chance of occurring from S_0^*, although bimolecular reactions will be rare.   Unless stated to the contrary the following discussion refers to solution photochemistry.

Isoenergetic Conversion of Excited States to the Ground State [48, 49, 52]

What might we expect as the criterion available for detecting "hot" ground-state reactions?   A negative criterion is proposed:[52] If a photo-chemical reaction produces a product which is thermodynamically unstable with respect to the starting material, and the product is formed irreversibly under the reaction conditions, formation of this product probably occurs in an excited state and not a "hot" ground state.   For example, suppose we attempt to convert butadiene into bicyclobutane or cyclobutene by a thermal path.   From thermochemical measurements, both of the latter compounds are expected to possess 6 to 10 more kcal mole^{-1} of excess energy than butadiene.   Therefore, under *equilibrium conditions*, the maximum amount of either isomer formed will be small in a thermal reaction.[50]

On the other hand, both of these compounds are *kinetically* stable with respect to butadiene at ordinary temperatures.   If they were formed in an excited state of butadiene and vibrational quenching was rapid, conditions might be found whereby the two unstable isomers could be produced in greater amounts than is possible by thermal equilibration. It is conceivable that formation of either unstable isomer from a butadiene "hot" ground state may be followed by extremely rapid vibrational deactivation and isolation of the thermodynamically unstable isomers.

A converse relationship *does not* necessarily hold however—i.e., *if* a product more stable than the starting material is formed *and* the same product is *also* produced thermally, it is not a necessary conclusion that the product is formed in a "hot" ground state. The reason for this lack of one-to-one correlation is due to the fact that the excited state may coincidentally produce the same products as obtained thermally. Other evidence is required to determine the site of reaction in this case. In other words, when an excited state undergoes isoenergetic conversion to the ground state, the latter species is "born" with a large excess (say 40 to 90 kcal mole^{-1}) of energy so that the rate of vibrational quenching which occurs must be compared with those unimolecular reactions possessing a comparable activation energy. Such reactions may not be observable experimentally if competition from other processes of lower activation energy destroys the molecule under consideration. Consequently, ground-state chemistry may or may not be useful in prediction of the site of photoreaction. *If* a photoreaction and a *known* thermal reaction are similar, the photoprocess may involve a high vibrational level of S_0. The identity of a $S_0{}^*$ reaction and a photoreaction will be exact if it can be demonstrated that the particular thermal reaction is the *only* one having an activation energy lower than the photoexcitation energy.

A final consideration in attempting to assess the probability of occurrence of "hot" ground-state reactions is the need for the energy of $S_0{}^*$ to exceed or equal that of the thermal process. When quenching removes sufficient energy from the "hot" ground state to produce a species of lower energy than the thermal-activation energy, the reaction will not occur. This fact is important because the *energy drop* from the initially

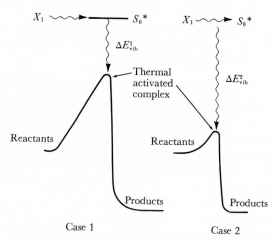

Case 1   Case 2

Fig. 7-6   *Reactions of hot ground states.*

formed S_0^* to the thermally activated complex will vary and may be small. If the energy gap is small, the reaction may be less probable because it requires only the removal of a small portion of vibrational energy to render the molecule unreactive.

From Fig. 7-6, if all other factors are equal, we expect that reaction 2 will be more probable because of the larger amount of vibrational energy ΔE^2_{vib} which must be removed from S_0^* (2) before it is rendered inactive, compared to the small amount E^1_{vib}, which, when removed, will render S_0^* (1) inactive. The implication here is that vibrational quanta are removed "one at a time," and the larger the number of quanta to be removed the longer it will take and the more probable the reaction.

"Hot" Ground-state Reactions in the Vapor Phase [52]

Another possible method for detection of "hot" ground reactions is to eliminate the excited states as possible sites for reaction and have the S_0^* win by default.[52] The vapor phase is best for study of these reactions because pressure dependence of product yields can be used as a probe to determine the nature of the states leading to products. A recent study will serve to illustrate this point. The photolysis of dilute ether solutions of 1,3,5-cycloheptatriene produces bicyclo-(3.2.0)-heptadiene-2,6 as the major product.[51]

$$\overset{h\nu}{\underset{Et_2O}{\longrightarrow}} \qquad 25\ (50\%) \qquad (7\text{-}33)$$

Irradiation of 1,3,5-cycloheptatriene in the vapor phase [52] produces toluene as the major product, and low yields of compound 25.

$$\overset{h\nu}{\underset{vapor}{\longrightarrow}} \underset{major}{CH_3} + \underset{25\ (minor)}{\qquad} \qquad (7\text{-}34)$$

The only important product detected in the pyrolysis of cyclohepta-triene at 480° was toluene.[52]

The yield of 25 and toluene from the photolysis of cycloheptatriene in the vapor phase showed an interesting pressure dependence. Added gases were used to vary the pressure in the photolysis system. Helium, xenon, methane, oxygen, nitric oxide, and ether were used and their effects were such that quenching efficiency seemed related to molecular weights and boiling points of the quenchers. As a result, the increased pressure apparently causes faster removal of excess vibrational energy, and *specific* quenching is absent. This result is of importance because oxygen and nitric oxide are often cited as efficient triplet scavengers.[53] This latter result means that either a triplet is not involved in this reaction *or* the isomeric products are formed from a very fast intramolecular reaction in the triplet, which is not completely quenched even by high pressures of good quenchers.[52]

The quantum yield for toluene formation is close to unity at $p = 0$ from an extrapolated plot of $1/\phi_{toluene}$ versus pressure of cycloheptatriene— i.e., the Stern-Volmer plot is linear. The quantum yield of toluene drops toward zero at high pressures and is apparently equal to zero in solution— i.e., infinite pressure. In contrast, the yield of bicycloheptadiene shows only a minor dependence on pressure and the formation of 25 persists in solution.

Integration of the first absorption band of cycloheptatriene and application of Eq. 4-1 yields a value of about 10^{-9} sec as the expected fluorescence lifetime of the molecule. Unfortunately, no emission data are available for cycloheptatriene. It may be *assumed* [52] that the triplet is not involved in the photochemistry of cycloheptatriene because

1. oxygen and nitric oxide *do not* quench the reaction;
2. the lowest triplet state of cycloheptatriene is probably lower than 50 kcal, resulting in a large $S_1 - T_1$ split ($S_1 \sim 98$) and presumably inefficient intersystem crossing.

The last point must be considered carefully if knowledge of the location of T_2 is not known. *If* the T_2 state should lie *below* S_1, the argument is vitiated—i.e., in Fig. 7-7, if T_2 in case (a) is the energy of the triplet of cycloheptatriene, the second point is invalid.

At any rate, having *assumed* that the T_1 state is not involved in the formation of compound 25 and toluene, we are left with only two states of interest, S_1 and $S_0{}^*$. Furthermore, quenching shows different effects

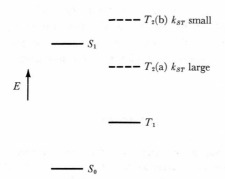

Fig. 7-7 *Possible energy relationships between the lowest excited singlet state, T_2 and the rate of intersystem crossing.*

on the formation of 25 (increases slightly with increasing p) and toluene (decreases dramatically with increasing p).

The effect of added quencher on the formation of toluene is greater than on the formation of bicycloheptadiene.

In the ground state the reverse of bicycloheptadiene formation occurs, so that it may be assumed that the formation of 25 does not occur in S_0^*, and

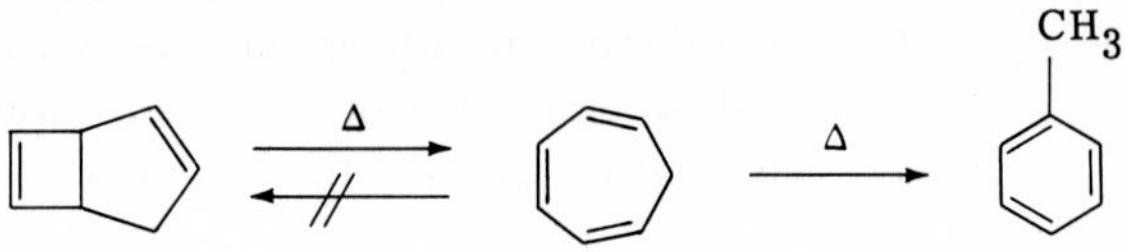

must therefore occur in S_1. On the other hand, formation of toluene from cycloheptatriene does occur in the ground state, and since the states responsible for formation of bicycloheptadiene and toluene in the vapor phase show different pressure dependences, they are not the same. The only choice left is S_0^* since *we have assumed* that T_1 is not involved. It is important that mercury sensitization of cycloheptatriene in the vapor *results in the formation of toluene*, demonstrating, that cycloheptatriene triplets *may* be involved in the direct photolysis.[54]

Under the assumptions above, however, the over-all photochemical process is envisioned as follows. The S_1 state of cycloheptatriene reaches a low-lying vibrational level and then rearranges to compound 25, which must be stabilized by collisions or revert back to cycloheptatriene. At low pressures conversion of cycloheptatriene to 25 is unlikely because the vibrationally excited 25 reverts back rapidly to cycloheptatriene, and internal conversion to S_0^* competes with formation of 25. Unless the excess vibrational energy of S_0^* is rapidly removed, these molecules rearrange to toluene.

It remains to be seen how extensive "hot" ground-state reactions will become in solution photochemistry, and the difficulty of rigorously establishing such a course under favorable conditions should lead one to evaluate carefully the arguments which may be presented to espouse such an occurrence.

PROBLEMS*

1. 4,4-Diphenylcyclohexenone undergoes the following reaction upon irradiation. Write a detailed mechanism for this reaction. How would you establish where S_1, T, or S_0^* were intermediates in this reaction?

* See Addendum for additional problems.

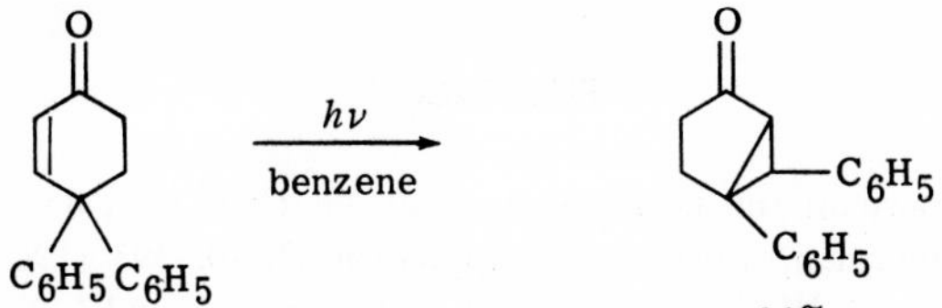

2. Write a mechanism for the rearrangements given in Eq. (7-8).
3. Predict the major products of the following reactions.

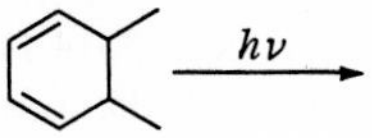

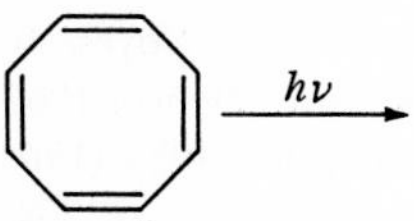

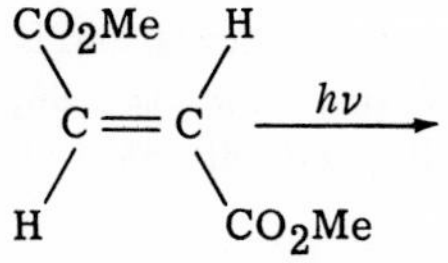

4. The following reactions have been proposed to occur in "hot" ground states. What other information would be helpful in appraising this hypothesis?

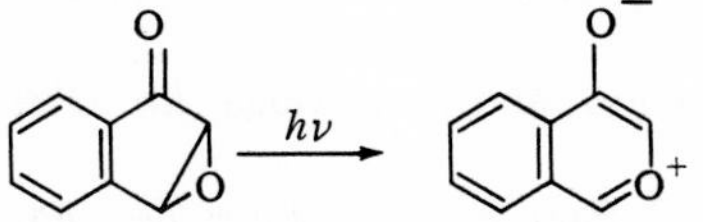

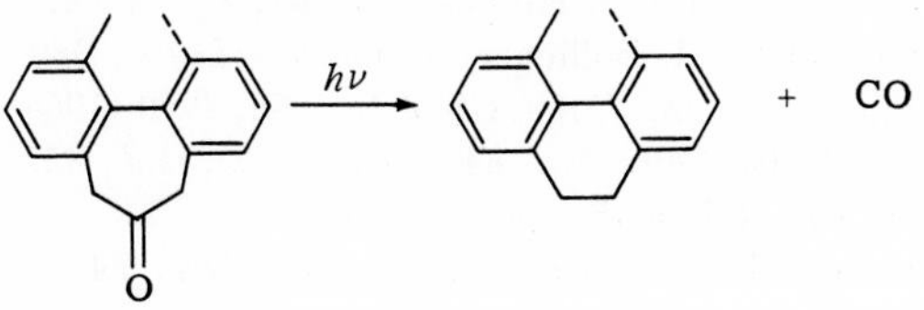

5. A compound X is an efficient photosensitizer of 1,3-pentadiene isomerization and produces a photostationary state consisting of 55% *trans*. What can you deduce about the triplet energy of X?

6. What stationary-state mixture of 1,3-pentadienes will the following sensitizers produce? (See Table 5-13.) 1. xanthone; 2. diphenyl selenium; 3. fluorene; 4. coronene 5. pyrene.

REFERENCES*

1. H. E. Zimmerman and D. I. Schuster, *J. Am. Chem. Soc.*, **83**, 4486 (1961).
2. H. E. Zimmerman, *Tetrahedron*, Supplement 2, **19**, 393 (1963); *Advances in Photochemistry*, ed. W. A. Noyes, Jr., G. S. Hammond, and J. N. Pitts, Jr. (vol. 1, New York: Interscience, 1963), p. 183.
3. G. S. Hammond, N. J. Turro, and P. A. Leermakers, *J. Phys. Chem.*, **66**, 1144 (1962).
4. H. E. Zimmerman and J. S. Swenton, *J. Am. Chem. Soc.*, **86**, 1436 (1964).
5. D. H. R. Barton *et al.*, *J. Chem. Soc.*, 3314 (1958) and earlier papers.
6. M. H. Fisch and J. H. Richards, *J. Am. Chem. Soc.*, **85**, 3029 (1963).
7. O. L. Chapman and L. F. Englert, *ibid.*, **85**, 3028 (1963).
8. For an excellent review of valence isomerizations see: O. L. Chapman, in *Advances in Photochemistry*, ed. W. A. Noyes, Jr., G. S. Hammond, and J. N. Pitts, Jr. (vol. I, New York: Interscience, 1963), p. 323.
9. P. J. Kropp, *J. Am. Chem. Soc.*, **86**, 4053 (1964); *ibid.*, **85**, 3779 (1963).
10. O. L. Chapman, *et al.*, *Tetrahedron Letters*, 2049 (1963).
11. G. W. Griffin and E. J. O'Connell, *J. Am. Chem. Soc.*, **84**, 4148 (1962); H. E. Zimmerman, H. G. C. Durr, R. G. Lewis, and S. Bram, *ibid.*, **84**, 4149 (1962).
12. H. E. Zimmerman, *et al.*, *J. Am. Chem. Soc.*, **86**, 948 (1964).
13. E. F. Ullman and J. E. Milks, *ibid.*, **86**, 3814 (1964); E. F. Ullman, *ibid.*, **86**, 5050 (1964).
14. For related rearrangements see J. M. Duston and P. Yates, *Tetrahedron Letters*, 505 (1964).
15. G. S. Hammond, N. J. Turro, and A. Fischer, *J. Am. Chem. Soc.*, **83**, 4674 (1961).
16. P. G. Gassman, D. H. Aue, and D. S. Patton, *J. Am. Chem. Soc.*, **86**, 4211 (1964).
17. R. J. de Kock, N. G. Minnard, and E. Havinga, *Rec. Trav. Chim.*, **79**, 922 (1960).
18. E. E. van Tamelen and S. P. Pappas, *J. Am. Chem. Soc.*, **85**, 3297 (1963).
19. E. E. van Tamelen and S. P. Pappas, *ibid.*, **84**, 3789 (1962).
20. E. M. Arnett and J. M. Bollinger, *Tetrahedron Letters*, 3803 (1964); A. W. Burgstahler and P. Chien, *J. Am. Chem. Soc.*, **86**, 2940 (1964).
21. R. Srinivasan, *J. Am. Chem. Soc.*, **84**, 4141 (1962); *ibid.*, **85**, 3048 (1963).
22. R. Srinivasan, *ibid.*, **85**, 4045 (1963).
23. H. Prinzbach and J. H. Hartenstein, *Angew. Chem.*, **74**, 5061 (1962); *ibid.*, **74**, 651 (1962).
24. G. S. Hammond, N. J. Turro, and R. S. H. Liu, *J. Org. Chem.*, **28**, 3297 (1963).
25. R. Srinivasan, *J. Am. Chem. Soc.*, **85**, 819 (1963).
26. R. Srinivasan, *ibid.*, **86**, 3318 (1964).
27. M. Stiles and U. Burckhardt, *J. Am. Chem. Soc.*, **86**, 3396 (1964).

* See Addendum for additional references.

28. O. L. Chapman, D. J. Pasto, and J. Griswald, Jr., *J. Am. Chem. Soc.*, **84,** 1213 (1962).

29. R. B. Woodward and R. Hoffmann, *J. Am. Chem. Soc.*, **87,** 395 (1965); *ibid.*, **87,** 2045 (1965); E. Heilbronner, in *Molecular Orbitals in Chemistry, Physics and Biology*, ed. P.-O. Löwdin and B. Pullman (New York: Academic Press, 1964), p. 329.

30. W. J. Potts, *J. Chem. Phys.*, **23,** 65 (1955); G. M. Wyman, *Chem. Rev.*, **55,** 625 (1955).

31. G. Zimmerman, L.-Y. Chow, and U.-J. Paik, *J. Am. Chem. Soc.*, **80,** 3528 (1958).

32. R. S. Mulliken and C. C. S. Roothan, *Chem. Rev.*, **41,** 219 (1947).

33. G. N. Lewis, T. T. Magel, and D. Lipken, *J. Am. Chem. Soc.*, **62,** 2973 (1940).

34. For an excellent review see J. Saltiel, Ph.D. Dissertation (Pasadena: California Institute of Technology, 1964).

35. D. Schulte-Frohlinde, H. Blums, and H. Gusten, *J. Phys. Chem.*, **66,** 2486 (1962); *Ann.*, **612,** 138 (1958); H. Dyck and D. S. McClure, *J. Chem. Phys.*, **36,** 2326 (1962).

36. G. S. Hammond and J. Saltiel, *J. Am. Chem. Soc.*, **85,** 2515 (1963).

37. R. B. Cundall, in *Progress in Reaction Kinetics*, ed. G. Porter (Vol. II, New York: Pergamon Press, 1964), p. 166.

38. G. S. Hammond, N. J. Turro, and P. A. Leermakers, *J. Phys. Chem.*, **66,** 1144 (1962).

39. G. S. Hammond and J. Saltiel, *J. Am. Chem. Soc.*, **84,** 4983 (1962).

40. G. S. Hammond, *et al., ibid.*, **86,** 3197 (1964).

41. F. R. Mallory, C. S. Wood, and J. T. Gordon, *ibid.*, **86,** 3094 (1964).

42. J. Saltiel and G. S. Hammond, *ibid.*, **85,** 2516 (1963).

43. A. Nickon and W. L. Mendelson, *ibid.*, **85,** 1995 (1963).

44. G. S. Hammond, P. Wyatt, C. D. DeBoer, and N. J. Turro, *ibid.*, **86,** 2533 (1964).

45. G. O. Schenck, H. Eggert, and W. Denk, *Ann.*, **584,** 176 (1953).

46. C. S. Foote and S. Wexler, *J. Am. Chem. Soc.*, **86,** 3879, 3880 (1964).

47. E. J. Corey and W. J. Taylor, *ibid.*, **86,** 3880 (1964).

48. H. Sponer, *Radiation Research*, Supplement I, 558 (1959).

49. J. Franck and H. Sponer, *Contribution à l'étude de la structure moléculaire*, Volume Commemoratif Victor Henri (Liege: Maison Desoer, Liege, 1948), p. 169.

50. J. P. Chesick, *J. Phys. Chem.*, **68,** 2033 (1964); H. E. Frey, *Trans. Faraday Soc.*, **60,** 83 (1964).

51. W. G. Dauben and R. L. Cargill, *Tetrahedron*, **12,** 186 (1961).

52. R. Srinivasan, *J. Am. Chem. Soc.*, **84,** 3432 (1962).

53. D. W. Setoer, *et al., Canad. J. Chem.*, **40,** 2179 (1962).

54. S. Arai, N. Maemori, K. Yamaguchi, and S. Sheda, *Bull. Soc. Chem. Jap.*, **36,** 590 (1963).

55. M. Stiles and U. Burckhardt, *J. Am. Chem. Soc.*, **86,** 3396 (1964).

chapter
eight

Photochemical
Cycloadditions

8-1. DIELS–ALDER REACTIONS

Cycloaddition reactions which form four-membered rings are commonly encountered when unsaturated compounds are irradiated.[1, 2, 7] The generally encountered thermal Diels-Alder reaction to form six-membered rings is a relatively rare course in photocycloadditions, except when the unsaturated units contain hetero atoms.[3, 7] These cycloaddition reactions are of importance in syntheses and possess some fascinating mechanistic aspects. In each case discussed below one should consider the following:

1. Which of the two partners is excited (or does a complex of both share the excitation energy)?

2. Can either partner be excited (and, if so, do the results differ)?

It is also of some interest to compare these photochemical cycloadditions to the corresponding thermal reactions if they exist. Finally, in many cases photosensitization and triplet-quenching experiments can be of some help in determining the mechanism of these reactions.

An interesting theoretical rationalization of the differences between thermal and photochemical cycloaddition reactions has appeared.[6] Correlation diagrams for the MO's involved in various cycloaddition reactions have been designed and then classified with respect to the symmetry elements of the (assumed) transition state. Such a device allows one to predict at once the selection rules for thermal and photochemical cycloadditions. This simple picture correctly predicts that the thermal Diels-Alder is allowed (on the basis of symmetry selection rules) while the photochemical Diels-Alder is forbidden. On the other hand, photochemical cyclobutane formation is allowed while thermal cyclobutane formation is forbidden on the basis of these selection rules.

The latter prediction is again consistent with a large portion of known experimental data.[2, 60]

Maleic Anhydride and Various Dienes

The addition of maleic anhydride to anthracene, which is one of the few examples of Diels-Alder photocycloaddition, proceeds with a quantum yield of about 0.02 in dioxane solution.[4] The product is the same as the thermal Diels-Alder adduct. One molar maleic anhydride com-

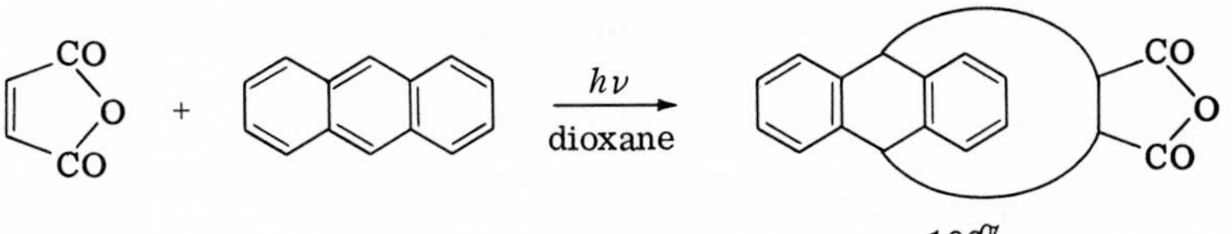

100%

pletely quenches the *fluorescence* of anthracene so that the reaction may be proceeding via the singlet state of the latter. However, this interpretation may be fallacious since a complex between maleic anhydride and anthracene exists, which may be responsible for the fluorescence quenching (Section 4–2).

The photochemical addition of maleic anhydride to cyclooctatetraene and cycloheptatriene produces the (thermal) Diels-Alder products.[5] No experiments which probe the mechanistic details of these additions are available.

Olefins and α-Dicarbonyl Compounds [1, 2, 6, 7]

The photochemical Diels-Alder addition of olefins to α-dicarbonyl compounds is well known.[2, 3, 7] Dicarbonyl compounds which are fixed in the *cis* configuration (e.g., phenanthrenequinone, compound 1) serve as efficient "diene" components. In the case of 1 and 1,1-diphenylethylene (compound 2), either component may be selectively excited by employing monochromatic light. Excitation of 1 in the presence of 2 leads to formation of the adduct (3), while excitation of 2 in the presence of 1 leads only to polymerization of 2.[6]

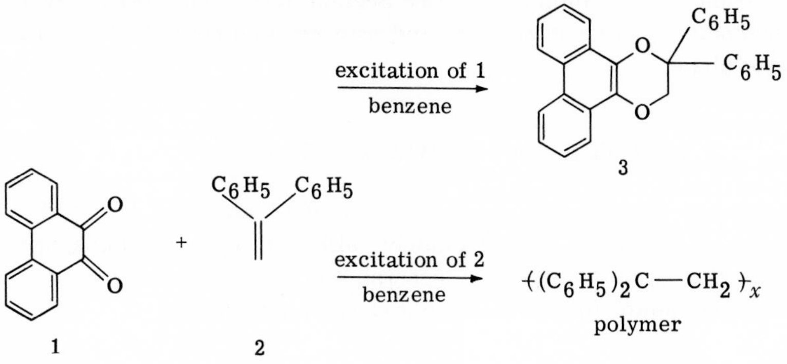

(8-2)

3

$$+(C_6H_5)_2C-CH_2\xrightarrow{}_x \quad (8\text{-}3)$$

polymer

1   2

The triplet energies of simple α-dicarbonyl compounds range from 56 to 50 kcal mole^{-1}, so that excitation transfer to the olefin partner ($E_T > 60$) is energetically unfavorable. Thus the triplet of 1 is probably attacking unexcited 2, in a concerted or two-step cycloaddition. Although a large number of these reactions are known,[7] virtually no mechanistic study of the course of reaction has been made.

Dienes and Oxygen

The 1,4-addition of oxygen to dienes is photosensitized by a large number of dyes.[2, 11, 12] Two possible mechanisms for these reactions are

1. Sensitizer (Sens) $\xrightarrow{h\nu}$ • Sens • (a biradical excited state)   (8-4)

   • Sens • $+ O_2 \rightarrow$ • Sens—O—O •   (8-5)

   • Sens—O—O • + [cyclohexadiene ring] $\longrightarrow$ [endoperoxide bicyclic structure]   (8-6)

2. Sens $\xrightarrow{h\nu}$ Sens(S_1) $\rightsquigarrow$ Sens(T_1)   (8-7)

   Sens(T_1) + $O_2(T_0) \rightarrow$ Sens(S_0) + $O_2(S_1$)   (8-8)

   $O_2(S_1)$ + [cyclohexadiene ring] $\longrightarrow$ [endoperoxide bicyclic structure]   (8-9)

Mechanism 1 formulates the reaction as a radical relay process in which the intermediate biradical • Sens—O—O • attacks the diene. Mechanism 2 formulates the addition as proceeding by way of singlet oxygen (remember O_2 is a triplet in its ground state) attack on the diene.   Since a singlet oxygen (generated by the reaction of hydrogen peroxide and sodium hypohalite) gives the same over-all products as the photosensitized reaction, mechanism 2 may be correct.[8]   However, in some cases the first mechanism may also be operating.   The lowest triplet $\rightarrow$ singlet transition [9] of oxygen only requires 22.5 kcal mole^{-1}, and spin-conservation rules do not inhibit [10] the rate of the process shown in Eq. 8-8. Indeed, triplet-triplet annihilation (see Section 5-4) usually occurs at a diffusion-controlled rate in solution and at a collision-controlled rate in the vapor phase.

8-2. CYCLOBUTANE FORMING CYCLOADDITIONS

Cyclobutane formation is a very important photoreaction from the standpoint of syntheses.   Unfortunately, although such reactions are numerous, they are not completely general, and the factors directing the course of cyclobutane formation are not clear in many cases.

Maleic Anhydride and Aromatic Compounds [13-18]

The photochemical reaction of benzene and maleic anhydride [13-15] yields the adduct (4). The two reactants form a charge-transfer complex

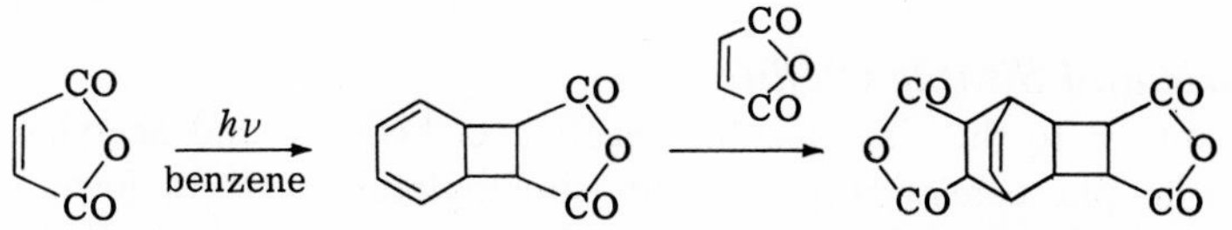

$$(8-10)$$

4 (95%)

which is required [4] for reaction since the addition does not occur in cyclohexane, in which no complex exists. Benzophenone ($E_T = 69$) sensitizes this reaction, but benzil ($E_T = 54$) inhibits it.[16, 17] This must result from the fact that the triplet of the complex lies between 69 and 54 kcal mole^{-1}. The phosphorescence 0—0 band of maleic anhydride lies at 70 to 72 kcal mole^{-1}. However, a solution of maleic anhydride in benzene quenches benzophenone triplets at a diffusion-controlled rate. In carbon tetrachloride, moreover, benzene and maleic anhydride do not form a complex and also do not quench benzophenone triplets. Table 8-1

Table 8-1   *Sensitizers for the addition of maleic anhydride to benzene* [17]

Compound	E_T (kcal mole^{-1})	Reaction
Acetophenone	74	Yes
Benzophenone	69	Yes
Anthroquinone	62	No
Benzil	54	No

lists some compounds which sensitize reaction 8-10. We may conclude from this table that the complex has $E_T \sim 65$.

The photoaddition of maleic anhydride to acenaphthylene and phenanthrene occurs with and without sensitizer.[18] In these cases, benzil is a sensitizer because the maleic anhydride-aromatic hydrocarbon complexes have a lower triplet than the diketone.

Acetylenes and Benzene

A number of acetylenes may be added to benzene photochemically.[19, 20] The isolated product is a cyclooctatetraene, presumably derived from ring opening of the initially formed bicyclooctatriene (Eq. 8-11). Benzo-

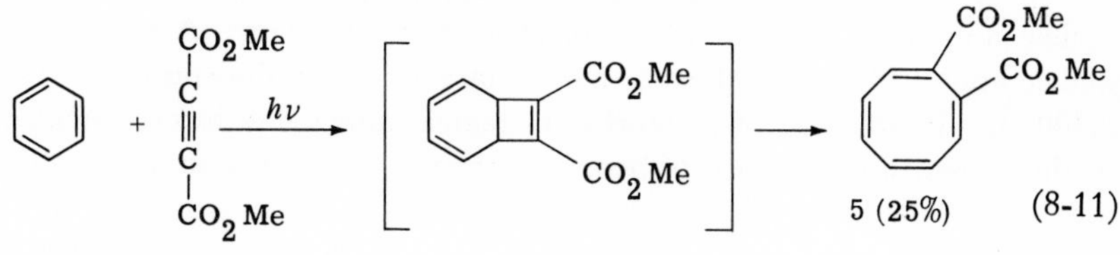

5 (25%)   (8-11)

phenone inhibits this reaction by serving as an internal filter and possibly a quencher. Thus, neither of the reactants possesses $E_T < 69$ (or the reaction may proceed via a singlet addition mechanism).

Aromatic and Simple Olefins

In contrast to the ring opening reaction of benzene and acetylenes, benzonitrile photochemically adds to trimethylethylene [19] to form the bicyclooctadiene (6). The mechanism of this reaction is not at all clear.

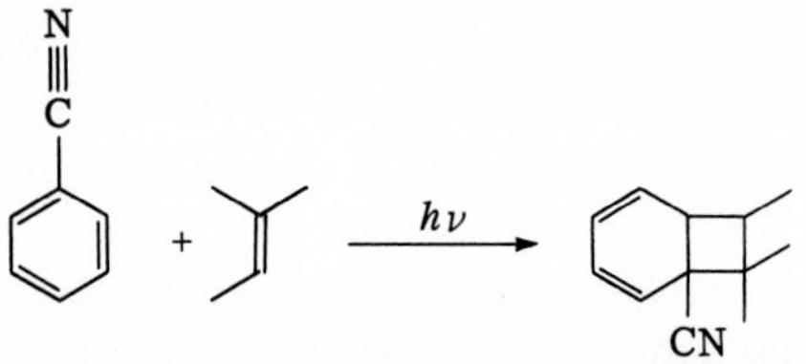

$$(8\text{-}12)$$

6 (63%)

Vinyl acetate, maleic anhydride, and 1,2-dichloroethylene do not react with the benzonitrile, but ethoxyethylene does. Benzophenone fails to sensitize the reaction, and, indeed reacts smoothly with the trimethylethylene [19] to form a trimethylene oxide, 7 (see Section 8-4). This

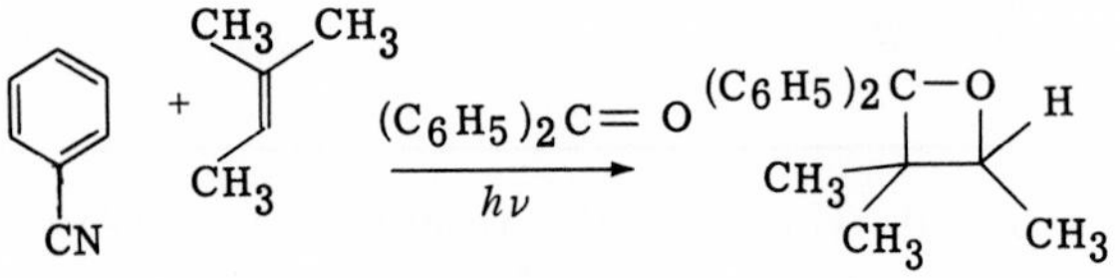

$$(8\text{-}13)$$

7 (90%)

result indicates that the triplet energy of benzonitrile or trimethylethylene (or a complex of the two compounds) is too high for efficient excitation transfer, so that a competing reaction (formation of compound 7) dominates.

Maleic Anhydride Derivatives and Olefins [22]

The formation of a charge-transfer complex between benzene and maleic anhydride is required for reaction 8-10 to occur. A solution of maleic anhydride in cyclohexene has a charge-transfer absorption band at 2,700 Å. Irradiation of a solution of maleic anhydride in cyclohexene in the presence or absence of benzophenone leads mainly to allylic substitution product, polymer, and a low yield of cyclobutanes.[21] Excitation

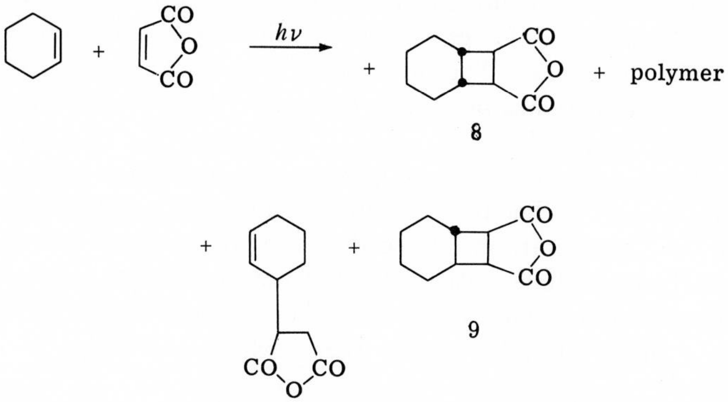

(8-14)

8

9

of the charge-transfer band of a cyclohexene solution of cyclohexene and
fumaronitrile, however, results in a good yield of the adduct (10):

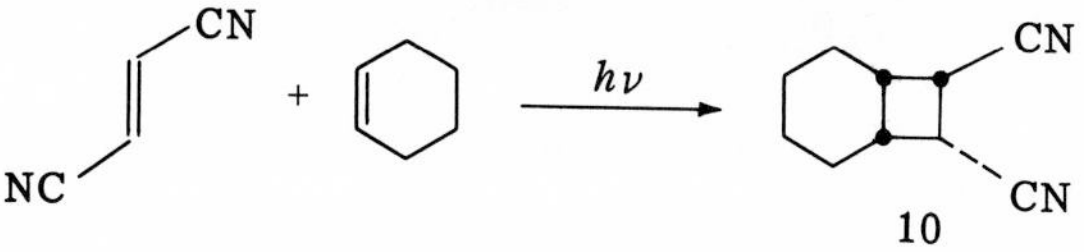

(8-15)

10

On the other hand, dimethyl maleate fails to show a charge-transfer band
in cyclohexene, yet yields a mixture of products similar to those shown in
Eq. 8-14. The fact that *trans* fused ring systems are formed in these
reactions [21] indicates that either (1) a two-step mechanism is operating—
i.e.,

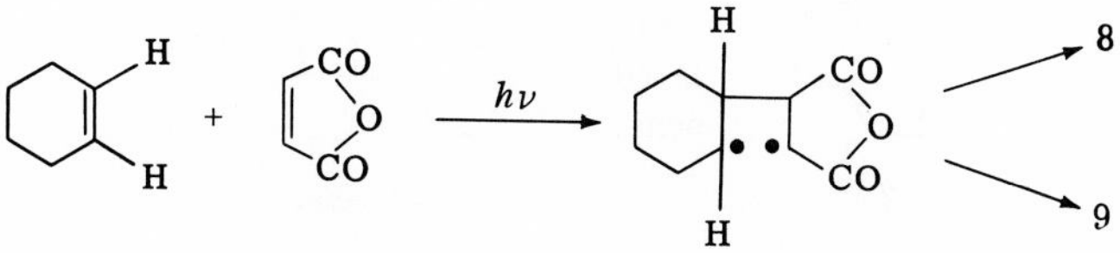

or (2) addition occurs to a mixture of excited *cis*- and *trans*-cyclohexene.

Irradiation of a solution of dimethylmaleic anhydride in cyclohexene
(no charge-transfer band) leads to a high yield [22] of the cyclic adduct (11).
In this case the yield is improved by benzophenone as sensitizer.

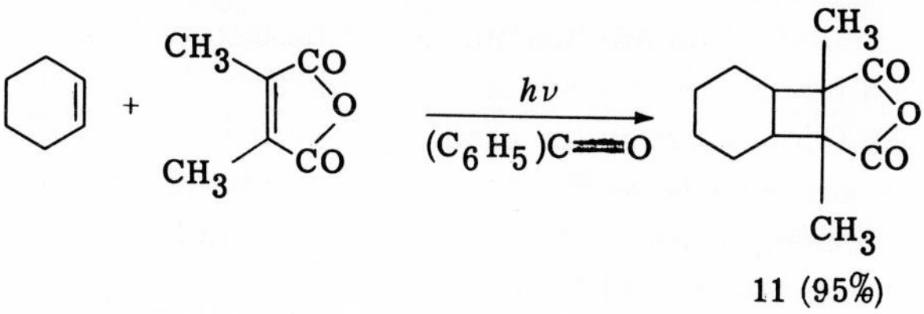

(8-16)

11 (95%)

Furthermore, dimethylmaleic anhydride does not add to benzene; instead, it dimerizes under direct irradiation or in the presence of benzophenone.[22] A number of derivatives of dimethylmaleic anhydride undergo similar reactions. The addition of maleic anhydride and its derivatives to acetylenes has been used to provide a convenient route to substituted cyclobutenes.[23]

Irradiation of cis-2-cyclooctenone induces isomerization to the highly strained trans isomer.[47] The latter compound dimerizes spontaneously in the dark at room temperature. Since the latter reaction is reminiscent of the photochemical dimerization of cyclic α,β-unsaturated ketones, it may be that the excited state involved in these reactions gains its reactivity from a highly strained double bond, which approaches a trans configuration.[47]

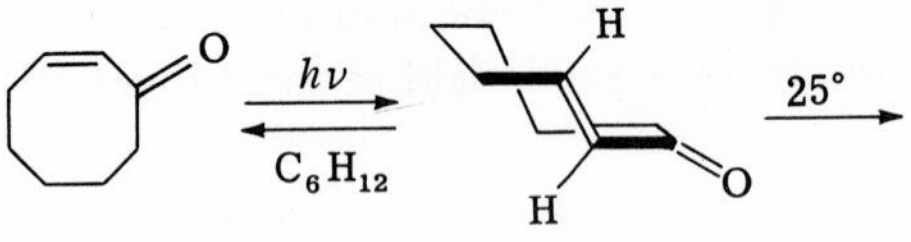

$$(8\text{-}17)$$

20%   80%

Dimerization Involving Double Bonds Conjugated to an Aromatic System [1, 2]

The dimerization of acenaphthylene occurs under both direct and sensitized conditions to produce two stereoisomeric dimers.[1, 2, 24]

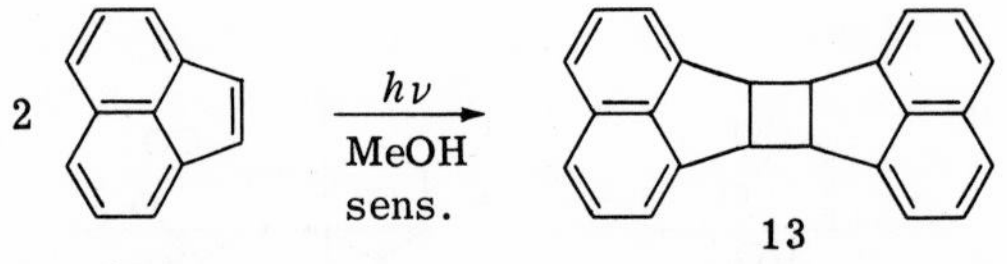

$$(8\text{-}18)$$

12   13
                         cis/trans = 2

Direct irradiation produces differing ratios of trans to cis isomers depending on the solvent employed. This effect is probably a result of photodissociation of the more soluble dimer—i.e., solubility of the two dimers in various solvents determines the final product ratio. Reaction 8-18 is sensitized by benzophenone,[24] so that it probably occurs by attack of the triplet of compound 12 on another unexcited molecule of 12.

The photodimerization of coumarin (14) in ethanol yields the head-to-head cis dimer (15) as the major product.[25] Furthermore, the reaction does not go in benzene solution.[26] The dimerization of compound 14 is sensitized by benzophenone, in benzene solution, and the predominant product [26] is the head-to-head trans dimer (16).

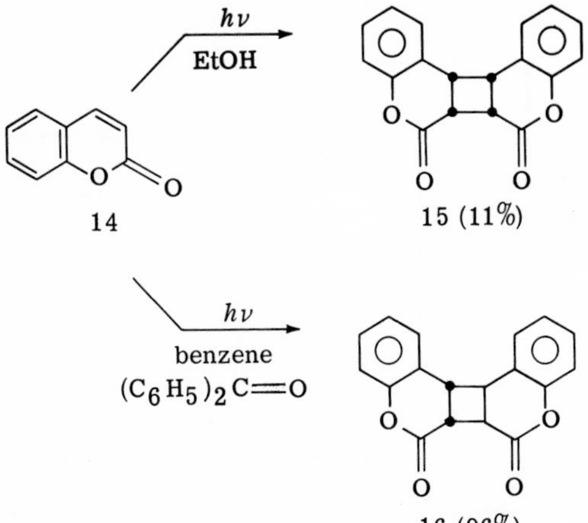

14   15 (11%)

(8-19)

16 (96%)

The difference in the course of the direct and sensitized reactions is the result of the involvement of different excited states in the two cases. The mechanism is probably the following [27]

$$C_0 \xrightarrow{h\nu} C_1$$

$$C_1 \rightarrow C_3$$

$$B_3 + C_0 \rightarrow C_3 + B_0$$

$$C_3 + C_0 \rightarrow \text{Compound 16}$$

$$C_1 + C_0 \rightarrow \text{Compound 15}$$

where C_0, C_1, and C_3 are coumarin ground state, lowest excited singlet state, and lowest triplet state, respectively, and B_0 and B_3 are benzophenone ground and triplet states (produced quantitatively by intersystem crossing from the singlet), respectively. In nonpolar solvents such as benzene, C_1 is deactivated by "self-quenching." In polar solvents such as ethanol, C_1 reacts with C_0 to produce compound 15. In the presence of B_3, C_3 is produced by triplet-energy transfer *in both polar and nonpolar solvents*. The reaction of C_3 with C_0 produces compound 16 predominately. Spectroscopic data [27] yield the energy diagram shown in Fig. 8-1. It is seen that singlet-singlet excitation transfer from C_1 to benzophenone is also possible—i.e., the C_1 molecules which absorb in the presence of benzophenone can be quenched by the latter compound, which in turn undergoes intersystem crossing to B_3. An elegant vindication of these hypotheses is the fact that in dilute concentration, coumarin yields compound 16, *under direct* excitation. Thus, coumarin singlets either cross over to C_3 or are deactivated to C_0 under these conditions— i.e., dimerization, a bimolecular reaction, does not compete efficiently

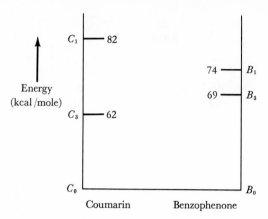

Fig. 8-1   *Energy-level diagram for the coumarin-benzophenone system.*[27]

with rapid unimolecular processes in dilute solution. The coumarin triplets thus produced react in exactly the manner as those produced by energy transfer, and compound 16 is produced by reaction of C_3 and C_0.

Dimerization in the Solid State [28]

Crystal structure plays an important role in the limitations and stereochemistry of photodimerizations in the solid state.[29, 30, 31] Crystallographic studies show that for dimerization to be efficient the reacting centers must be no more than 4 Å apart.   In addition, the stereochemistry of the dimer is controlled by the relative orientation of the monomer in the crystal.   Thus, for *trans*-cinnamic acid, there are two crystal forms which have different nearest neighbor orientations in the crystals and therefore yield different photodimers,[29, 31] as shown in Eqs. 8-20 and 8-21.

Cycloaddition Reactions of α,β-Unsaturated Ketones and Related Compounds [39, 40, 43]

Irradiation of cyclopentenone leads to the formation of two dimers (compounds 19 and 20) in nearly equal amounts.[32] Cyclohexenone produces at least four dimers under similar conditions:

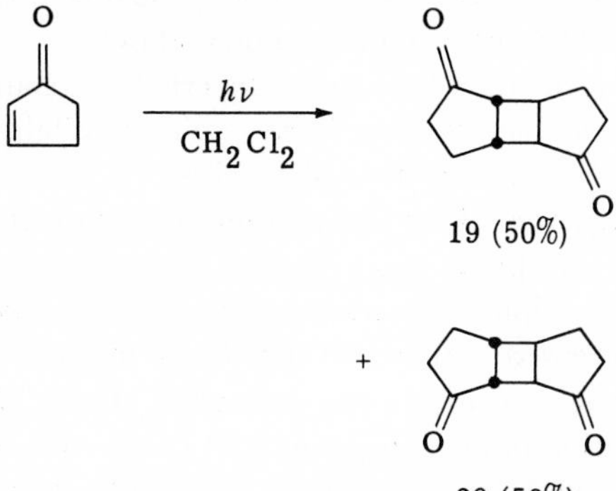

19 (50%)

20 (50%)

(8-22)

On the other hand, 3-phenylcyclohexenone yields only the *syn* dimer under irradiation:[33]

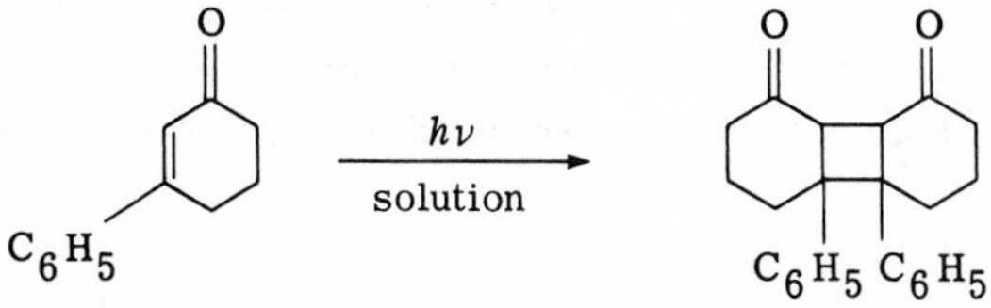

21

(8-23)

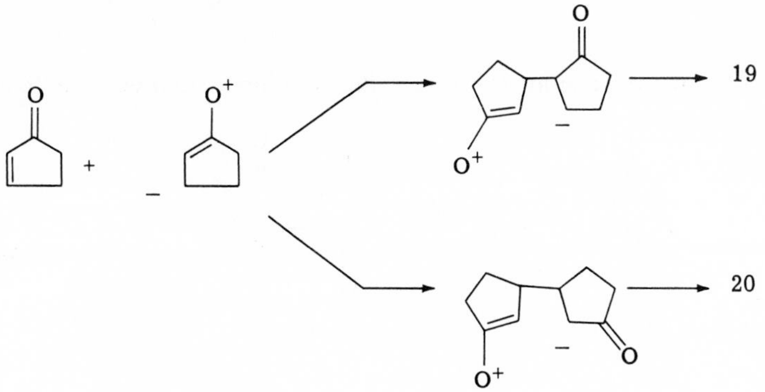

The nonselectivity of the first two examples may result from the occurrence of a singlet dimerization which should show low sensitivity to structural effects. Thus, if the dimerization of cyclopentenone is pictured as a two-step addition, the formation of 20 should predominate because of the stabilizing interaction of the adjacent carbonyl with the negative charge in the intermediate (assuming the transition state for addition resembles these intermediates). This mechanism (as well as a similar biradical intermediate mechanism) conflicts with the experimental fact that compounds 19 and 20 are produced in nearly equal amounts, so that the transition state for addition probably does not resemble a dipolar or biradical intermediate as shown above.

On the other hand, a one-step concerted mechanism involving an excited singlet state may be more likely. The possibility that two excited states participate in this reaction also exists. A study of the ratio of 19 and 20 as a function of cyclopentenone concentration would provide information on this point since singlet dimerization will become less competitive with triplet dimerization as the concentration of cyclopentenone is decreased. It would also be of interest to note the course of the reaction when sensitizers and quenchers are added to the system.

The dimerization of benzoquinone and its derivatives sometimes leads to the formation of "cage" structures.[35-37] The stereochemical course of these dimerizations is sensitive to reaction conditions—e.g., wavelength of the exciting light, solvent composition, state of aggregation, etc. For example, irradiation of 2,5-dimethylbenzoquinone in the solid state results in the formation of the cyclobutane (22) which may be isolated and closed to the "cage" compound (23) upon further irradiation.[35] However, the analogous photoreaction produces only the isomeric cyclo-

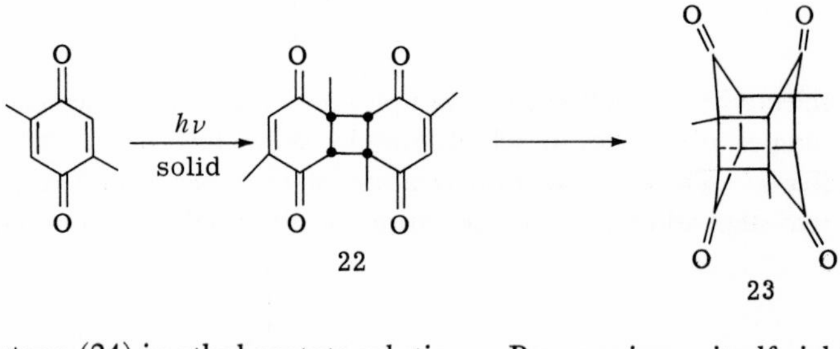

$$(8\text{-}24a)$$

butane (24) in ethyl acetate solution. Benzoquinone itself yields a "cage"

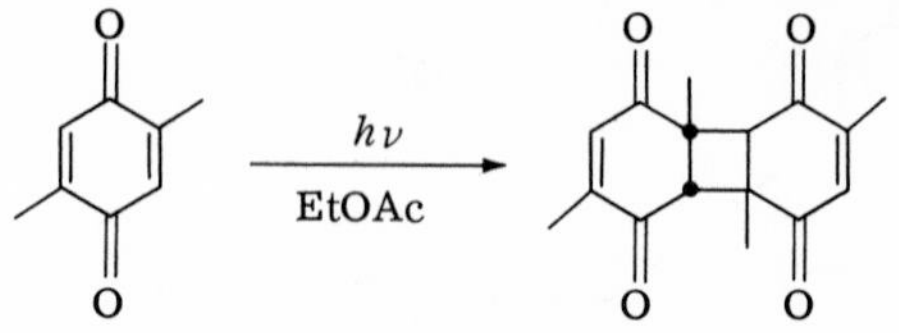

$$(8\text{-}24b)$$

compound when irradiated in the melt.

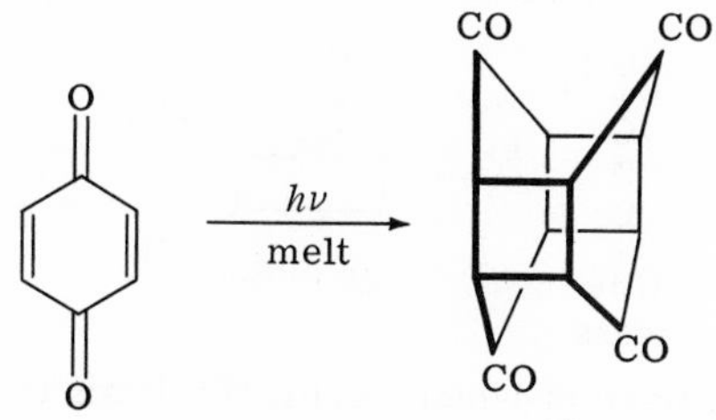

$$(8\text{-}25)$$

25

Irradiation of certain pyridine derivatives leads to a dimerization analogous to that of anthracene.[38]

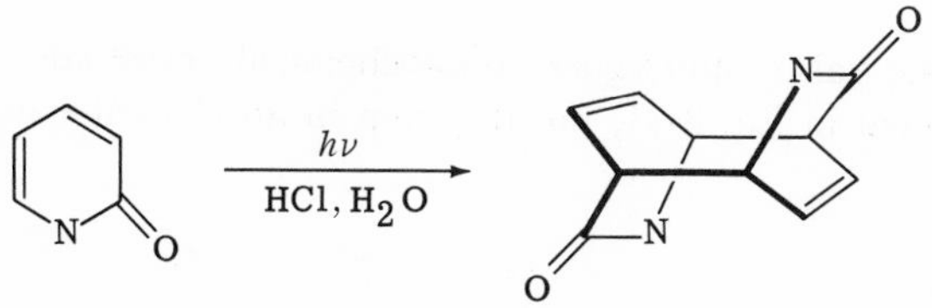

$$(8\text{-}26)$$

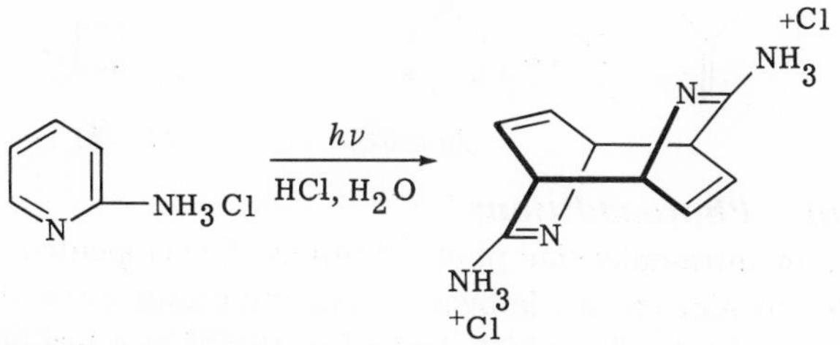

$$(8\text{-}27)$$

Little is known about the excited states involved in these reactions and much mechanistic work remains before a detailed understanding of the course of these dimerizations can be had.

Intermolecular Photoadditions

Irradiation of cyclopentenone in a ten-fold excess of cyclopentene leads to a high yield [39] of the tricyclic ketone (27).

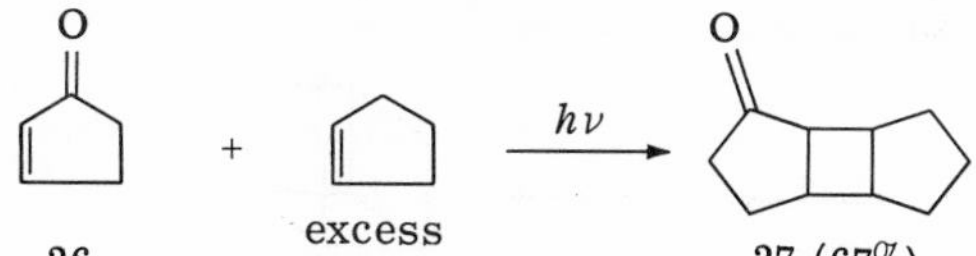

$$(8\text{-}28)$$

26   excess   27 (67%)

The addition of cyclopentenone to alkenes is quite general and alkynes also undergo smooth addition.[40, 41]   The primary photoproduct

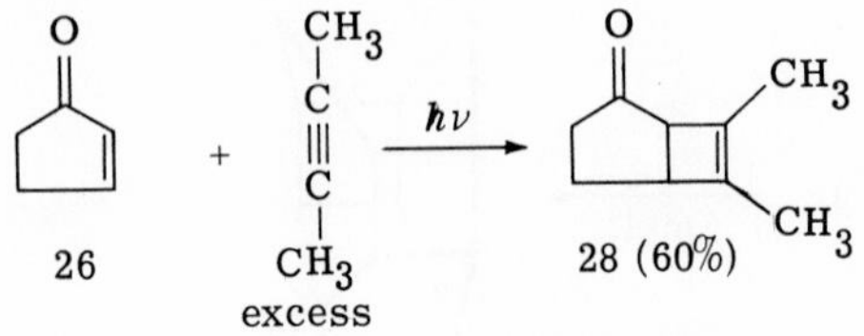

$$(8\text{-}29)$$

(28) undergoes an isomerization which eventually leads to the following photoequilibrium.[40]

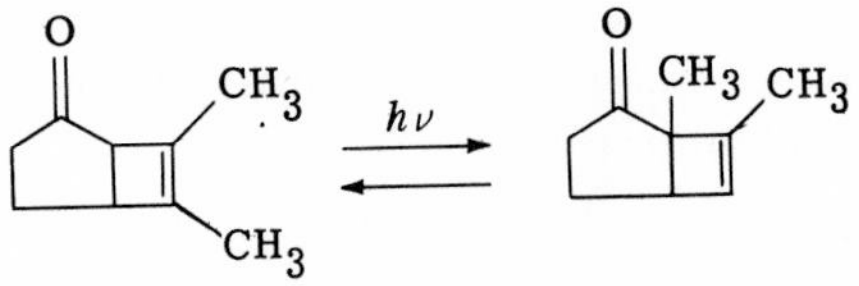

$$(8\text{-}30)$$

Cyclohexenone also undergoes photochemical cross-addition to alkenes, as is shown in Eq. 8-31, the first step in an elegant synthesis of caryophyllene.

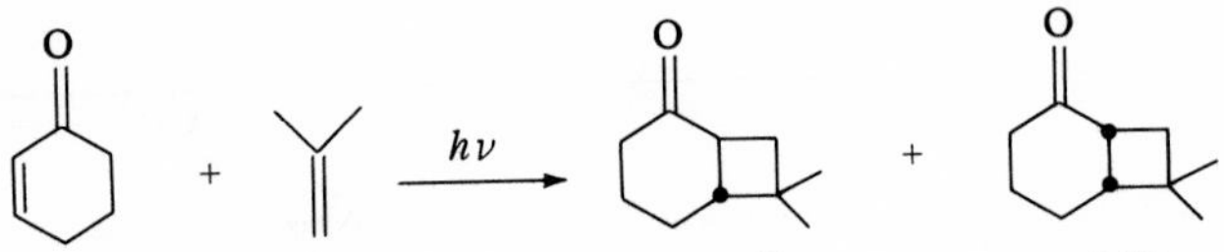

$$(8\text{-}31)$$

Intramolecular Photoadditions [1-3]

A number of intramolecular photoadditions of cyclopentenones and cyclohexenones to alkenes are known.[37]   An important example is the closure of the dibromide (31) which was a key step [42] in a brilliant route to cubane (32).

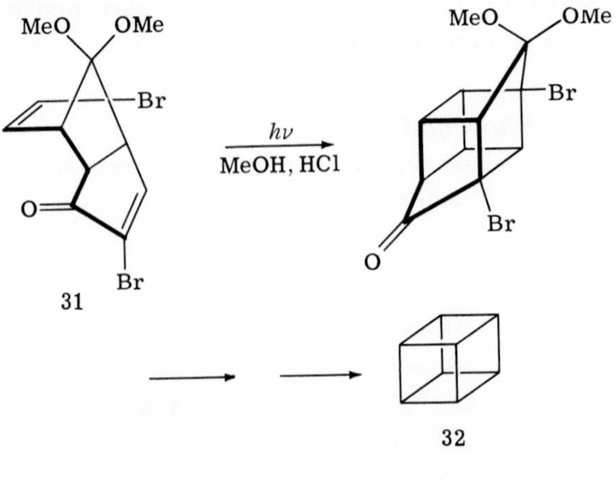

$$(8\text{-}32)$$

Mechanism of the Addition of α,β-Unsaturated Ketones to Alkenes

Again, very little is known concerning the nature of the excited states involved in these photocross-additions. The predominant cross-adducts are not predicted by consideration of the most stable "one-bond" intermediate in a two-step reaction. It is interesting to note that both cyclohexenone [43] and cyclopentenone transfer triplet excitation to dienes (*vide infra*, Section 8–4) but *do not add efficiently to dienes*.

The reactivity of cyclohexenone towards alkenes seems to parallel the ionization potential of the latter, indicating that photoaddition may be directed by formation of the first bond by a kinetic phenomenon which results from polar complexing forces.[43] The second bond has no choice as to closure after rotation. Thus, both *cis*- and *trans*-dichloroethylene lead to the same mixture of cyclobutanes upon cross-addition to cyclohexenone, under conditions such that the alkene does not isomerize.[44] Recall, however, that in the case of maleic anhydride and its derivatives, the appearance of a charge-transfer band did not correlate with reactivity toward cycloaddition.[21]

The fact that cyclopentenone and cyclohexenone can sensitize the dimerization of dienes is evidence that some triplets are being formed upon irradiation of these compounds.[45] An interesting experiment is to attempt 1. to sensitize the dimerization and additions of these enones with triplet sensitizers and 2. to attempt to quench the same reactions with triplet quenchers. Finally, one can conceive of kinetic controlled attack of the positively polarized carbon α to the carbonyl in some cases to describe the preferred path of certain photochemical additions:

major

minor

Such a phenomenon would have to be peculiar to the excited state since ground-state reactivity would very probably favor the second intermediate above, which would lead to the minor adduct.

This entire discussion emphasizes the need for a better description of electronic excited states and should remind us of the possible hazards which exist when we attempt to correlate the course of photochemical processes with known ground-state reactivities.

One generalization appears possible at this time concerning photochemical additions involving carbonyl compounds and unsaturated systems: Addition competes with energy transfer, and the latter dominates if the carbonyl compound possesses a higher triplet state than the unsaturated substrate. This rule correctly predicts that most carbonyl compounds *will not* add to dienes since the latter compounds usually possess low triplet excitation energies ($E_T < 60$).

An example of an addition [46] to a diene which conforms to this rule is shown in Eq. 8-33:

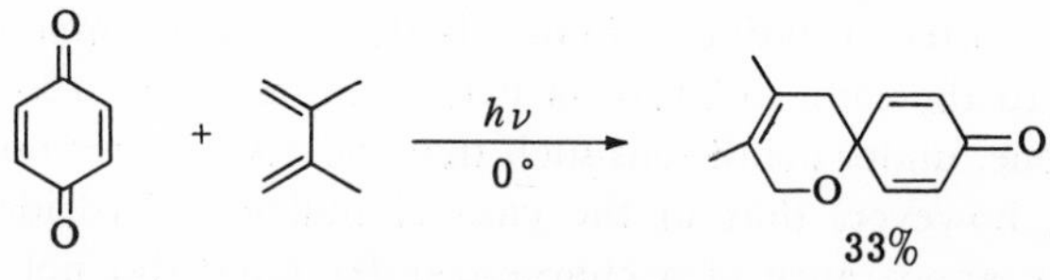

$$\text{(8-33)}$$

33%

Presumably energy transfer to the diene ($E_T \sim 58$) is relatively inefficient because of the relatively low triplet energy of benzoquinone ($E_T \sim 50$). As a result, addition becomes an important process.

8-3. PHOTOCYCLOADDITIONS INVOLVING HETERO ATOMS

Except for trimethylene oxide formation, photochemical cycloadditions which lead to heterocyclic rings have not been extensively or systematically studied, although such reactions potentially provide an attractive entry to small ring heterocyclic systems.

Trimethylene Oxide Formation [48, 49]

At the end of the last section the photochemical addition of a carbonyl group to form a trimethylene oxide (oxetane) was mentioned. For example, benzophenone adds smoothly to isobutylene as follows:[47-50]

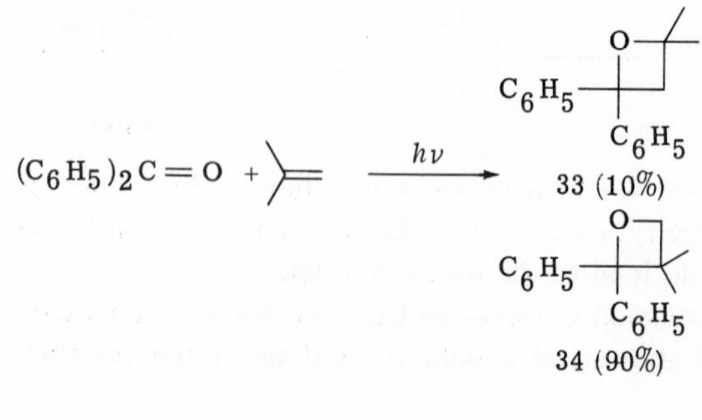

$$(C_6H_5)_2C=O \ + \ \text{(isobutylene)} \ \xrightarrow{h\nu} \ \text{(8-34)}$$

33 (10%)

34 (90%)

These reactions involve the n,π^* triplet state of the carbonyl system. A large number of such reactions are known and it appears that in general *the predominate isomer is correctly predicted from consideration of the more stable biradical (ground-state) intermediate* (see Table 8-2). Thus, in contrast to

Table 8-2   *Trimethylene oxide formation* [48, 49]

Carbonyl Compound	Alkene	Major Product	Quantum Yield
$C_6H_5COCH_3$	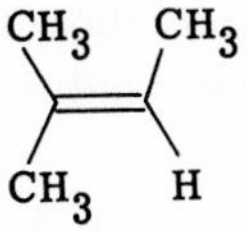 $(CH_3)_2C{=}C(CH_3)H$	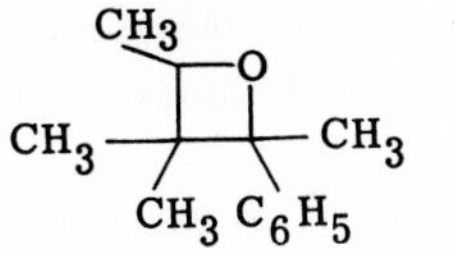 (oxetane)	0.10
$(C_6H_5)_2CO$	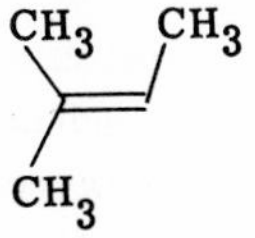 $(CH_3)_2C{=}CH(CH_3)$	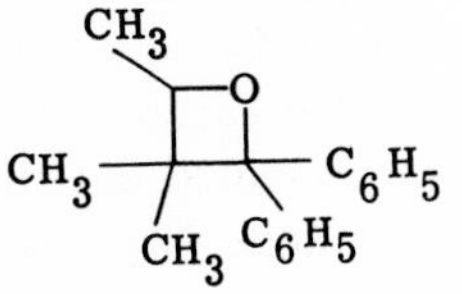 (oxetane)	0.50
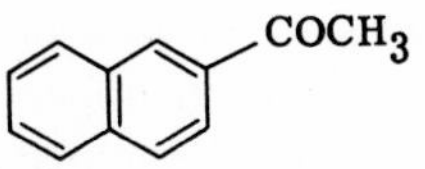 naphthyl-$COCH_3$	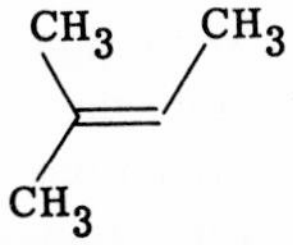 $(CH_3)_2C{=}C(CH_3)CH_3$		0.00

the difficulty in rationalizing the orientational problems of the additions of enones to alkenes, trimethylene oxide formation is nicely explained by a two-step reaction with intermediates whose relative concentrations are determined by the stability of the various "one-bond" biradicals. For example, the addition of isobutylene to benzophenone might produce one of the four biradical intermediates, 35, 36, 37, or 38.

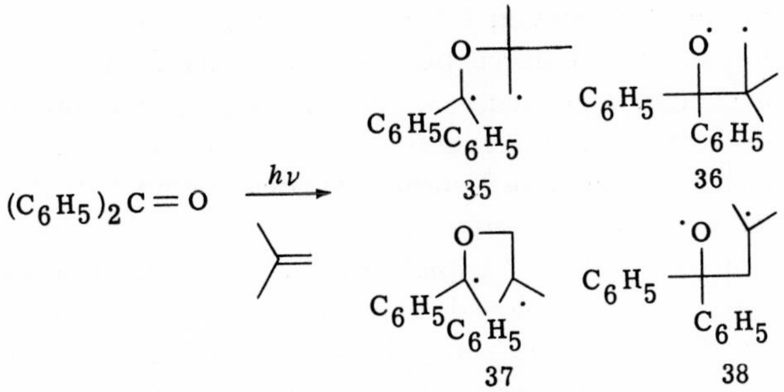

$$(C_6H_5)_2C{=}O \quad \xrightarrow{h\nu} \quad 35 \quad 36 \quad 37 \quad 38$$

Of these compounds, listed above, 37 is predicted to be the most stable, while compound 35 is predicted the next stable on the basis of stabilizations of the radical centers involved because the odd electrons experience greatest stabilization by being conjugated with the maximum number of phenyl groups and the maximum number of methyl groups.

The following criteria for trimethylene oxide formation [48] appear to be fairly general:

1. The alkene must possess a *triplet energy* comparable to or *higher* than the carbonyl compound so that energy transfer from carbonyl triplet to alkene is inhibited.

2. The carbonyl must possess a lowest n,π^* triplet configuration.

3. Other reactions of the triplet carbonyl compounds (e.g., hydrogen abstraction) will compete with cycloaddition.

Thus, there is a parallelism between the requirements for oxetane formation and photoreduction (see Section 6-2). The remarkable conformity of oxetane formation to the requirements of the biradical mechanism indicates that carbonyl triplets are selective in addition reactions.

Yang [49] has pointed out that the photoreactions of certain aromatic carbonyl compounds (e.g., oxetane formation with olefins, photoreductions, etc.) may depend on factors other than the nature of the lowest triplet state (see Section 6-2). If the lowest triplet state of an aromatic carbonyl compound is π,π^* but internal conversion from an upper n,π^* triplet is slow, then bimolecular reactions may occur for the upper n,π^* state. At first this may seem to be an extremely unlikely event because internal conversion is expected to be extremely rapid in solution. Recall, however, that the rate of internal conversion among triplets has been *assumed* to be of the same order as the rate of internal conversion among excited singlets. Direct information concerning this point is scarce. Since the rate of phosphorescence from triplets is of the order of 100 to 0.1 sec^{-1}, the rates of internal conversion among triplets could be any value from about 10^3 to 10^{12} sec^{-1} and still be in agreement with the experimental data (see Section 4-3, note added in proof).

For example, the photoreactions of 9-anthraldehyde show a pronounced wavelength dependence, which is indicative of a slow rate (compared to the rate of photoreaction) of internal conversion. As shown in Eq. 8-35, when a solution of 9-anthraldehyde in isobutylene is irradiated with light of wavelength shorter than 4,100 Å, oxetane formation, a reaction characteristic of n,π^* triplets occurs. When light of wavelength longer than 4,100 Å is employed, only the dimer of 9-anthraldehyde is found. This effect may be rationalized by assuming that when the shorter wavelength light is used, intersystem crossing from the initially produced singlet to an upper n,π^* triplet occurs. This state persists long enough to react with the isobutylene solvent, and oxetane formation results. When wavelengths greater than 4,100 Å are employed, the excited singlet formed undergoes intersystem crossing to the lowest π,π^* triplet, presumably because it is lower in energy than the n,π^* triplet.

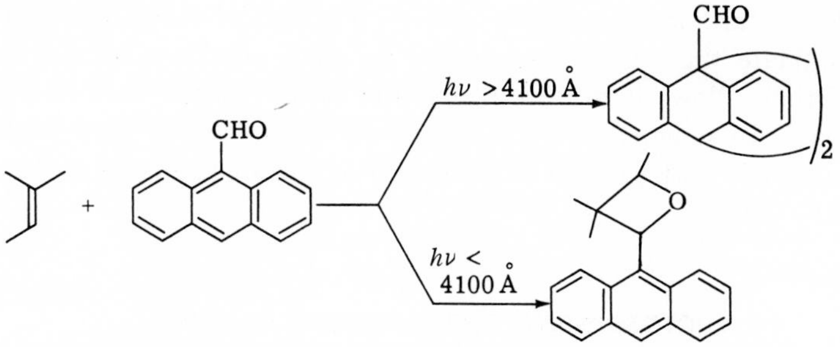

$$(8\text{-}35)$$

Addition of Carbonyl Groups to Ketenimines

The photoaddition of carbonyl compounds to ketenimines yields two cyclic adducts [51] of the same type as compounds 39 and 40, as shown for benzophenone and dimethyl-N-(2-cyano-2-propyl) ketenimine.

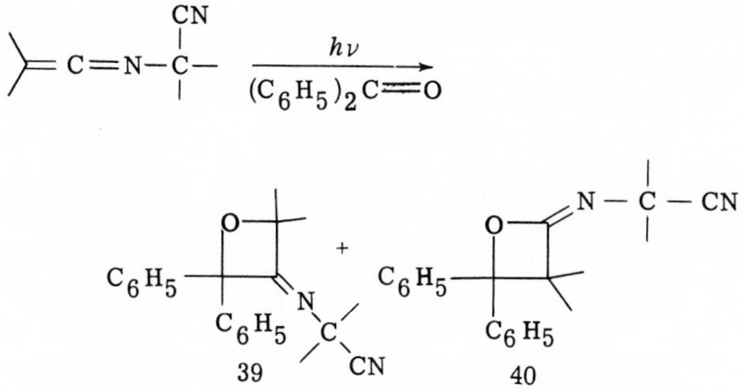

$$(8\text{-}36)$$

39   40

There is a parallelism between the photoreduction, trimethylene oxide formation, and the addition of ketenimines to carbonyl compounds.[51] For high-energy ketones ($E_T > 70$ kcal mole^{-1}), energy transfer to ketenimine (causing radical formation followed by cage recombination) competes with adduct formation.

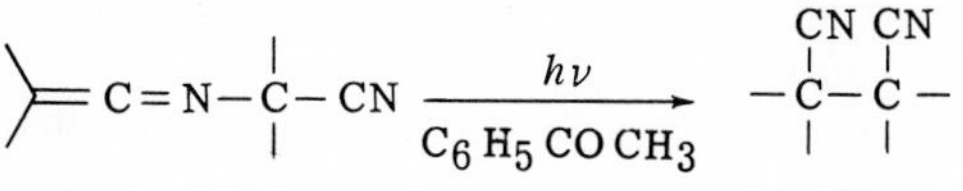

$$(8\text{-}37)$$

41

Furthermore, carbonyl compounds possessing lowest π,π^* triplets are inert toward addition, and the structure of the adduct depends on the energy of the particular carbonyl compound involved.

Summary

Photochemical cycloaddition reactions represent an important synthetic route to four-membered ring systems. Diels-Alder and 1,4-1,4-cycloadditions are less frequently noted. The triplet state is a more likely candidate than an excited singlet for these reactions because its longer lifetime allows it to "hunt" for and find a partner before it is deactivated. In some cases the intermediacy of triplets has been established, but much work remains to be done before far-reaching generalizations can be made.

8-4. PHOTOSENSITIZED CYCLOADDITIONS OF DIENES

Photosensitization provides an important method for the selective cycloaddition reaction of conjugated dienes. The mechanisms of these reactions have received considerable attention and are discussed below.

Dimerization [45, 52, 53]

The irradiation of concentrated solutions of dienes in the presence of photosensitizers leads to dimerizations of the dienes (Eqs. 8-38 and 8-39).[52, 53] A striking difference exists for the effect of variation of

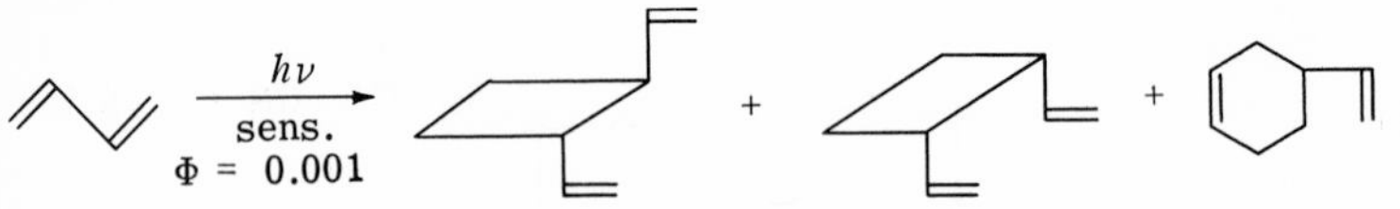

42   43   44

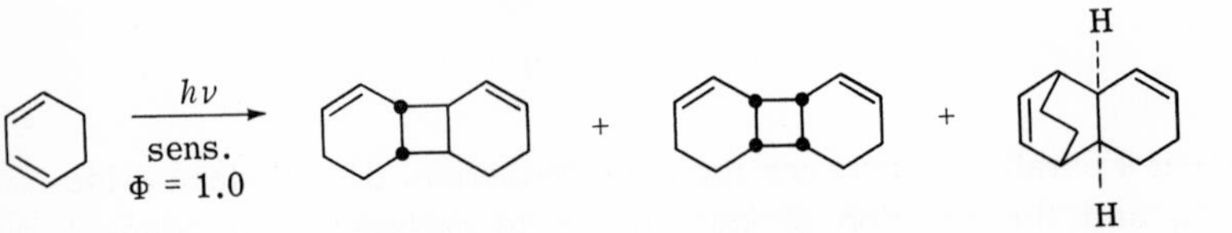

(8-38)

45 (60%)   46 (20%)   47 (20%)

(8-39)

sensitizer for the two cases given in Eqs. 8-38 and 8-39: *The use of different sensitizers leads to wide variations in the relative amounts of dimers for butadiene, but no corresponding variation is found in the composition of the mixture of dimers produced from cyclohexadiene.*

Some typical data are given in Table 8-3 for the effect of sensitizer on the ratio of butadiene dimers and in Table 8-4 on the ratio of cyclohexadiene dimers.[33, 44] Two other points of difference contrast the course of dimerization of the linear and cyclic dienes.

1. An increase in temperature produces a large relative increase in the amount of vinylcyclohexene (44) formed in the butadiene

dimerization, but the same temperature increase does not affect the relative yield of cyclohexadiene dimers.

2. The quantum yield for dimerization of cyclic dienes (cyclohexadiene, cyclopentadiene) is about 1,000 times greater than that for butadiene.

Table 8-3   *Dimerization of butadiene by various sensitizers* [46]

Sensitizer	Relative Yields of Dimers 42	43	44	E_T (Sens) (kcal mole^{-1})
Acetophenone	78	18	4	74
Benzophenone	78	18	4	69
Michler's ketone	78	18	4	61
Anthraquinone	78	18	4	61
2-Acetonaphthone	76	16	8	59
2-Naphthaldehyde	72	16	12	59
2-Naphthylphenyl ketone	72	16	12	58
1-Acetonaphthone	63	17	20	57
Biacetyl	52	13	35	55
Fluorenone	44	13	43	53
3-Acetylpyrene [a]	43	12	45	50

[a] Dimerization is much less efficient than that with the other sensitizers listed.

Table 8-4   *Photosensitized dimerization of cyclohexadiene* [46]

Sensitizer	E_T (kcal mole^{-1})	Relative Yield of Dimers 45	46	47
Benzophenone	69	62	16	22
2-Acetonaphthone	59	58	19	23
Biacetyl	55	60	19	21
Fluorenone	53	58	19	23

The result of plotting the $S_0 \rightarrow T_1$ excitation energies of various sensitizers versus the sum of the yields of cyclobutanes for the dimerization of butadiene is shown in Fig. 8-2. The main features of this curve are:

1. a region ($E_T > 60$) for which sensitizers give the same result;

2. a region ($53 < E_T < 60$) for which sensitizers give varying relative yields of dimers;

3. a region ($53 > E_T$) for which the efficiency of dimerization falls off drastically.

It is significant that the drop in the curve begins at 60 kcal, *the energy reported for the* $S_0 \rightarrow T_1$ *transition of butadiene.* It is further interesting to

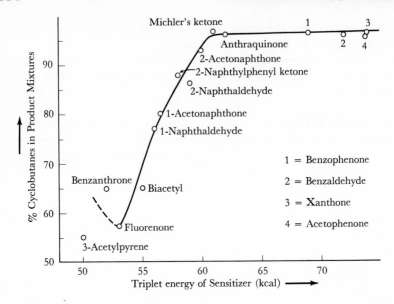

Fig. 8-2   *Variation of product distribution with triplet energy of sensitizer.*[45]

note that the rather sharp cut off in efficiency of dimerization occurs at about 54 kcal, *the energy reported for the* $S_0 \rightarrow T$ *transition of 1,3-cyclohexadiene*.[54]   Since butadiene exists as a mobile equilibrium mixture of s-*cis* and s-*trans*-rotomers, the latter predominating at ordinary temperatures, the $S_0 \rightarrow T$ energy reported pertains to the s-*trans* isomer.   Let us assume then that the value of $S_0 \rightarrow T$ transition reported for 1,3-cyclohexadiene approximates the energy necessary to excite the triplet state of s-*cis* butadiene.

Simple molecular orbital calculations [5] for *linear* butadiene predict the first excited state of the molecule will result from excitation of an electron, antibonding between atoms 2 and 3, to an orbital which is bonding between these centers.   Therefore, the lowest excited states of 1,3-butadiene are expected to have a larger barrier to rotation about the central bond in the excited state than in the ground state.   The bond orders calculated for the simplest model are given in Eq. 8-40.   Although

$$CH_2 = CH = CH = CH_2 \xrightarrow{\;h\nu\;} CH_2 = CH = CH = CH_2 \qquad (8\text{-}40)$$

$$\underset{1.88}{\uparrow} \quad \underset{1.44}{\uparrow} \qquad\qquad\qquad \underset{1.44}{\uparrow} \quad \underset{1.72}{\uparrow}$$

these calculations are crude, more refined treatments also indicate that a substantial barrier to rotation about the 2-3 bond exists for the lowest excited states of butadiene.   Havinga [56] has pointed out the possible significance of stereoisomeric excited states in the vitamin D series.

We can now conceive of two transitions involving Franck-Condon excitation of s-*trans*- and s-*cis*-butadiene to form *noninterconvertible* stereoisomeric *trans* and *cis* triplets, respectively. Such a scheme may be represented in exaggerated valence bond terms as follows:

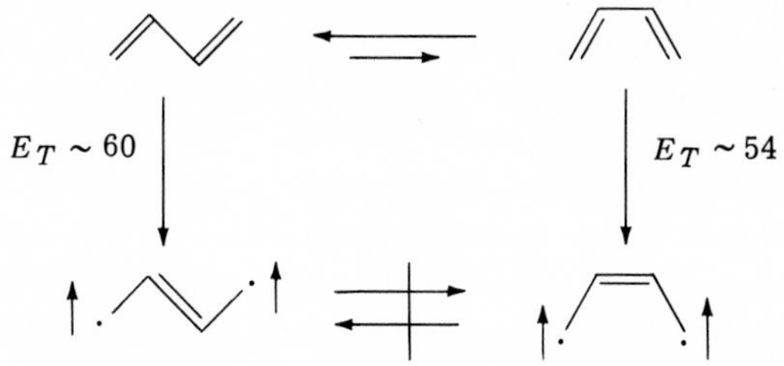

$E_T \sim 60$ $E_T \sim 54$

48   49

The data in Tables 8-3 and 8-4 can then be explained in the following manner: The *trans* triplet (48), which possesses the greater excitation energy, reacts predominately with s-*trans*-butadiene molecules to yield cyclobutanes since it is not favorably disposed to form cyclohexenes. The *cis* triplet (49) reacts predominately with s-*trans*-butadiene to yield mainly vinylcyclohexene. Either triplet is expected to react predominately with s-*trans*-butadiene because of the concentration advantage of the latter rotomer over s-*cis*-butadiene, all other factors being equal. The high-energy sensitizers transfer excitation to either s-*cis*- or s-*trans*-butadiene on every collision, and the ratio of *trans* and *cis* triplets produced reflects the relative concentrations of their precursor—i.e., *overwhelming* predominance of *trans* triplets is produced, and greater than 95% of the dimers are cyclobutanes. When the energy of the sensitizer falls below 60 kcal, however, transfer to s-*trans*-butadiene becomes measurably inefficient, and relatively larger amounts of *cis* triplets are formed as a result of the selective excitation of s-*cis*-butadiene molecules, and the relative yield of vinylcyclohexene increases. Finally, sensitizers having less than 53 kcal of excitation energy do not transfer efficiently to either isomer and non-Franck-Condon excitations, which may be governed by different rules than usual, are possible.

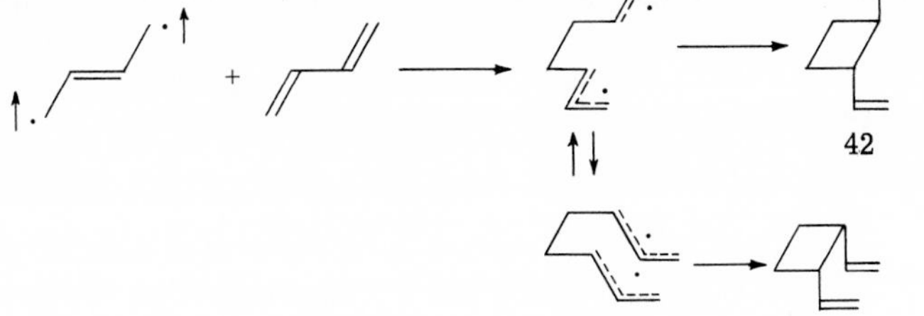

42   (8-41)

43

44   (8-42)

On the other hand, the carbon skeleton of cyclic dienes is rigidly held in the *cis* configuration and *only cis* triplets can be formed upon energy transfer from triplet sensitizers.

An important feature of these diene dimerizations is the generality with which the unit C=C—C—C—C=C appears. No exceptions to this rule are known at this time. This may be taken as evidence for a two-step process in which the triplet diene adds to an unexcited diene *in a manner such as to produce the most stabilized one-bond intermediate*—i.e., the diradicals which are most stable on electronic grounds predominate, and stabilization of the allylic unit controls the point of attack of a triplet to a conjugated diene.

In contrast, direct irradiation of concentrated butadiene solutions produces a host of dimers, among which the following are formed.[45] The dimer (50) may result from reaction of initially formed bicyclobutane with butadiene:

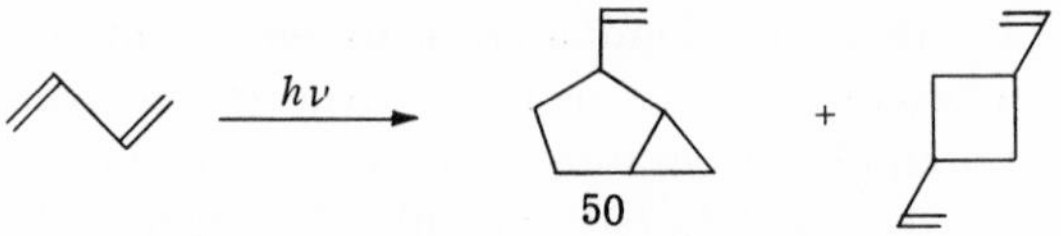

$$\text{(8-43)}$$

$$\text{50}$$

+ other dimers

The direct irradiation of cyclohexadiene leads to a mixture of dimers similar in composition to that produced in the sensitized reaction but in considerably lower yield.[57]

Cross-additions to Alkenes

Although the cross-addition of butadiene and cyclohexadiene is effected efficiently by photosensitizers, simple alkenes have not been efficiently added to dienes under photosensitizing conditions. Thus, cyclohexadiene gives at best poor yields of cross-adducts when it is irradiated in the presence of a sensitizer and a large excess of cyclopentene, norbornene, or 1,5-hexadiene.[58] However, an intramolecular cross-addition of myrcene to produce compound 53, has been reported. This reaction is of interest

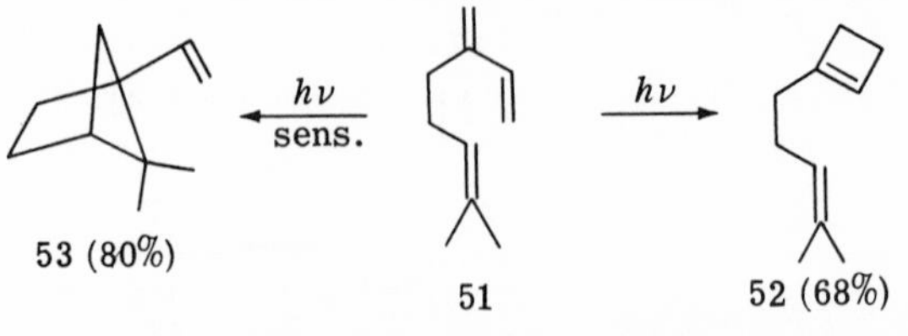

$$\text{(8-44)}$$

53 (80%)   51   52 (68%)

because direct irradiation of myrcene yields a cyclobutene (52) as the major product, indicating that the reaction occurs in the singlet state and few molecules cross over to the triplet state.[58, 59]

Cross-additions to Halogenated Olefins

In contrast to the low efficiency of photosensitized cross-addition of dienes to simple alkenes, halogenated ethylenes are excellent substrates for such reactions.[60, 61]   Let us briefly review the thermal counterpart of these reactions so that we may later compare the two.

Although the dichloro- and monochloroethylenes form Diels-Alder adducts with certain dienes, trichloro- and tetrachloroethylene are very inert to cycloaddition.   Fluorinated ethylenes, on the other hand, tend to react with dienes to yield cyclobutanes predominately.   Evidence has recently been produced which is consistent with the hypothesis that a bifunctional "biradical" intermediate is formed as the first step in 1,2-cycloaddition.[60]   Several schools of thought exist concerning the timing of bond formation in Diels-Alder reactions for which biradical intermediates, two-step, and one-step mechanisms have been proposed.[62]

For example, 1,1-dichloro-2,2-difluoroethylene (1122) reacts with butadiene at 80° to yield only one product.

$$ \text{(8-45)} $$
$$ \text{(8-46)} $$

with the reactions:
$\xrightarrow[80°]{CF_2=CCl_2}$ $\underset{F_2}{\overset{Cl_2}{\square}}$ (54) $\xleftarrow[h\nu, 0°]{CF_2=CCl_2}$

A number of photosensitized cycloadditions of 1122 to various dienes have been found [61] and are listed below in Table 8-5.   Where more than one adduct is formed, the ratio of these adducts is independent of sensitizer for the cases studied.

Chlorinated ethylenes, which are not very reactive in either 1,4- or 1,2- addition to dienes, undergo smooth photosensitized cycloaddition to cyclopentadiene and cyclohexadiene.   The yields with linear dienes are lower, due to the preponderant dimerization of the dienes.   Some examples are listed in Table 8-5.

Mechanisms of Photosensitized Cross-addition to Dienes [45, 52, 53]

It appears that the diene triplet is the chemically active species in these photosensitized reactions.   Evidence for this conclusion is based on the following facts:

1. Diene dimers are formed in addition to cross-adducts.
2. No evidence for significant dimerization of the haloethylenes has been found.
3. Many compounds which possess insufficient triplet energy to excite halo-olefins, sensitize cross-addition and dimerization.

The diene triplets therefore demonstrate a marked selectivity since they will react selectively with diene molecules if the concentration of halo-olefin is not sufficiently high, and they will not react efficiently even with

Table 8-5 *Photosensitized addition[a] of 1122 and 1,1-dichloroethylene to dienes* [61]

Diene	*Products*

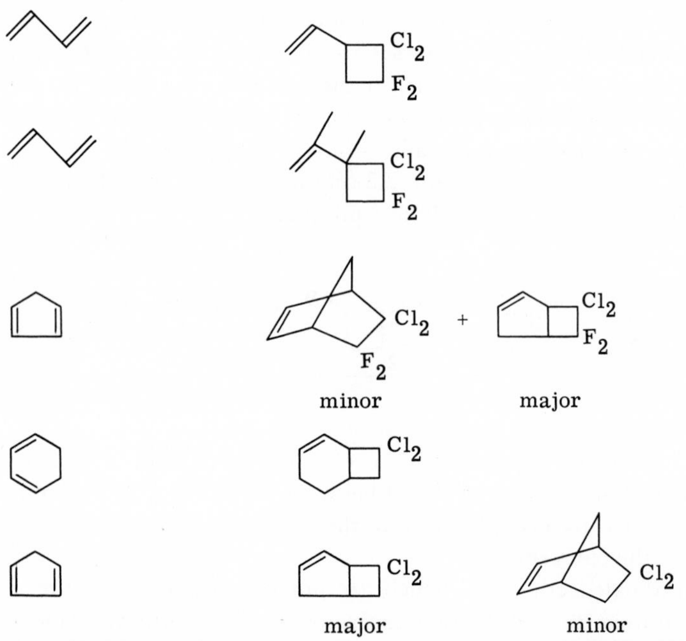

Cl2
F2
Cl2
F2
Cl2
F2
+
Cl2
F2
minor
major
Cl2
Cl2
Cl2
major
minor

[a] Diene dimers also formed.

a large excess of simple alkene. Therefore, a reactivity scale of substrates for diene triplets may be formulated as

$$\text{diene} > \text{halo-olefin} \gg \text{alkene}$$

It will be interesting to enlarge this list and determine the effect of substrate structure on the features of these reactions. It appears that formation of a stabilized biradical intermediate in the photosensitized reactions, as in the thermal 1,2 cycloadditions, explains the observed results. The preponderance of cyclobutanes in the adduct reaction mixtures indicates a preference for the biradical formed from triplet diene and substrate to close 1,2 rather than 1,4.

Photosensitized Dimerization of Simple Alkenes

Irradiation of norbornene in the presence of acetophenone as sensitizer leads to the formation of dimers.[48, 63]

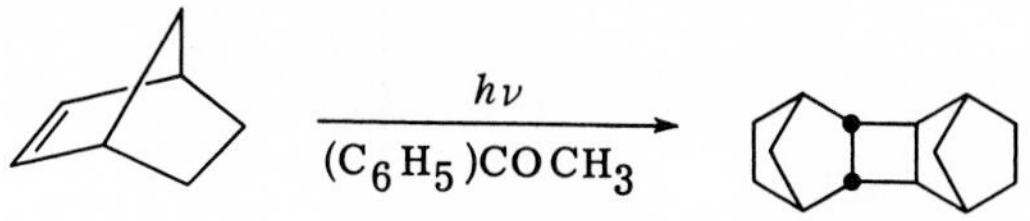

$$\text{(structure)} \xrightarrow[\text{(C}_6\text{H}_5\text{)COCH}_3]{h\nu} \text{(structure)} \quad 55 \qquad (8\text{-}47)$$

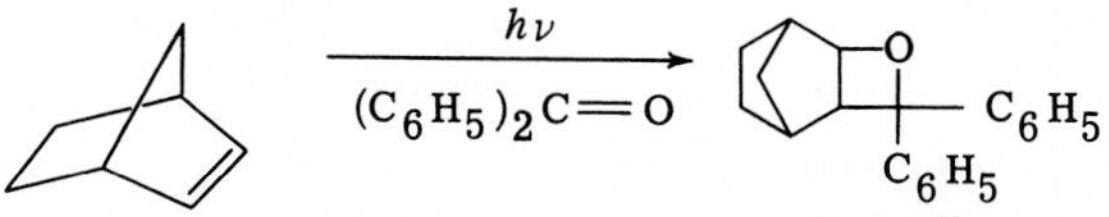

+ other dimers

$$\text{(structure)} \xrightarrow[\text{(C}_6\text{H}_5\text{)}_2\text{C}=\text{O}]{h\nu} \text{(structure)} \quad (8\text{-}48)$$

56 (80%)

Irradiation of benzene solutions of norbornene containing benzophenone, however, yields mainly an oxetane (see Eqs. 8-47 and 8-48). A competition between energy transfer and cycloaddition occurs in this case. Acetophenone $(E_T = 74)$ has a higher triplet than norbornene, while benzophenone $(E_T = 69)$ has a lower triplet. Sensitizers of intermediate energy such as xanthone $(E_T = 72)$ produce comparable amounts of dimers and oxetane.

Similarly, cyclopentene is dimerized to the tricyclodecane (57), when an acetone solution of the olefin is irradiated.[64]

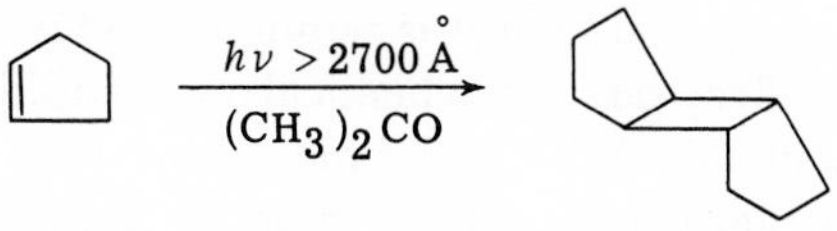

$$\text{(structure)} \xrightarrow[\text{(CH}_3\text{)}_2\text{CO}]{h\nu > 2700\,\text{Å}} \text{(structure)} \qquad (8\text{-}49)$$

57 (56%)

Benzophenone, which does not possess sufficient energy to transfer excitation efficiently to cyclopentene, does not photosensitize the reaction, but rather yields benzpinacol when irradiated in cyclopentene. Presumably, benzene $(E_T \sim 85$ kcal mole$^{-1})$ should be capable of effecting such dimerizations, although its efficiency as a sensitizer may be low. However, the inertness of benzene to photoreactions may be of great advantage to avoid side reactions of the sensitizer and olefin. It is the anomalously large singlet-triplet splitting of simple ethylenes $(\sim 100$ kcal mole$^{-1})$ which allows benzene, whose S_1 state lies about 40 kcal mole^{-1} *lower* than that of cyclopentene, to have a T_1 state which is several kcal mole^{-1} *higher* than that of cyclopentene.

Only a few simple alkenes have been shown to undergo sensitized dimerization, e.g., 1,3,3-trimethylcyclopropene.[65] The major product is not predicted by consideration of the most stable one-bonded inter-

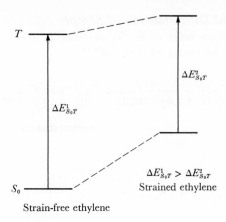

Fig. 8-3   *Possible energy relationships for strained and strain-free ethylenes.*

mediate (Eq. 8-50). Apparently, steric factors overcome the energetic advantages, if a two-step mechanism operates.[66]

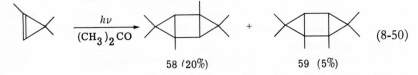

$$\begin{array}{ccc} & 58 \ (20\%) & 59 \ (5\%) \end{array} \tag{8-50}$$

The scant number of simple alkenes which dimerize under sensitized conditions indicates a "special" effect is required. This may be the first example of a strain effect on photochemical cycloadditions. Consider the energy diagram in Fig. 8-3. A simple alkene such as ethylene or butene possesses a triplet energy greater than 75 kcal. *If* the effect of strain, which is pronounced on the ground-state energies, influences the energy of excited states to a lesser degree, then the energy *gap* between the ground state and the excited states of strained olefins will be smaller and more accessible to low-energy sensitizers. This hypothesis needs further development before a detailed evaluation of its validity can be made.

PROBLEMS*

1. Which of the following compounds do you expect to be *efficient* sensitizers of the dimerization of cyclohexadiene-1,3?

1. benzene, 2. acetophenone, 3. 1-bromonaphthalene, 4. 2-acetonaphthone, 5. quinoline, 6. anthracene, 7. phenanthrene, 8. pyrene, 9. triphenylamine.

2. Show that for any sensitizer which is quenched at a diffusion-controlled rate by cyclohexadiene-1,3 the intersystem crossing efficiency (triplet yield) for

* See Addendum for additional problems.

the sensitizer is given by the following expression

$$\Phi_{ST} = \frac{\Phi_{dim}}{\Phi^0_{dim}}$$

where Φ_{ST} is the yield of triplets for the sensitizer, Φ_{dim} is the yield of dimerization produced by the sensitizer and Φ^0_{dim} is the yield of dimerization produced by benzophenone ($\Phi_{ST} = 1$).

3. Predict whether $(C_6H_5)_2C\!\!=\!\!O$ will add efficiently to 1. tetramethylethylene, 2. cyclohexene, 3. cyclohexadiene-1,3.

4. A compound is found to sensitize the dimerization of butadiene as efficiently as benzophenone and produces a mixture of dimers containing 98% divinylcyclobutanes and 2% vinylcyclohexene. What can you say about the triplet energy of this compound?

5. Predict the major products from the photosensitized dimerization of isoprene. Will the ratio of diene dimers vary as the sensitizer is varied?

6. Predict the products of the following reactions:

(a) 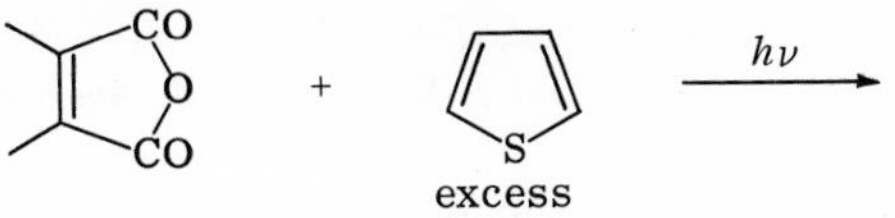
excess

(b) 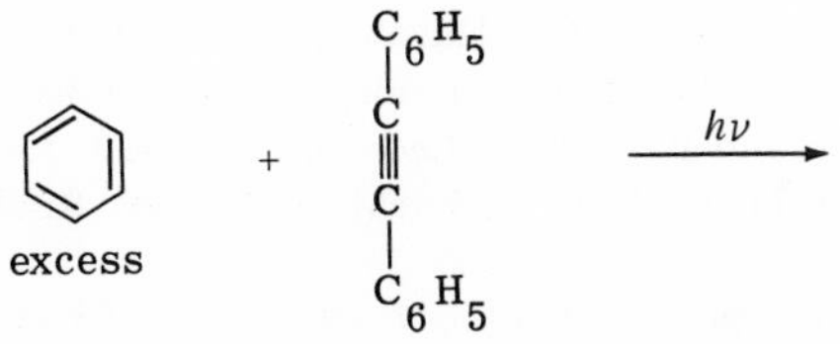
excess

(c) 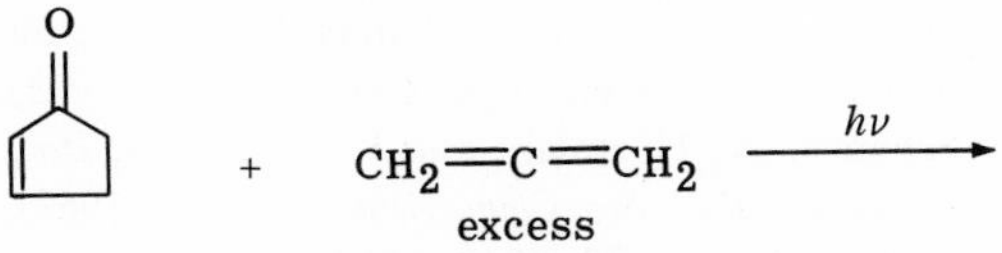
excess

7. Cyclopentadiene undergoes photosensitized dimerization. Predict the products of the dimerization and whether the relative ratio of dimers will depend on the sensitizer employed.

REFERENCES*

1. A. Mustafa, *Chem. Rev.*, **51**, 1 (1952); *ibid.*, **40**, 181 (1947).
2. A. Schonberg, *Praeparative Organische Photochemie* (Berlin: Springer-Verlage, 1958).
3. P. deMayo, in *Advances in Organic Chemistry* (Vol. II, New York: Interscience, 1960) p. 367; P. deMayo and S. T. Reid, *Quart. Rev.*, **15**, 393 (1961).

* See Addendum for additional references.

4. J. P. Simons, *Trans. Faraday Soc.*, **56,** 391 (1960).
5. G. O. Schenck, *Angew. Chem.*, **73,** 413 (1961); G. O. Schenck, *Strahlentheropie* **114,** 22 (1961).
6. H. C. Longuet-Higgins and E. W. Abrahamson, *J. Am. Chem. Soc.*, **87,** 2045 (1965); R. Hoffmann and R. B. Woodword, *ibid.*, **87,** 2046 (1965).
7. C. R. Masson, V. Bockelheide, and W. A. Noyes, Jr., in A. Weissberger *Technique of Organic Chemistry* (Vol. II, New York: Interscience, 1956), p. 257.
8. C. S. Foote and S. Wexler, *J. Am. Chem. Soc.*, **86,** 3879, 3880 (1964); E. J. Corey and W. C. Taylor, *ibid.*, **86,** 3881 (1964).
9. G. Herzberg, *Molecular Spectra and Molecular Structure*, Vol. I, "Spectra of Diatomic Molecules," 2d ed. (Princeton, N.J.: Van Nostrand).
10. G. Porter and M. R. Wright, *Disc. Faraday Soc.*, **27,** 18 (1959).
11. E. J. Bowen, in *Advances in Photochemistry*, ed. W. A. Noyes, Jr., G. S. Hammond, and J. N. Pitts, Jr. (Vol. I, New York: Interscience, 1963), p. 23.
12. G. O. Schenck and K. Ziegler, *Naturwiss.*, **32,** 157 (1944).
13. H. F. Angus and D. Bryce-Smith, *Proc. Chem. Soc.*, 327 (1959); *J. Chem. Soc.*, 4791 (1960).
14. G. O. Schenck and R. Steinmetz, *Tetrahedron Letters*, 1 (1960).
15. E. Grovenstein, D. V. Rao, and J. W. Taylor, *J. Am. Chem. Soc.*, **83,** 1705 (1961).
16. D. Bryce-Smith, A. Gilbert, and B. Vickery, *Chem. and Ind.*, 2060 (1960); *J. Chem. Soc.*, 2675 (1962); *J. Chem. Soc.* 918 (1965).
17. G. S. Hammond and W. M. Hardham, *Proc. Chem. Soc.*, 63 (1963); G. S. Hammond and W. M. Hardham, unpublished results.
18. D. Bryce-Smith and B. Vickery, *Chem. and Ind.*, 429 (1961).
19. J. G. Atkinson, D. E. Ayer, G. Buchi, and E. W. Robb, *J. Am. Chem. Soc.*, **85,** 2257 (1963).
20. D. Bryce-Smith and J. E. Lodge, *J. Chem. Soc.*, 695 (1963); E. Grovenstein and D. V. Rao, *Tetrahedron Letters*, 148 (1961).
21. J. A. Barltrop and R. Robson, *Tetrahedron Letters*, 597 (1963); P. deMayo, R. W. Yip, and S. T. Reid, *Proc. Chem. Soc.*, 54 (1963).
22. G. O. Schenck, W. Hartman, and R. Steinmetz, *Ber.*, **96,** 498 (1963); *ibid.*, **95,** 1642 (1962); *Bull. Soc. Chim. Belges*, **71,** 781 (1962).
23. R. Criegee, *et al.*, *Ber.*, **97,** 2947 (1964).
24. G. O. Schenck and R. Wolgast, *Naturwiss.*, **48,** 737 (1961); *ibid.*, **49,** 36 (1962).
25. R. Anet, *Chem. and Ind.*, 897 (1960); *Canad. J. Chem.*, **40,** 1249 (1962).
26. G. O. Schenck, I. von Wilucki, and C. H. Krouch, *Ber.*, **95,** 1409 (1962).
27. G. S. Hammond, C. A. Stout, and A. A. Lamola, *J. Am. Chem. Soc.*, **86,** 3103 (1964).
28. For an excellent review of photoreactions in the solid state see: H. S. A. Gilmore, in *Physics and Chemistry of the Solid State*, ed. D. Fox, *et al.* (New York: Interscience, 1963).
29. M. D. Cohen and G. M. J. Schmidt, *J. Chem. Soc.*, 1996 (1964).
30. G. W. Griffin, A. F. Vellturo, and K. Furukawa, *J. Am. Chem. Soc.*, **83,** 2725 (1961).
31. J. Bregman, K. Osaki, G. M. J. Schmidt, and F. I. Sonntag, *J. Chem. Soc.*, 2021 (1964).

32. P. Eaton, *J. Am. Chem. Soc.*, **84**, 2344 (1962).
33. D. Valentine, N. J. Turro, and G. S. Hammond, *J. Am. Chem. Soc.*, **86**, 5202 (1964).
34. G. Buchi, unpublished results.
35. R. C. Cookson and J. Hudec, *Proc. Chem. Soc.*, 11 (1959); *J. Chem. Soc.*, 4499 (1961).
36. D. Bryce-Smith and A. Gilbert, *J. Chem. Soc.*, 2428 (1964).
37. See R. C. Cookson, *et al.*, *J. Chem. Soc.*, 3062 (1964) for a review of photochemical "cage" closures.
38. E. C. Taylor, R. O. Kan, and W. W. Pauller, *J. Am. Chem. Soc.*, **83**, 4484 (1961); *ibid.*, **83**, 2967 (1961); G. Slomp, F. A. MacKellar, and L. A. Paquette, *J. Am. Chem. Soc.*, **83**, 4472 (1961).
39. P. Eaton, *J. Am. Chem. Soc.*, **84**, 2454 (1962).
40. P. Eaton, *Tetrahedron Letters*, 3695 (1964).
41. R. Criegee, *et al.*, *Ber.*, **97**, 2949 (1964).
42. R. Eaton and T. W. Cole, Jr., *J. Am. Chem. Soc.*, **86**, 963 (1964).
43. E. J. Corey, R. B. Mitra, and H. Uda, *ibid.*, **86**, 485 (1964); E. J. Corey, *et al.*, *ibid.*, **86**, 5570 (1964).
44. G. S. Hammond and N. J. Turro, unpublished results.
45. N. J. Turro, Ph.D. Thesis (Pasadena: California Institute of Technology, 1963).
46. J. A. Barltrop and B. Hesp, *Proc. Chem. Soc.*, 195 (1964).
47. P. E. Eaton and K. Lin, *J. Am. Chem. Soc.*, **86**, 2088 (1964).
48. D. R. Arnold, R. L. Hinman, and A. H. Glick, *Tetrahedron Letters*, 1425 (1964); G. Buchi, *et al.*, *J. Am. Chem. Soc.*, **78**, 876 (1956).
49. N. C. Yang, M. Nussim, M. J. Jorgenson, and S. Murov, *Tetrahedron Letters*, 3657 (1964).
50. J. F. Harris, Jr. and D. D. Coffman, *J. Am. Chem. Soc.*, **84**, 1553 (1962).
51. L. A. Singer and P. D. Bartlett, *Tetrahedron Letters*, 1887 (1964).
52. G. S. Hammond, N. J. Turro, and A. Fischer, *J. Am. Chem. Soc.*, **83**, 4674 (1961); N. J. Turro and G. S. Hammond, *ibid.*, **84**, 2841 (1962).
53. G. S. Hammond, N. J. Turro, and R. S. H. Liu, *J. Org. Chem.*, **28**, 3297 (1963); G. S. Hammond and R. S. H. Liu, *J. Am. Chem. Soc.*, **85**, 477 (1963); *ibid.*, **87**, 3406 (1965).
54. D. F. Evans, *J. Chem. Soc.*, 1987 (1961).
55. R. Daudel, *et al.*, *Quantum Chemistry* (New York: Interscience, 1959), p. 59.
56. E. Havinga, R. J. deKock, and M. P. Roppoldt, *Tetrahedron*, **11**, 276 (1960); E. Havinga, *Chimia*, **16**, 145 (1962).
57. G. O. Schenck, *et al.*, *Z. Naturforsch.*, **19b**, 18 (1964).
58. R. S. H. Liu and G. S. Hammond, *J. Am. Chem. Soc.*, **86**, 1892 (1964).
59. K. J. Crowley, *Proc. Chem. Soc.*, 245, 334 (1962).
60. P. D. Bartlett, *et al.*, *J. Am. Chem. Soc.*, **86**, 616 (1964).
61. N. J. Turro and P. D. Bartlett, *J. Org. Chem.*, **30**, 1849 (1965).
62. C. Walling and H. G. Shugar, *J. Am. Chem. Soc.*, **85**, 607 (1963).
63. H. D. Scharf and F. Korte, *Tetrahedron Letters*, 821 (1963).
64. H. D. Scharf and F. Korte, *Ber.*, **97**, 2425 (1964).
65. H. H. Stechl, *Ber.*, **97**, 2681 (1964); *Angew. Chem.*, **75**, 1176 (1963).

chapter nine

Photochemical Fragmentations and Related Reactions

9-1. PHOTOLYTIC PRODUCTION OF FREE RADICALS AND CARBENES

A frequent course of reaction during irradiation of compounds in the vapor phase is the dissociation of the absorbing molecule into free radicals. In fact, the best studied of all photochemical reactions is probably the photolysis of aldehydes and ketones in the vapor phase.[1, 2, 3]

Photolysis of Carbonyl Compounds [1-3, 5]

Three general types of reaction occur when noncyclic aliphatic carbonyl compounds are irradiated in the vapor phase:

1. α-bond cleavage (type I cleavage) to form radicals [1] (Eq. 9-1);
2. γ-hydrogen atom abstraction,[2, 5] followed by elimination of an olefin (type II cleavage, Eq. 9-2);
3. cyclobutanol formation [4] (Eq. 9-3).

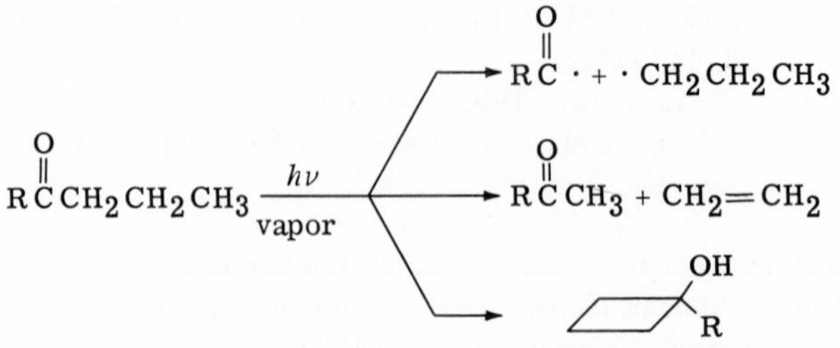

$$R\overset{\overset{\displaystyle O}{\|}}{C}CH_2CH_2CH_3 \xrightarrow[\text{vapor}]{h\nu}$$

$$\longrightarrow R\overset{\overset{\displaystyle O}{\|}}{C}\cdot + \cdot CH_2CH_2CH_3 \qquad (9\text{-}1)$$

$$\longrightarrow R\overset{\overset{\displaystyle O}{\|}}{C}CH_3 + CH_2{=}CH_2 \qquad (9\text{-}2)$$

$$\longrightarrow \ \text{(cyclobutanol, OH, R)} \qquad (9\text{-}3)$$

Reaction 9-1 is frequently followed by elimination of carbon monoxide (in the vapor-phase photolysis), but this reaction is almost entirely suppressed in solution at room temperature. The "cage effect" may be responsible for the quenching of reaction 9-1 in solution—i.e., the radicals formed as a result of light absorption cannot separate immediately because of the solvent "cage" which surrounds them. As a result, recombination of the radicals occurs faster than elimination of carbon monoxide and no net reaction occurs.

$$R_2C\!\!=\!\!O \underset{\substack{\text{fast}}}{\overset{\substack{h\nu,\ \text{solution, }25°}}{\rightleftharpoons}} \underset{\text{solvent cage}}{R\cdot + R\overset{\cdot}{C}O} \rightarrow 2R\cdot + CO \qquad (9\text{-}4)$$

On the other hand, suppose that decarbonylation either:

   1. occurs from an upper vibrational level of an excited state;
   2. requires a crossover to a dissociative state from an upper vibrational level.

Rapid vibrational quenching in solution will cause such a short lifetime in upper vibrational levels that decarbonylation will be inefficient. However, as the temperature is raised the lifetime and population of these upper levels will increase, so that decarbonylation should occur.

In fact, it is found that at temperatures above 100° reaction 9-1 occurs in solution with quantum efficiencies approaching those obtained in gas-phase photolysis.[5] This does not serve to differentiate between the two mechanisms mentioned above, however, since both the dissociation of RCO· to carbon monoxide and the population of upper vibration levels are favored by an increase in temperature.

Certain cyclic ketones undergo type I cleavage followed by elimination of carbon monoxide even in solution.[2] The process probably occurs in two steps. For example, 9-ketobicyclo-(4,2,1)-nonane (compound 1) and related compounds [6] are photolyzed in solution as shown below.†

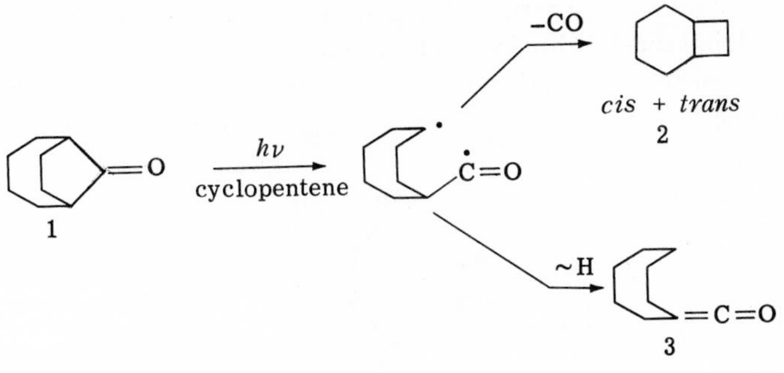

$$(9\text{-}5)$$

cis + trans
2

$$(9\text{-}6)$$

Two effects appear to promote efficient photodecarbonylation:

   1. ring strain, and
   2. stabilization of the radicals formed by α cleavage.

† Note in proof: see, however, *Tetrahedron Letters*, 2301 (1965).

Thus, cyclopentanone is stable under irradiation conditions [6] which produce complete decarbonylation of 1.

As another example, 2-indanone (4) and its derivatives are of some
interest. The parent compound 4, when irradiated in cyclohexane,
yields mainly photoreduction products, while the diphenyl derivative (5)
gives a good yield of carbon monoxide under the same conditions.[7]

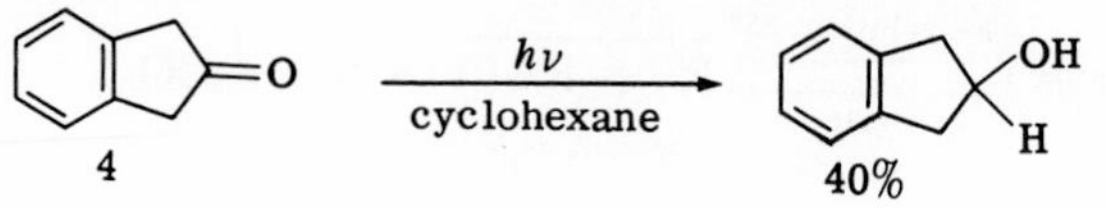

$$(9\text{-}7)$$

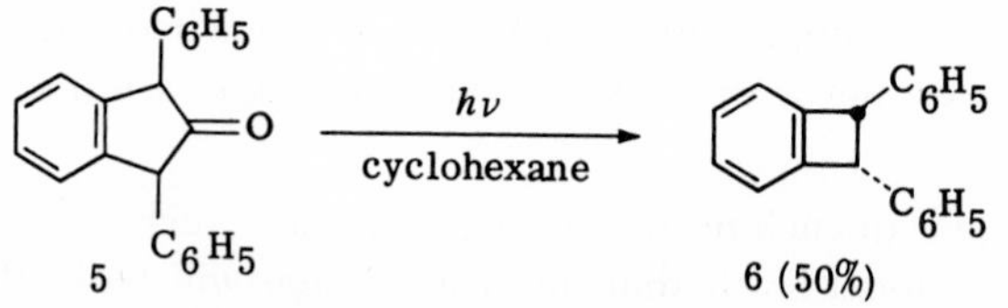

$$(9\text{-}8)$$

Reaction 9-8 provides a facile preparation of the diphenylbenzocyclo-
butane (6). A combination of strain and stabilization of a biradical
intermediate (7) presumably enhances the photodecarbonylation of
compound 5.

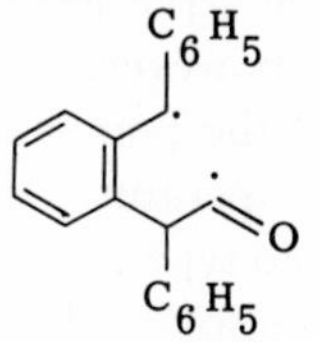

Although cyclobutanone might be expected to undergo facile decarbonylation in solution as a result of ring strain, in fact, it does not.[2]   In
contrast, cyclobutane-1,3-diones, such as compound 8, undergo rapid
elimination of carbon monoxide when they are irradiated in inert solvents
such as benzene.[8]   The over-all process yields the ethylene (10), probably
via the cyclopropanone (9):

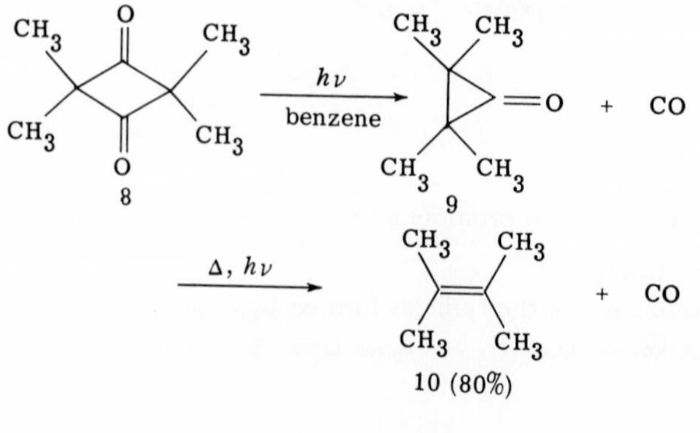

$$(9\text{-}9)$$

In this case, both ring strain and biradical stabilization contribute to facilitate decarbonylation. The intermediate, compound 9, may be isolated [8] or trapped by inclusion of a hydroxylic solvent or oxygen in the system.

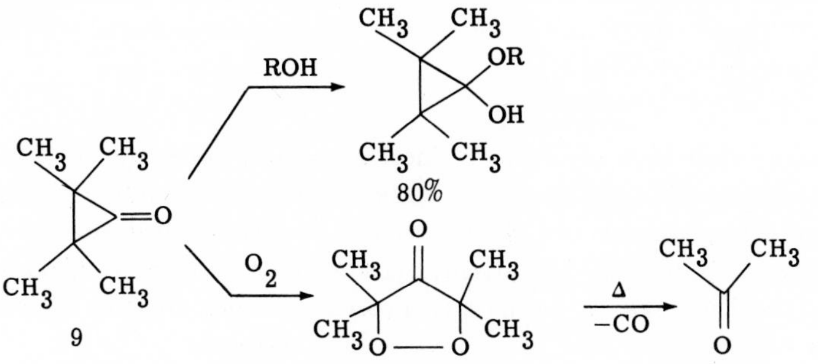

$$(9\text{-}10)$$

$$(9\text{-}11)$$

70%

Stabilization of the radicals formed from α cleavage also results in efficient decarbonylation of noncyclic ketones,[7] as shown in Eq. 9-12

$$(C_6H_5)CH_2\overset{\overset{\displaystyle O}{\|}}{C}CH_2(C_6H_5) \xrightarrow[-CO]{h\nu} (C_6H_5)CH_2CH_2(C_6H_5) \quad (9\text{-}12)$$

11   85%

In this case, the radicals formed are truly free of "cage" recombination since irradiation of 12 leads to a statistical mixture of three possible radical recombination products.

$$(C_6H_5)_2CH\overset{\overset{\displaystyle O}{\|}}{C}CH_2(C_6H_5) \xrightarrow[-CO]{h\nu} \begin{array}{l} C_6H_5CH_2\cdot \\ + (C_6H_5)_2CH\cdot \end{array}$$

12

$$\longrightarrow (C_6H_5)_2CH)_2 + (C_6H_5)CH_2)_2$$
$$\qquad\qquad 25\% \qquad\qquad 25\%$$

$$(9\text{-}13)$$

$$+ \quad (C_6H_5)_2CHCH_2(C_6H_5)$$
$$\qquad\qquad 50\%$$

Formation of Carbenes [9]

Diazo compounds may be decomposed thermally or photochemically to produce carbenes.[9]   One of the best known examples of such a process is the photochemical dissociation of diazomethane. Methylene, the product of photolysis of diazomethane, is of theoretical interest [10] because its singlet state is predicted to be bent while its triplet state should be linear. Spectroscopic evidence [11] from the flash photolysis of diazomethane indicates the following mechanism for photodecomposition to form methylene.

$$CH_2N_2 \xrightarrow{h\nu} CH_2N_2(S_1) \longrightarrow \underset{singlet}{CH_2\,(\uparrow\downarrow)} + N_2$$

$$\xrightarrow[\text{gas}]{\text{inert}} \underset{triplet}{CH_2(\uparrow\uparrow)}$$

(9-14)

It was found that high pressures of inert gas *favored* formation of triplet CH_2, but singlet CH_2 was produced initially from diazomethane photolysis, so that the *ground state* of CH_2 is a *triplet*.   A chemical criterion for the assignment of multiplicity has arisen: Stereospecific addition of CH_2 into a double bond indicates a singlet-step process in which rotation of intermediates cannot occur and must involve a *singlet* state.   On the other hand, triplet CH_2 will form a biradical intermediate in which spin inversion must occur before final bond formation and *may* result in some loss of stereospecificity.[12]   For this criterion to be of use, we should find *both* examples of stereospecific and nonstereospecific additions for comparison.

The addition of CH_2 to *cis-* and *trans-*butene in the vapor and solution phase has been studied in some detail.[13, 14] At relatively high concentrations of olefin the following paths are important:

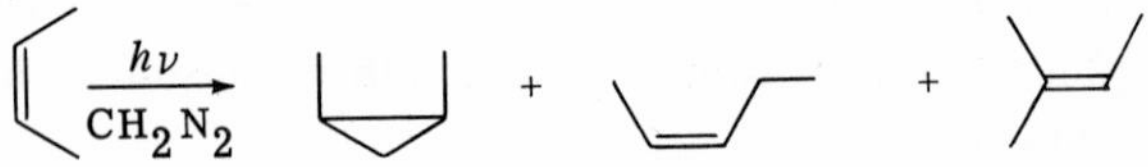

(9-15)

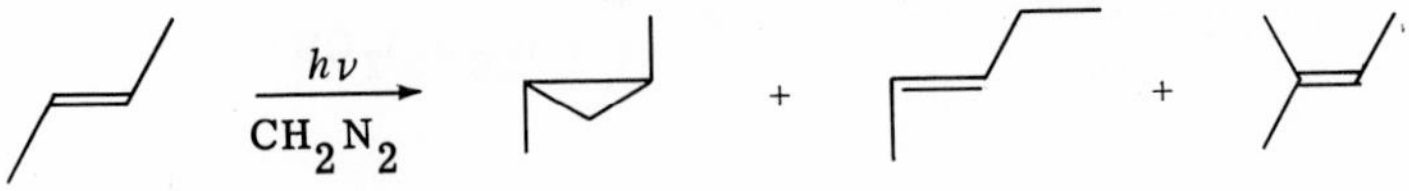

(9-16)

Table 9-1 *Photolysis of CH_2N_2 and the butenes in the vapor phase with added nitrogen gas as diluent* [13, 14]

Partial Pressures Compound (mm)				Relative Yields	
		CH_2N_2	N_2		
370	—	400	—	10	1
1	—	2	100	10	8
0.6	—	6	560	2	10
0	360	300	—	1	10
0	2	5	560	2	10

Both the addition and insertion reactions which occur are stereospecific and by the aforementioned criterion must occur from the singlet state.

A marked pressure dependence on the types of products obtained in vapor photolysis was found.[13] Some data are listed in Table 9-1. The results indicate that CH_2 ($\uparrow\downarrow$) must collide many times with an inert gas before it can locate an olefin molecule and be converted into CH_2 ($\uparrow\uparrow$) which then reacts *nonstereospecifically* with an olefin molecule.

In other words, the following path predominates at low pressures of inert gas:

$$CH_2N_2 \quad \xrightarrow{h\nu} \quad CH_2N_2{}^* \text{ (singlet)} \tag{9-17}$$

$$CH_2N_2{}^* \quad \longrightarrow \quad CH_2(\uparrow\downarrow) \;+\; N_2 \tag{9-18}$$

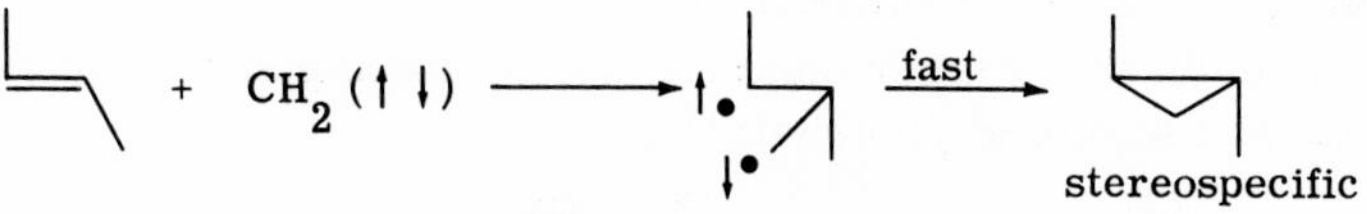

$$\tag{9-19}$$

Under conditions whereby the CH_2 ($\uparrow\downarrow$) is deactivated before it encounters an olefin the following sequence predominates:

$$CH_2N_2 \quad \xrightarrow{h\nu} \quad CH_2N_2{}^* \text{ (singlet)} \tag{9-20}$$

$$CH_2N_2{}^* \quad \longrightarrow \quad CH_2(\uparrow\uparrow\downarrow) \;+\; N_2 \tag{9-21}$$

$$CH_2(\uparrow\uparrow\downarrow) \quad \xrightarrow[\text{collisions}]{\text{many}} \quad CH_2(\uparrow\uparrow) \tag{9-22}$$

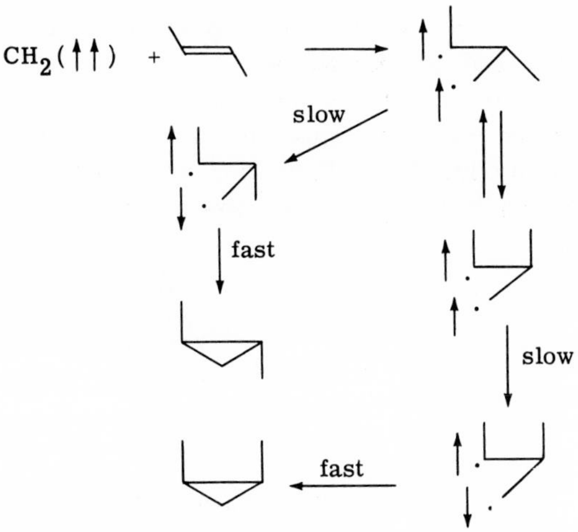

$$\tag{9-23}$$

The same type of reaction has been photosensitized by mercury triplets and *nonstereospecific* addition of CH_2 ($\uparrow\uparrow$) occurs.[13]

Triplet CH_2 has been produced in solution by sensitization with benzophenone.[15] Again nonstereospecific addition is observed, although equilibration of the products did not occur.

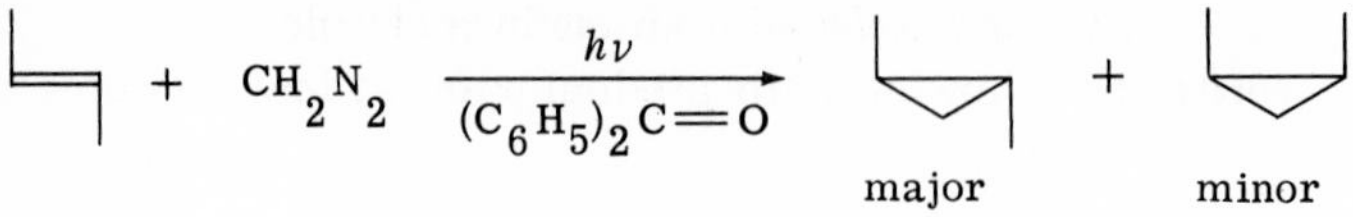

$$\text{[structure]} + CH_2N_2 \xrightarrow[\ (C_6H_5)_2C=O\ ]{h\nu} \text{[structure]} + \text{[structure]} \qquad (9\text{-}24)$$

major   minor

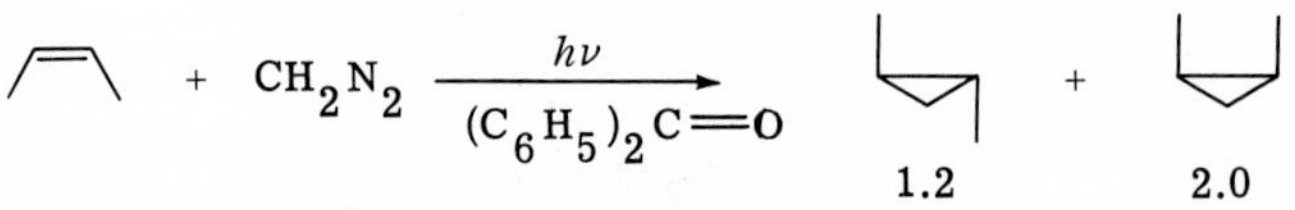

$$\text{[structure]} + CH_2N_2 \xrightarrow[\ (C_6H_5)_2C=O\ ]{h\nu} \text{[structure]} + \text{[structure]} \qquad (9\text{-}25)$$

1.2   2.0

Free Radicals from Azo Compounds [24]

Azo compounds, such as compound 13, may be decomposed thermally and by direct and sensitized photolysis.[16]

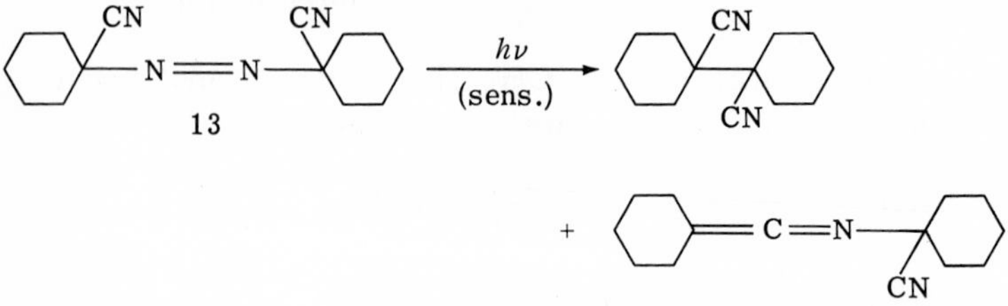

$$\text{[structure of compound 13]} \xrightarrow[(\text{sens.})]{h\nu} \text{[structure]}$$

13

$$+ \text{[structure]} \qquad (9\text{-}26)$$

Photochemical decomposition is fairly general for alkyl azo compounds, but aryl azo compounds, (e.g. azobenzene) undergo *cis-trans* isomerization [17] rather than decomposition (see Section 7-3). The elimination of nitrogen under the relatively mild conditions of solution photolysis at room temperature (or lower) is of great synthetic value in the preparation of highly strained compounds.

Although the elimination of nitrogen is usually a very exothermic process over-all, in solution excess excitation energy is rapidly quenched and strained structures produced by elimination and cyclization may survive. Several examples [18, 19, 20] are given below in Eqs. 9-27 through 9-29.

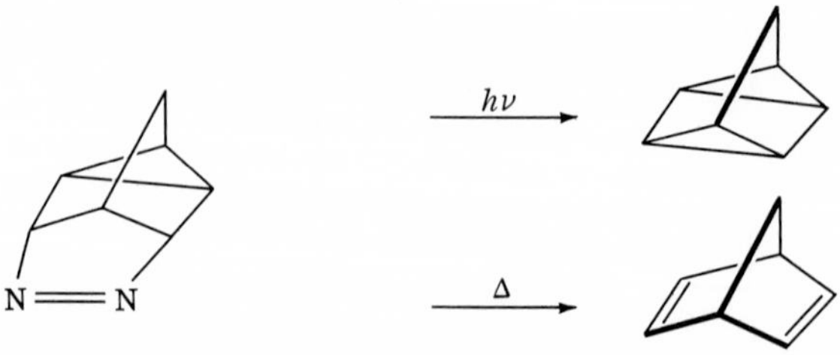

$$\text{[structure]} \xrightarrow{h\nu} \text{[structure]}$$

$$\xrightarrow{\Delta} \text{[structure]} \qquad (9\text{-}27)$$

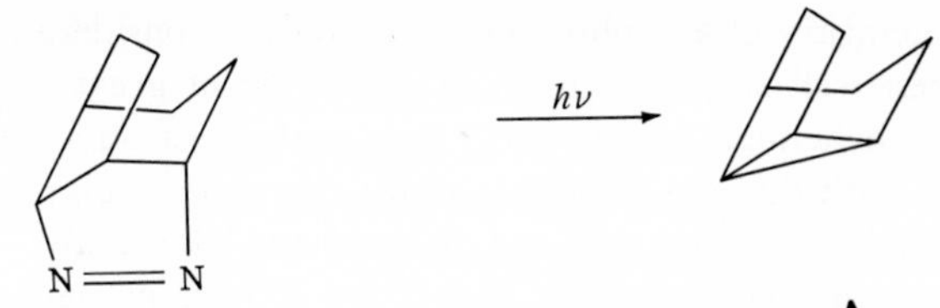

$$\xrightarrow{h\nu} \qquad\qquad (9\text{-}28)$$

$$\xrightarrow{h\nu} \qquad\qquad (9\text{-}29)$$

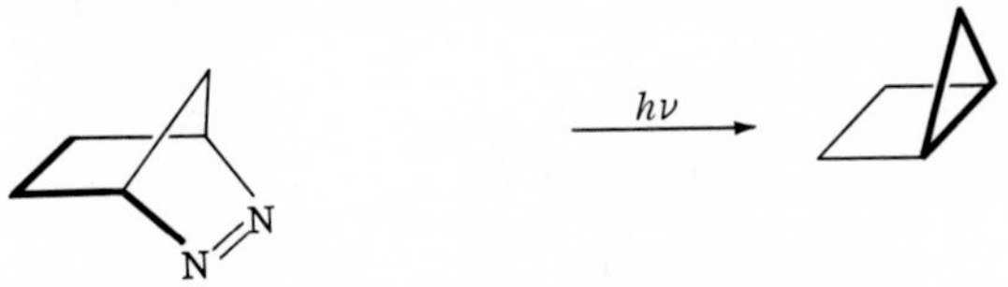

Excitation of the $n\text{-}\pi^*$ transition of azo compounds causes these reactions to proceed efficiently, but it is not known whether the $S_1(n,\pi^*)$, $T_1(n,\pi^*)$, or "hot" ground state is the site of nitrogen elimination. Unfortunately, azo compounds (like olefins) do not luminesce, in general. Those that do, usually lose nitrogen only slowly.[20]

Cyclopropenes [21] and cyclic acetylenes [22] may also be prepared by photolysis of appropriate azo compounds:

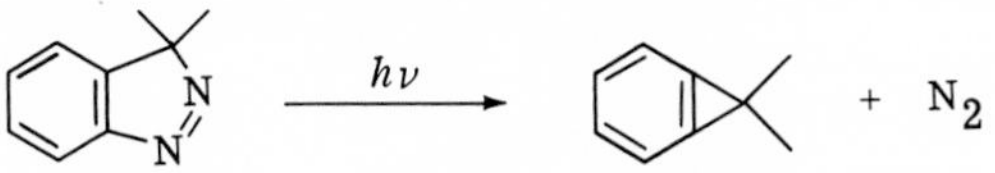

$$\xrightarrow{h\nu} \qquad\qquad + \ N_2 \qquad\qquad (9\text{-}30)$$

$$\xrightarrow{h\nu} \qquad\qquad + \ N_2 \qquad\qquad (9\text{-}31)$$

$$\xrightarrow{h\nu} \qquad\qquad + \ 2\,N_2 \qquad\qquad (9\text{-}32)$$

$$+ \ Ts^-$$

A spectacular solvent effect on the course of such reactions is given in Eqs. 9-33 and 9-34:

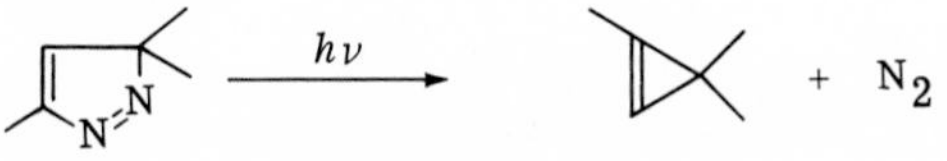

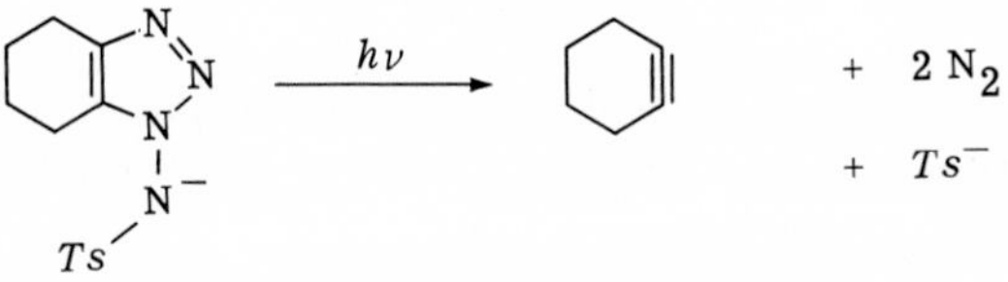

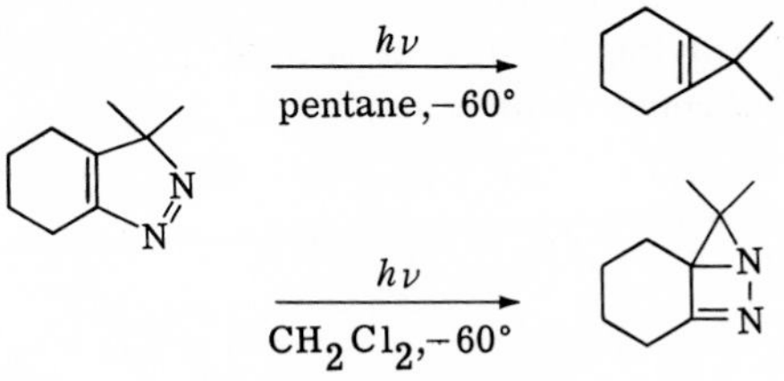

$$\xrightarrow[\text{pentane,}-60°]{h\nu} \qquad\qquad (9\text{-}33)$$

$$\xrightarrow[\text{CH}_2\text{Cl}_2,-60°]{h\nu} \qquad\qquad (9\text{-}34)$$

The stereochemistry of azo photolysis, although of considerable interest, has not been well worked out.[24] It would be of great interest to compare the stereochemical paths of sensitized and direct photolyses with one another and with thermal decompositions. As a particular example, the azo compounds (14 and 15) are decomposed thermally to yield the same mixture of cyclopropanes, indicating a lack of stereospecific decomposition.[25]

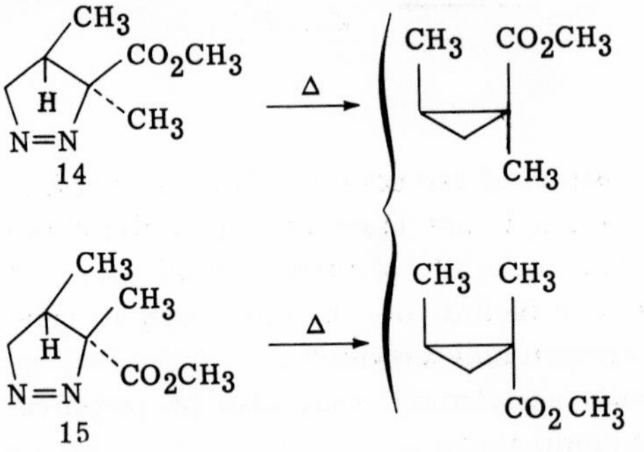

$$ \text{14} \xrightarrow{\Delta} \left\{ \begin{array}{c} \text{non-stereospecific} \end{array} \right. \tag{9-35} $$

On the other hand, photochemical decomposition leads to stereochemical retention.[25]

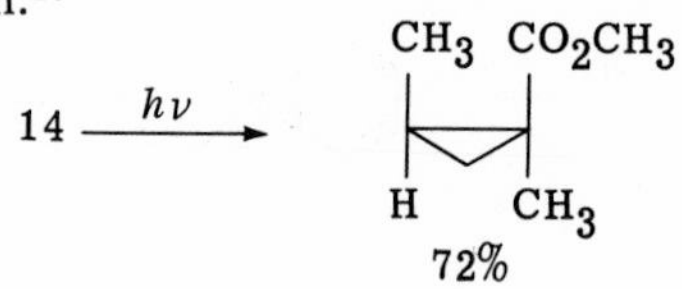

$$ \text{14} \xrightarrow{h\nu} \quad 72\% \tag{9-36} $$

$$ \xrightarrow{h\nu} \quad 75\% \tag{9-37} $$

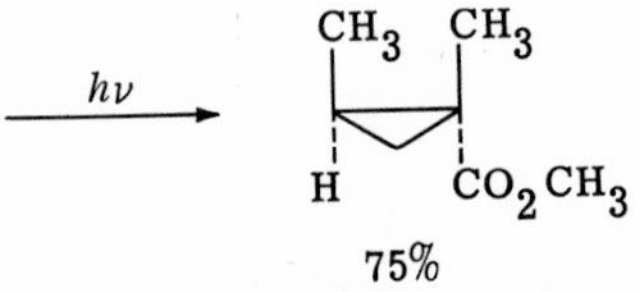

It would be of some interest to see if the sensitized (triplet) decomposition results in any loss of stereospecificity as a result of the (possibly) slow rate of spin inversion.

Miscellaneous Photochemical Eliminations

A number of stable molecules may be eliminated photochemically, in addition to those mentioned above. For example, ketenes [8, 26, 27] have been found to be leaving groups in several photodecompositions, as shown in Eqs. 9-38 through 9-40:

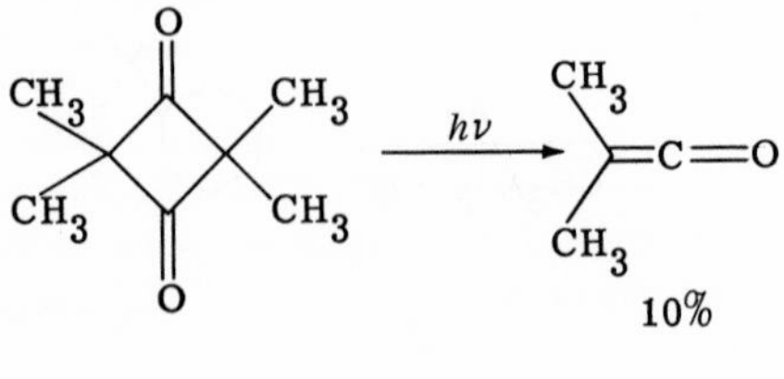

$$ \xrightarrow{h\nu} \quad 10\% \tag{9-38} $$

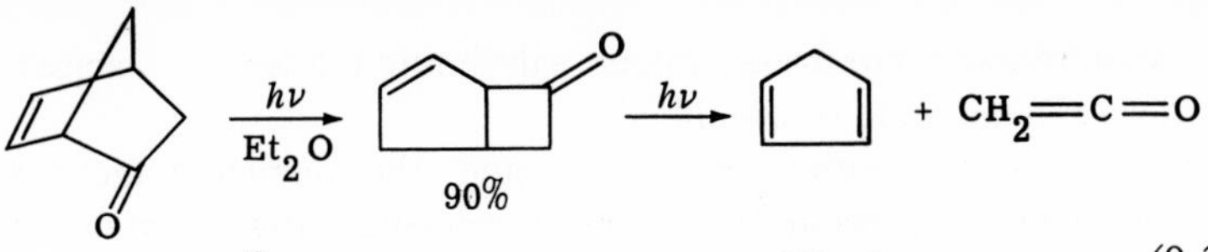

(9-39)

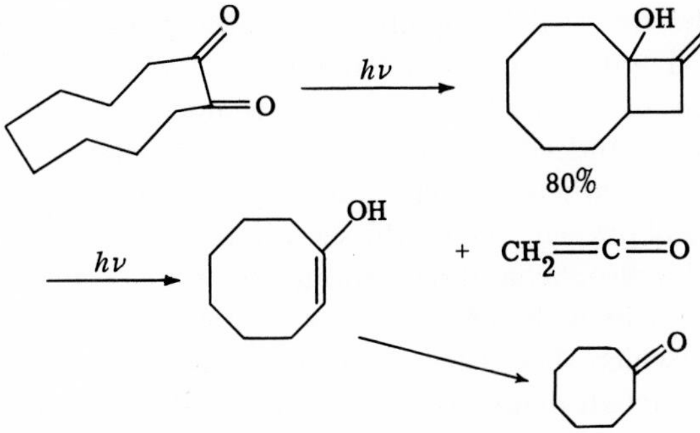

(9-40)

In each case, the elimination appears to be enhanced by a combination of ring strain and radical stabilization.

The fascinating and fluctuating molecule, "bullvalene" (16), has been synthesized by photoelimination of benzene from a molecule of a dimer of cyclooctatetraene.[28, 29]

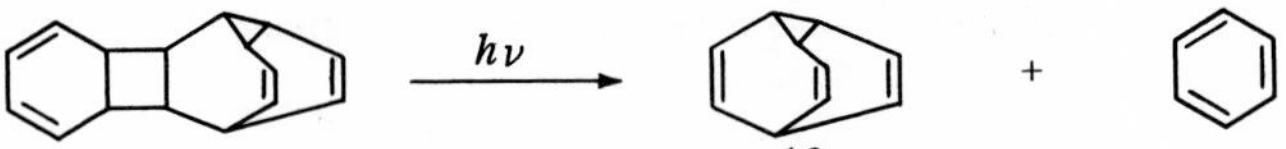

(9-41)

9-2. PHOTOCHEMICAL REARRANGEMENTS AND RELATED REACTIONS

Photochemical rearrangements (sometimes followed by the elimination of a molecule or group) are fairly common occurrences.   Often the same, or a similar reaction occurs thermally, perhaps implying that "hot ground states" are involved.

Photochemical Formation of Phenanthrenes [31]

For example, irradiation of *cis*-stilbene vapor at 170° yields *trans*-stilbene, phenanthrene, and hydrogen as the major products:[30]

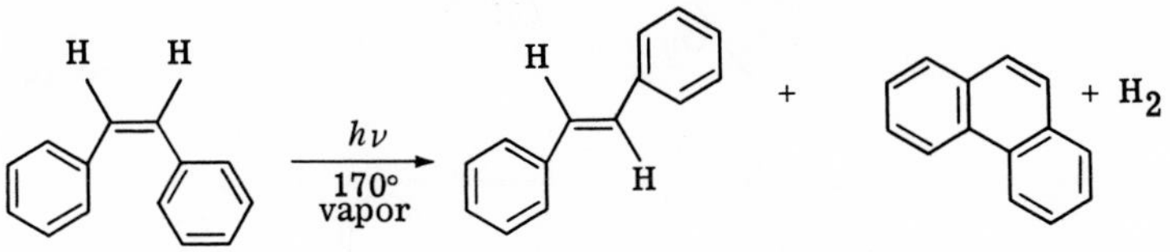

(9-42)

The same products are produced in the pyrolysis of *cis*-stilbene at 550°. The photoreaction is not quenched by oxygen or nitric oxide, indicating that radicals of significant lifetime are not present, and suggesting a one-step simultaneous closure-hydrogen elimination from an excited state or "hot" ground state of cis-stilbene.

In contrast, in solution, oxygen or some other oxidizing agent is *necessary* for reaction to occur.[31, 32] The intermediate dihydrophenanthrene (see Eq. 9-43) has been detected by its ultraviolet absorption spectrum and apparently plays a critical role in phenanthrene formation. The sensitized isomerization of cis- and trans-stilbene is uncomplicated by phenanthrene formation. Indeed, the isomerization is strongly *quenched* by the presence of oxygen, whereas phenanthrene formation is strongly quenched by the *absence* of oxygen. Since the sensitized reaction proceeds via the triplet state, dihydrophenanthrene formation must occur via a singlet state. In agreement with this conclusion is the fact that acetyl and nitro cis-stilbenes (which should form triplets in good yield), *do not* form phenanthrenes, although many other substituted stilbenes do. It is not gratifying, however, that *p*-bromo-cis-stilbene does go. If trans-stilbene is irradiated alone under conditions where the cis-stilbene formed does not absorb, no phenanthrene is formed.

The evidence then suggests the following mechanism for phenanthrene formation:

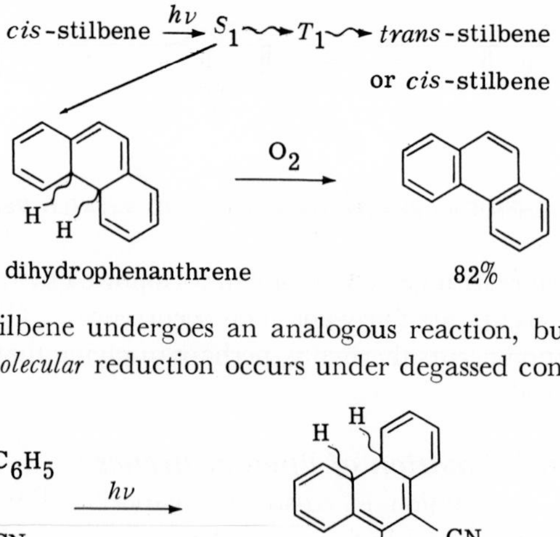

(9-43)

1,2-Dicyanostilbene undergoes an analogous reaction, but in addition a *formally intramolecular* reduction occurs under degassed conditions.[33]

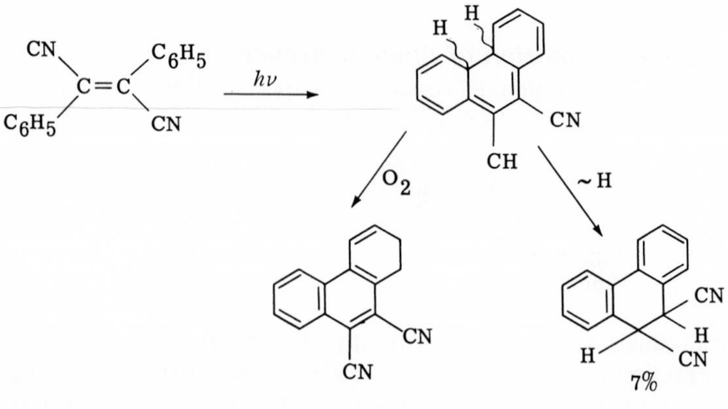

(9-44)

Photochemical Conversion of N-Methyl Diphenylamine to N-Methyl Carbazole

A similar oxidative cyclization reaction occurs with diphenyl-amine:[34, 35]

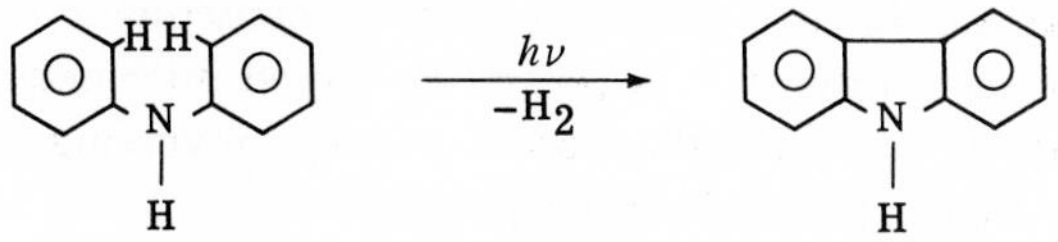

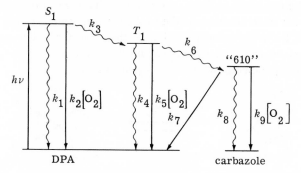

$$(9\text{-}45)$$

A transient having an absorption maximum at 610 mμ has been detected in this reaction by flash photolysis. Furthermore, two concurrent paths exist for conversion of this intermediate to carbazole, one involving oxygen, the other not. In hexane at room temperature, ϕ_C, the quantum yield of carbazole formation as function of oxygen concentration passes through a maximum.

At 60° a triplet transient is formed which leads to formation of the 610 mμ transient, and the disappearance of "610" and formation of carbazole occur at the same rate. The maximum in the ϕ_C vs $\lceil O_2 \rceil$ profile may result from competing oxygen quenching of the triplet and oxygen-dependent conversion of 610 to carbazole.[34]

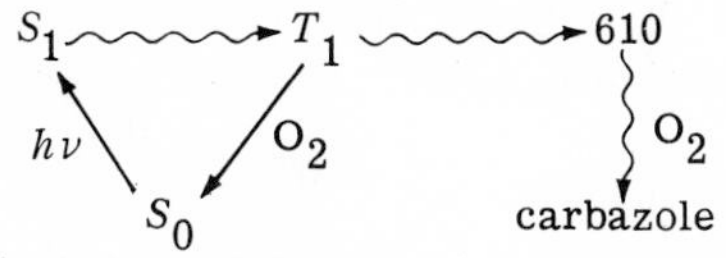

For temperatures down to $-70°$, 610 converts to S_0 by a first-order process with $\Delta E \sim 10$ kcal. Below $-70°$, 610 decay becomes *independent of temperature and carbazole is formed irreversibly.* The following scheme attempts to explain these results:

A maximum in ϕ_C also occurs as the temperature is lowered. At room temperature the yield of 610 is high in degassed solutions (i.e., k_6 is fast) but k_7 is fast and ϕ_C is low. As the temperature is lowered a strong decrease in k_7 ($E_a \sim 10$ kcal) occurs, the temperature-independent step, k_8, predominates, and ϕ_C rises. At still lower temperature k_6 slows down, the yield of 610 decreases, and a final decrease in ϕ_C is noted.

The nature of the 610 transient and its consequent conversion to carbazole is of some interest. A polar ring-closed intermediate has been suggested, and a "tunnelling" process perhaps involving simultaneous elimination of hydrogen has been proposed.

Photochemical Fries Rearrangements

Irradiation of phenylferrocene carboxylate leads to the formation of (p-hydroxyphenyl)-ferrocenyl ketone only.[37]

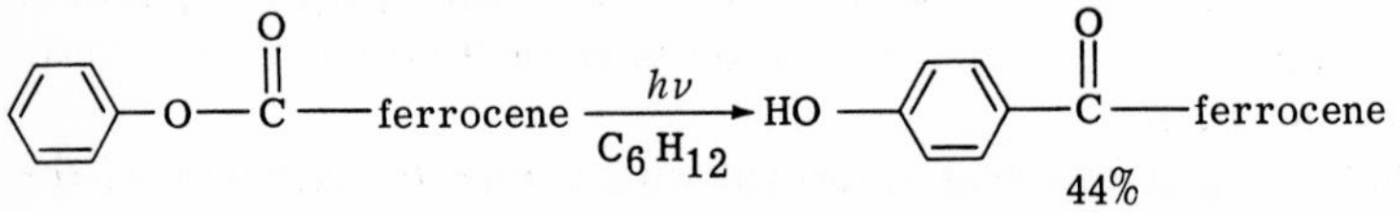

$$\text{(9-46)}$$

In contrast, phenyl benzoate yields both 2- and 4-hydroxylbenzophenones upon photolysis.

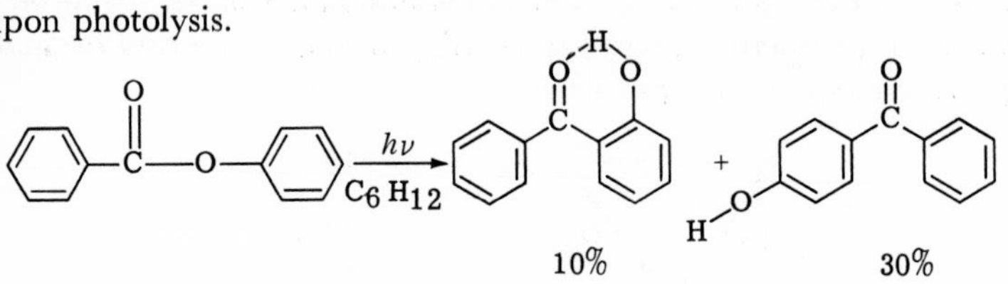

$$\text{(9-47)}$$

Little work has been done on the mechanism of such rearrangements, other than to study the effect of substituents on the course of reaction.

cis-trans Interconversions

Irradiation of the 2,3-dimethyl-spiro-(cyclopropane-1,9-fluorene) leads to their cis-trans interconversion.[39] This reaction is of interest because the bond which must be broken before isomerization can occur is remote from the excited portion of the molecule. The energy from absorption by the biphenyl system must "migrate" in some fashion to the cyclopropane ring, which then breaks open.

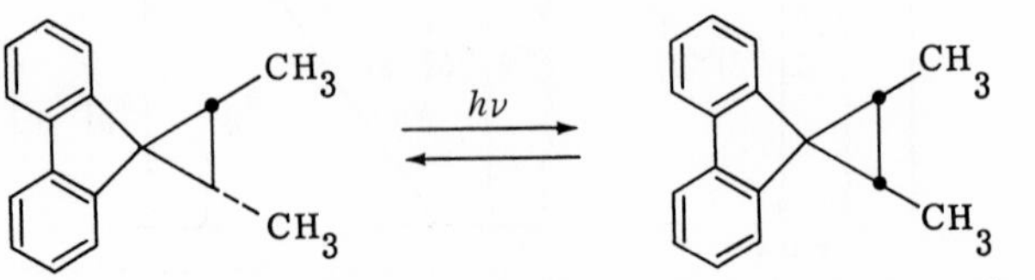

$$\text{(9-48)}$$

Both cis- and trans-dibenzoyl cyclopropane are similarly interconverted when they are irradiated.[40] A different course is followed, however, in hydrogen-donating solvents in the presence of a photosensitizer. Irradiation of an isopropanol solution of *trans*-dibenzoylcyclopropane in the presence of benzophenone leads to the production of 1,3-dibenzoylpropane, probably by the following mechanism:

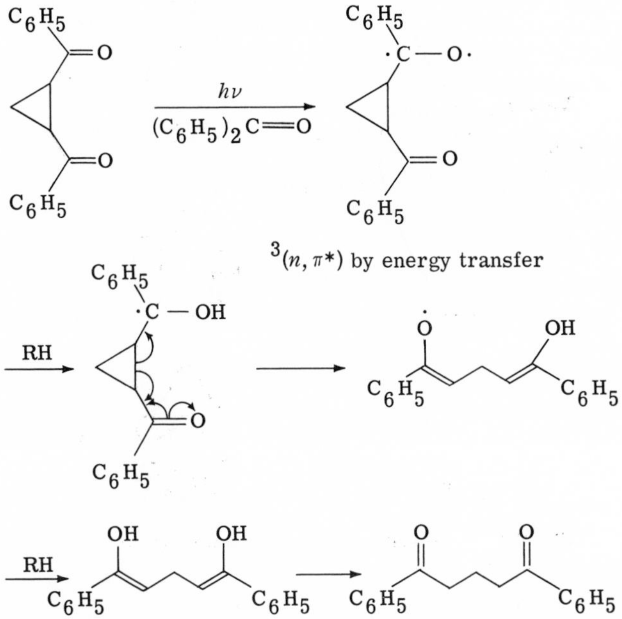

$$^3(n, \pi*) \text{ by energy transfer} \tag{9-49}$$

Photochemical Solvolysis [41]

As we have seen, π,π^* excitation causes an electron to be promoted from a π orbital of the S_0 state to a higher energy π^* orbital of the same π system. These two orbitals will in general occupy more of the same region of space than is the case of n and π^* orbitals. The electronic distribution is more delocalized than in the case of n,π^* excitation. An attempt to gain some insight into the expected reactivity of states of simple aromatic molecules has been made by simply investigating the elementary MO description of such states.[41] In particular an attempt to correlate the solvolysis behavior of disubstituted benzenes, in which there is a single electron-withdrawing or electron-releasing group, with the photochemically induced solvolysis of related compounds has been made.

What has been done is simply to construct the benzyl molecular orbitals and then notice the expected electronic distribution in the excited states derived from the six (carbonium ion) and eight (carbanion) electron species. The form of these orbitals is given below in Fig. 9-1.

It is then noted that substitution of the benzyl $C_7^{(+)}$ carbon by

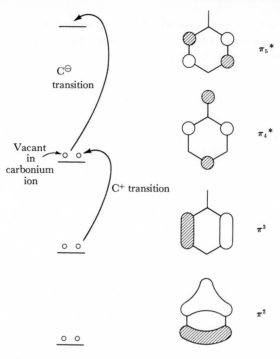

Fig. 9-1   *Molecular orbitals of the benzylic system.*

$-NO_2$ or the $C_7^{(-)}$ carbon by $-O-CH_3$ leads to the same qualitative conclusions for the electronic distribution of the π orbitals.

In order to predict the effect of excitation in the carbonium ion (or $-NO_2$) systems, we simply note the change produced upon excitation of an electron from the π_3 to the π_4^* orbital, and compare the resulting

$$(\pi_3)^2 (\pi_4)^0 \xrightarrow{\ h\nu\ } (\pi_3)^1 (\pi_4)^1$$

distribution with that for the ground state. In this case the S_0 state possesses six π electrons occupying π_1, π_2, and π_3, so that π,π^* excitation promotes an electron from π_3 to π_4^*. This causes an electron with density on the *ortho* and *meta* positions to be placed in an orbital which has density on the *ortho* and *para* but *not* the *meta* position. We thus expect *diminution* of electron density on the *meta* position upon π,π^* excitation.

In the case of the aromatic ring with a $-CH_2^-$ (or $-O-CH_3$) substituent, there are eight π electrons which occupy in pairs the π_1, π_2, π_3, and π_4 orbitals. Here promotion of an electron from π_4 to π_5^* occurs upon π,π^* excitation. The excitation removes an electron from π_4 which

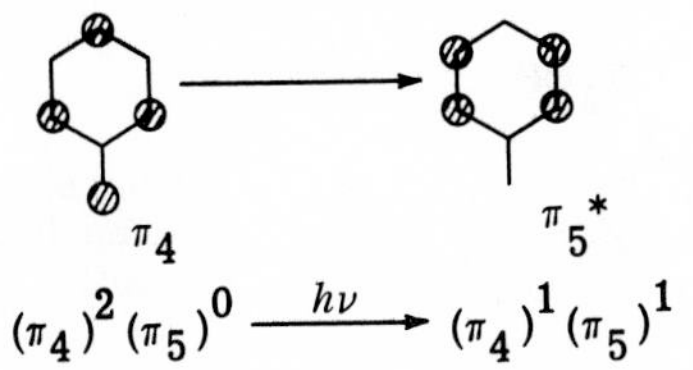

$$(\pi_4)^2 (\pi_5)^0 \xrightarrow{\ h\nu\ } (\pi_4)^1 (\pi_5)^1$$

has no electronic density on the *meta* positions into π_5^* which has *ortho* and *meta* but *no para* electron density. We therefore expect π,π^* excitation to lead to *enhanced meta* electron density.

It has been proposed that, for purposes of predicting reactivity, the following crude valence bond structures may be convenient:

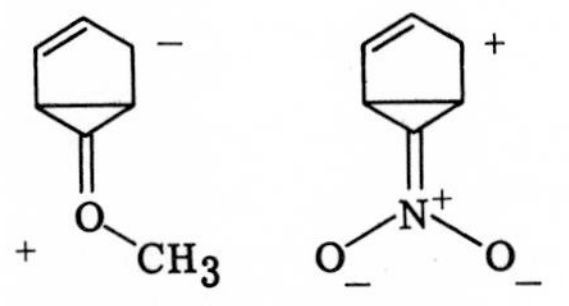

At this point it should be pointed out that the case of nitro substitution may lead to a lowest n,π^* state which would vitiate the basis of these calculations which were made for π,π^* states only!

Several examples which seem to be experimental verification of the qualitative correctness of these calculations have been found.[41]

An electron-donating substituent is expected to enhance reactivity towards electrophilic substitution at the *meta* position in the excited state and the *para* position in the ground state. The photolyses of 3-methoxybenzyl acetate and 4-methoxybenzyl acetates in aqueous dioxane are given below in Eq. 9-50.

One must be careful to consider an alternative possibility when interpreting these solvolysis reactions: the difference in *para* vs. *meta* reactivity *may simply reflect a shorter lifetime of the para isomer.*

There is no observable dark reaction under the conditions of the photolysis. Although the irradiation of 4-methoxybenzylacetate gave mainly free radical products, indicating a homolytic rather than heterolytic cleavage, 3-methoxy- and 3,5-dimethoxybenzyl acetate gave greater amounts of solvolysis products than free radical products.

The solvolytic reaction is formulated as follows:

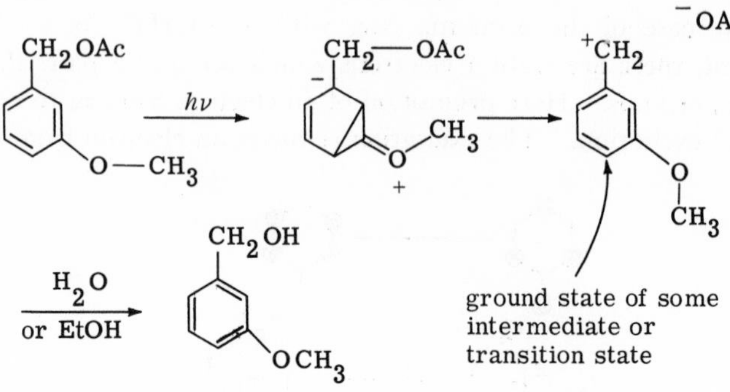

$$(9\text{-}50)$$

The argument is made that the excited state corresponding to

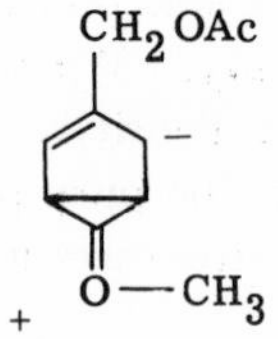

does not enhance heterolytic cleavage and a familiar photoreaction, homolytic fission, predominates.

Experimentally, evidence for selective *meta* withdrawal in the excited states of benzene compounds with nitro and cyano substituents has been found. For example, although *meta*-nitrophenyl trityl ether is unreactive in the dark in 90% aqueous dioxane, and the *para* isomer solvolyses smoothly, under irradiation the *rate* of solvolysis of the *meta* compound is greater than that of the *para* compound, the latter rate being scarcely enhanced from the dark rate.

This solvolysis is formulated as follows:

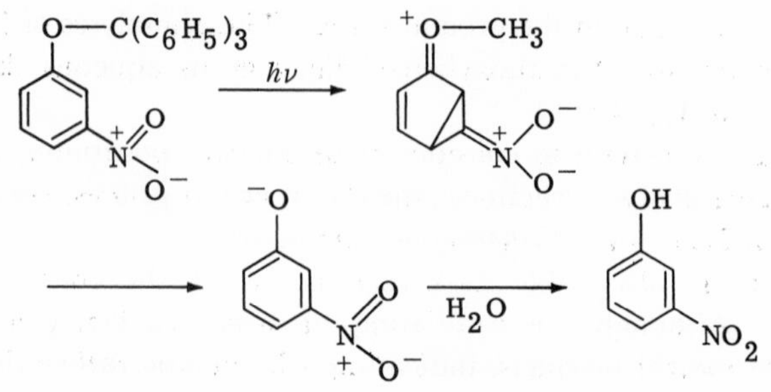

$$(9\text{-}51)$$

In contrast, the electronic distribution of the excited state of the *para* isomer is unfavorable for heterolytic fission.

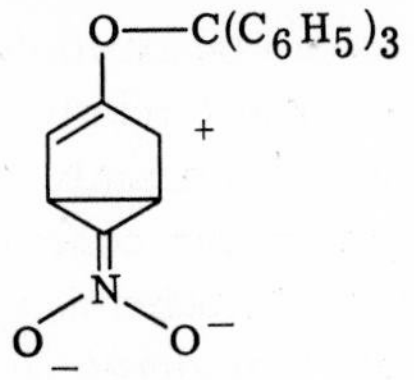

An example of a photo-induced aromatic substitution which may apparently have pertinence to the discussion above is the following reaction:[42]

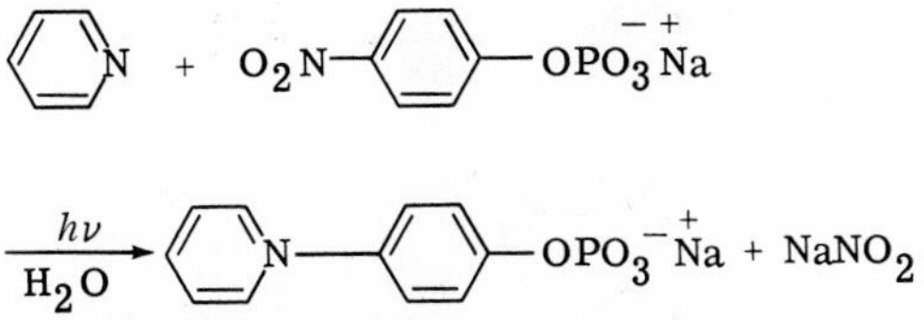

$$(9\text{-}52)$$

The Barton and Related Reactions [44]

An important photoisomerization of nitrite esters (called the Barton reaction) has recently been developed for the selective introduction of functionality at certain saturated centers,[44] as is shown in Eq. 9-53:

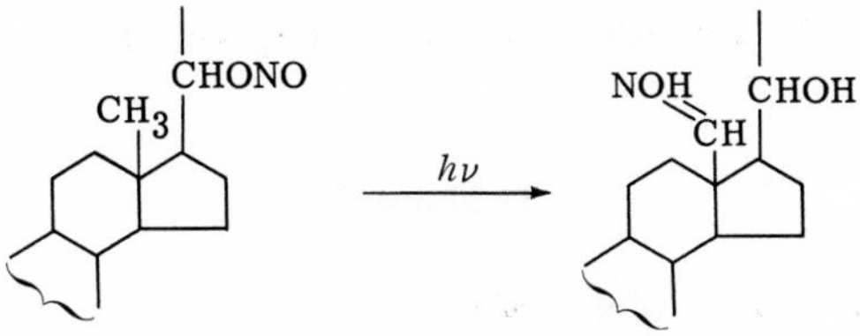

$$(9\text{-}53)$$

The mechanism of such reactions is believed to involve the following steps:

1. homolysis of the nitrite;
2. internal hydrogen abstraction by an alkoxy radical;
3. radical coupling;
4. isomerization of a nitroso compound to an oxime.[43]

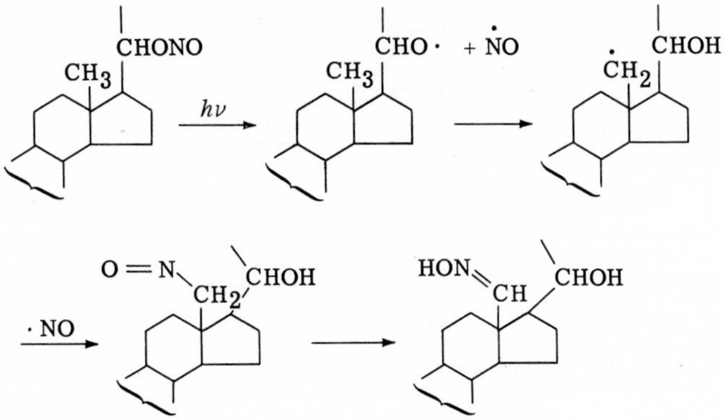

$$(9\text{-}54)$$

Although Barton reactions can be attributed to known transformations of alkoxy radicals, in certain cases relatively minor variations in the nature of a remote group may significantly alter the course of the reaction.[45]   It is not known whether the control of such reactions rests in the radical chemistry or in the photochemistry.

Hypophalites [44] and azides [44] undergo similar transformations when they are irradiated.

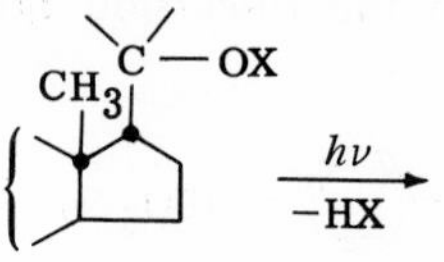

$$\text{(9-55)}$$

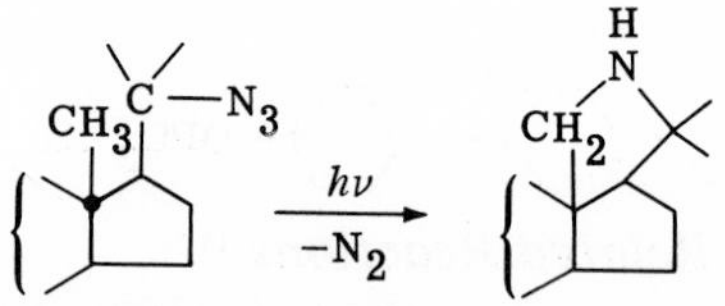

$$\text{(9-56)}$$

A nitrene intermediate is probably involved in the azide photolysis. Like carbenes, nitrenes should have low-lying excited singlet or triplet states.   A great deal of work remains to be done before the nature of the excited states and intermediates involved in these reactions will be known.

PROBLEMS*

1. Predict the products of the following reactions:

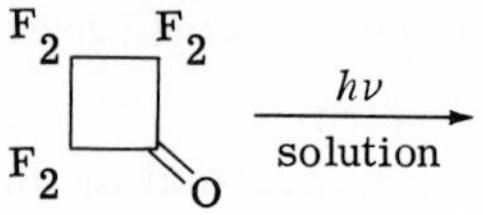

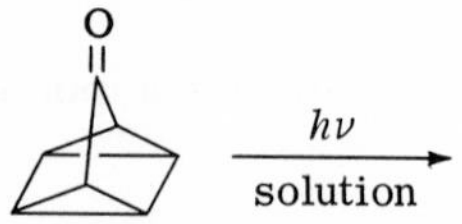

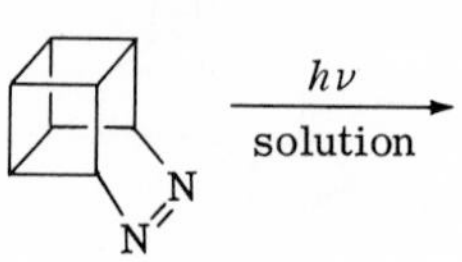

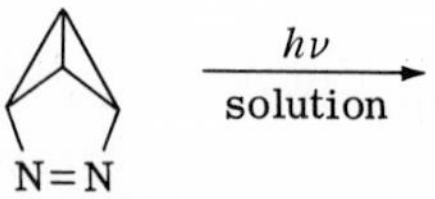

* See Addendum for additional problems.

2. Propose a detailed mechanism for the following reaction. Support your reasoning with known facts.

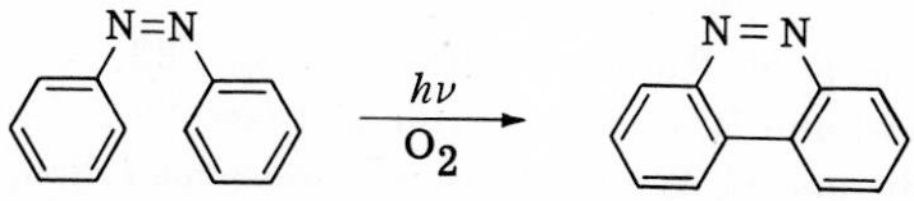

3. Do you expect the following reaction to occur in a hot ground state?

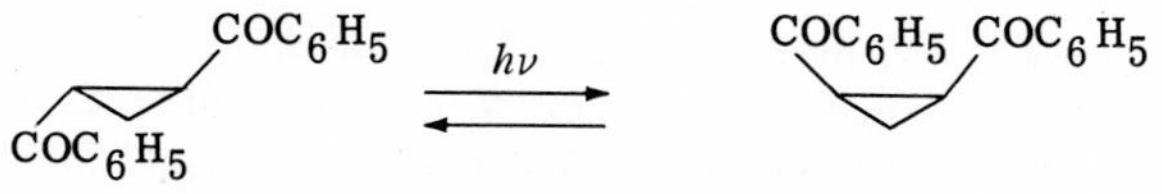

How would you test for the active site of reaction?

4. Which of the following solvolyses do you expect to be accelerated by irradiation?

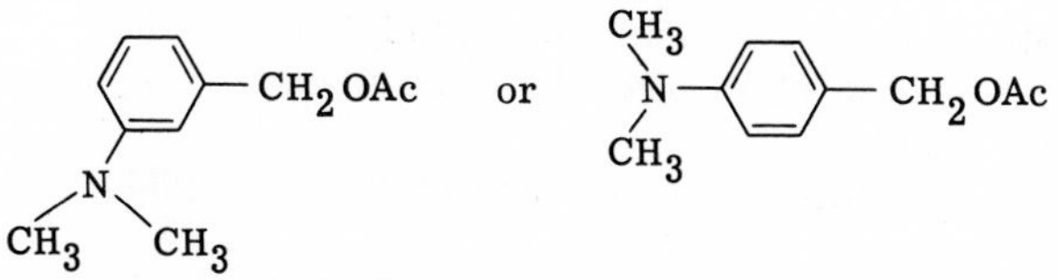

5. Benzophenone *sensitizes* the following reaction:

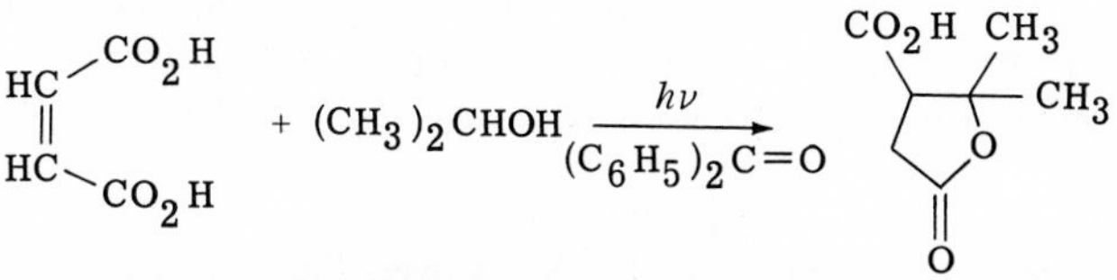

Propose a mechanism for this reaction.

6. In reference 6-40 the following relative rate data are presented for the rates of quenching of cyclobutanone formation from 2,7-dimethyl-4,5-octanedione.

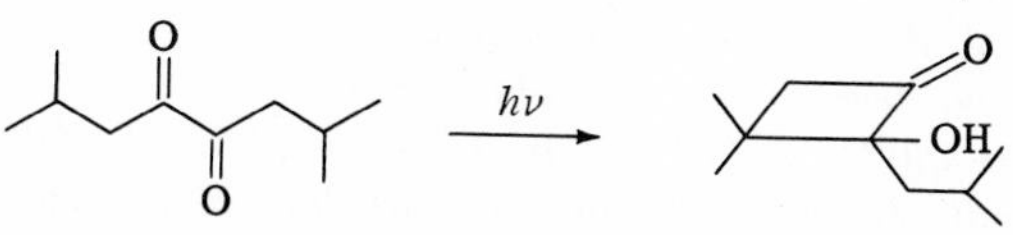

Rate ratios: control (no quencher), 1.0; with added naphthalene, 0.88; with added oxygen, 0.62; with added anthracene, 0.41. What conclusions can you make concerning the excited states involved in cyclobutanone formation? Explain.

REFERENCES*

1. C. R. Masson, V. Boekelheide, and W. A. Noyes, Jr., in *Technique of Organic Chemistry*, ed. A. Weissberger (Vol. II, New York: Interscience, 1956), p. 257.

* See Addendum for additional references.

2. R. Srinivasan, in *Advances in Photochemistry*, ed. W. A. Noyes, Jr., G. S. Hammond, and J. N. Pitts, Jr. (Vol. I, New York: Wiley, 1963), p. 83.
3. J. N. Pitts, Jr., *J. Chem. Ed.*, **34**, 112 (1957).
4. P. Ausloos and R. E. Robert, *J. Am. Chem. Soc.*, **83**, 4897 (1961).
5. C. H. Bamford and R. G. W. Norrish, *J. Chem. Soc.*, 1544 (1938).
6. C. D. Gutsche and C. W. Armbruster, *Tetrahedron Letters*, 1297 (1962).
7. G. Quinkert, *et al.*, *Angew Chem.*, **74**, 507 (1962); *Tetrahedron Letters*, 1863 (1963).
8. N. J. Turro, G. W. Byers, and P. A. Leermakers, *J. Am. Chem. Soc.*, **86**, 955 (1964); P. A. Leermakers, G. Vesley, N. J. Turro, and D. C. Neckers, *J. Am. Chem. Soc.*, **86**, 4213 (1964); R. C. Cookson, M. J. Nye, and G. Subrahmanyan, *Proc. Chem. Soc.*, 144 (1964); H. G. Richey, Jr., J. M. Richey, and D. C. Clogett, *J. Am. Chem. Soc.*, **86**, 3906 (1964).
9. W. Kirmse, *Angew. Chem.*, **71**, 537 (1959); **73**, 161 (1961).
10. A. D. Walsh, *J. Chem. Soc.*, 2260 (1953).
11. G. Herzberg and J. Shoosmith, *Nature*, **183**, 1801 (1959).
12. P. S. Skell and R. C. Woodworth, *J. Am. Chem. Soc.*, **78**, 4496 (1956); *ibid.*, **82**, 3217 (1960).
13. F. L. Duncan and R. J. Cvetanovic, *ibid.*, **84**, 3593 (1962).
14. F. A. L. Anet, *et al.*, *ibid.*, **82**, 3217 (1960).
15. K. R. Kopecky, G. S. Hammond, and P. A. Leermakers, *ibid.*, **84**, 1015 (1962).
16. J. R. Fox and G. S. Hammond, *J. Am. Chem. Soc.*, **86**, 4031 (1964); **86**, 1918 (1964); P. Smith, J. E. Sheafs, and P. E. Miller, *J. Org. Chem.*, **27**, 4053 (1962).
17. G. Zimmerman, L.-Y. Chow, and U.-J. Paik, *J. Am. Chem. Soc.*, **80**, 3528 (1958).
18. R. Moriarty, *J. Org. Chem.*, **28**, 2385 (1963).
19. M. Schwarz, Abs. Meeting, A.C.S., Denver, 1963, p. 34C.
20. C. Steel, *et al.*, *J. Am. Chem. Soc.*, **86**, 679 (1964); *J. Phys. Chem.*, **67**, 1779 (1963).
21. R. Anet and F. A. L. Anet, *J. Am. Chem. Soc.*, **86**, 525 (1964); G. L. Closs and W. Boll, *Angew. Chem.*, **75**, 64 (1963).
22. F. G. Willey, *Angew. Chem.*, **76**, 144 (1964).
23. G. L. Closs and W. A. Boll, *J. Am. Chem. Soc.*, **85**, 3905 (1963).
24. For a recent review see the following articles and references therein: C. G. Overberger and J. P. Anselme, *J. Am. Chem. Soc.*, **86**, 658 (1964); W. M. Jones and W.-T. Tai, *J. Org. Chem.*, **27**, 1030 (1962); C. G. Overberger and J. P. Anselme, *J. Am. Chem. Soc.*, **84**, 869 (1962).
25. V. von Auken and K. L. Rinehart, *J. Am. Chem. Soc.*, **84**, 3736 (1962).
26. D. I. Schuster, M. Axelrod, and J. Auerbach, *Tetrahedron Letters*, 1911 (1963).
27. W. H. Urri and D. J. Tucker, *ibid.*, 609 (1962).
28. W. von E. Doering and W. R. Roth, *Angew. Chem.*, **2** (Eng. ed.) 115 (1963).
29. G. Schroder, *Angew. Chem.*, **75**, 722 (1963); *Angew. Chem.*, **75**, 91 (1963).
30. R. Srinivasan and J. C. Powers, *J. Chem. Phys.*, **39**, 580 (1963).
31. F. R. Mallory, C. S. Wood, and J. T. Gordon, *J. Am. Chem. Soc.*, **86**, 3094 (1964); W. M. Moore, D. D. Morgan, and F. R. Stermitz, *ibid.*, **85**, 829 (1963).

32. For the analogous reaction of azo compounds see G. M. Badger, R. J. Drewer, and G. E. Lewis, *Australian J. Chem.*, **16,** 1042 (1963).

33. M. V. Sargent and C. J. Thomas, *J. Am. Chem. Soc.*, **85,** 2186 (1963).

34. H. Linschitz and K. H. Grellman, *ibid.*, **86,** 303 (1964).

35. E. J. Bowen and J. H. D. Eland, *Proc. Chem. Soc.*, 202 (1963).

36. M. Feldkimela and Y. Mazur, *Tetrahedron Letters*, 369 (1963).

37. R. A. Finnegan and A. W. Hagen, *ibid.*, 365 (1963).

38. D. Elad, *ibid.*, 873 (1963).

39. W. von E. Doering and N. Jones, *ibid.*, 791 (1963).

40. G. W. Griffin and E. J. O'Connell, *J. Am. Chem. Soc.*, **85,** 1001 (1963).

41. H. E. Zimmerman and V. R. Sandel, *ibid.*, **85,** 915 (1963); **86,** 922 (1963); E. Havinga, R. O. deJongh, and W. Dorst, *Rec. Trav. Chim.*, **75,** 378 (1956).

42. R. L. Letsinger and O. B. Ramsay, *J. Am. Chem. Soc.*, **86,** 1147 (1964).

43. M. Akhtar and M. M. Pecket, *J. Am. Chem. Soc.*, **86,** 268 (1964).

44. M. Akhtar, in *Advances in Photochemistry*, ed. W. A. Noyes, Jr., G. S. Hammond, and J. N. Pitts, Jr. (Vol. II, New York: Interscience, 1964).

45. D. H. R. Barton and J. M. Beaton, *J. Am. Chem. Soc.*, **83,** 750 (1961); *ibid.*, **84,** 1496 (1962).

chapter
ten

Miscellaneous
Topics

10-1. PHOTOCHEMICAL TECHNIQUES

The technique of photochemistry differs from ordinary chemical technique in that the prime reactant, light, must be added somehow to the system, which itself is usually contained in a glass vessel. The source of light may be the sun or a lamp of some type.

General Considerations

Since our major concern is the absorption of light by a particular reactant, we must know the absorption spectrum of the glass vessel, the solvent, all of the reactants (and intermediates, if any), and the products. The latter may become the predominately absorbing species in certain cases unless care is taken. Furthermore, an intense absorption by a reactant is of little use in a photoreaction if the lamp employed does not emit in the region of absorption. Mercury lamps of varying pressure, which are frequently employed for photoreactions, vary in their ability to produce light at different wavelengths.

Generation of Light and Absorption by the System [1–4]

Photoreactions can proceed only if the system in question absorbs light. Yet it is remarkable how researchers occasionally ignore this fact and fail to consider three very important factors controlling the rate of photoreactions: the absorption spectrum of the system, the transparency of the reaction cell, and the emission spectrum of the source.

A system which has negligible absorption above 3,000 Å will not undergo a photoreaction at a significant rate when irradiated in a pyrex cell by sunlight. The reasons for this slow rate should be clear: The

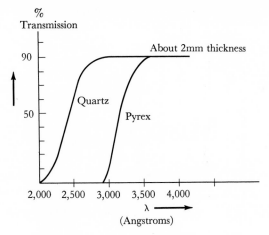

Fig. 10-1   *Transmission of pyrex and quartz.*

effective emission of the sun is at wavelengths greater than 3,000 Å, and neither the absorption spectrum of the system nor the optical properties of the reaction vessel are suited for photoreaction in this particular case. Pyrex transmits only a tiny fraction of any light with a wavelength shorter than 3,000 Å.   In order to give this particular system a decent opportunity for photoreaction, we would have to employ a quartz vessel for reaction since this material transmits light down to about 2,000 Å. Although quartz and pyrex vessels are both widely employed for the running of photoreactions, we see that they are by no means interchangeable.[2, 3]   Figure 10-1 shows the transmission properties of pyrex and quartz.   Simple schematics of two typical photochemical systems are shown in Figs. 10-2 and 10-3.

Before the discovery of lasers, monochromatic light of intensities greater than 10^{16} to 10^{17} photons per second was virtually impossible to obtain.   Lasers have not achieved popularity to date as photochemical sources because of the fact that most of the intense lasers do not emit

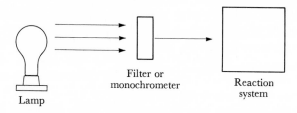

Fig. 10-2   *Schematic of a simple photolysis system.*

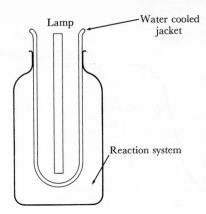

Fig. 10-3   *Diagram of a preparative scale photolysis system.*

below 7,000 Å.   When this limitation is removed and high intensity lasers are available in the visible and ultraviolet, we can expect them to see more widespread use, especially for mechanistic studies.

The attainment of monochromatic light is usually achieved by placing either a filter (or series of filters) or a monochromator between the source and the reaction cell.   The monochromaticity of the emerging beam is increased only at the sacrifice of intensity, so that a compromise is usually required.   It is often convenient to employ a mercury arc for ultraviolet work since the lines of the mercury-emission spectrum are somewhat separated, and the isolation of a particular line from a group of neighboring lines may be possible.[4]   The relative intensities of the lines from a 200 watt high-pressure mercury lamp are shown in Fig. 10-4.

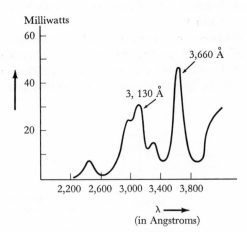

Fig. 10-4   *Relative intensities of the lines from a 200 watt mercury lamp.*

If the system is appropriate, the problem of monochromaticity can be overcome by choosing a lamp which gives a very high intensity for one particular line, with the complete exclusion of others, as for example the 2,537 Å mercury line. This is achieved in the latter case by employing a low pressure of mercury so that "resonance radiation" is the main source of emission. Thus, mercury is excited by an electrical discharge of some sort to a state corresponding to absorption of 2,537 Å radiation. In the absence of collisions, this state persists briefly and then emits a photon of 2,537 Å light and returns to the ground states. As the pressure of mercury increases in these lamps, this emission line gets weaker due to the strong absorption of mercury at this wavelength, and new broad lines characteristic of emission from lower excited states of mercury appear, as is shown in Fig. 10-4.

The choice of the source for a particular photoreaction depends on many factors, and we have already indicated that the most primitive information necessary is the absorption spectrum of the reactants and products, the transmission properties of the reaction vessel, and the emission characteristics of the source.

Control of Light [1, 4]

A number of chemical and glass filters and monochromators are available for the isolation of mercury arc lines. Most of these devices suffer from disadvantages such as relatively broad transmission band width or undesirably low transmittance. The transmission characteristics of some glass filters available commercially from Corning are given in Fig. 10-5. For an intensive list of chemical filters of use for photochemical work the exhaustive work of Pitts and Calvert should be consulted.[1]

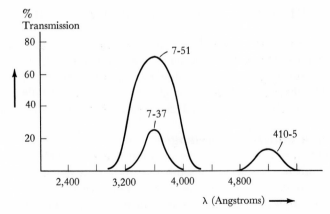

Fig. 10-5 *Typical ultraviolet and visible Corning Glass filters. The numbers above the curve are the catalogue numbers.*

Measurement of Light Intensity [1, 2, 5]

An *actinometer* is a chemical or physical device that measures the total amount of incident radiation. A chemical method has advantages over physical methods of light measurements, but for general use it should have

1. constant quantum efficiency and high absorption over a wide range of wavelengths and intensities;
2. high sensitivity and precision;
3. simplicity of operation;
4. availability of chemical material.

Of the many systems proposed for chemical actinometers, few display all of these features. Perhaps the most promising of the solution chemical actinometers employs potassium ferrioxalate. For the details in establishing an actinometer the reader is referred to the original literature.[5] The ferrioxalate system is usable in the wavelength region from 2,540 to 5,780 Å and is quite sensitive for a chemical actinometer. Its other advantages are

1. a small temperature coefficient for the wavelength region 3,000 to 5,000 Å, which eliminates the need for accurate temperature control between 20 to 30° C;
2. quantum efficiency independent of intensity;
3. quantum efficiency not critically dependent upon the solution composition;
4. high precision;
5. ease of operation.

The stoichiometry of the reaction is

$$\text{Fe(III) } (C_2O_4)_3 \xrightarrow[H_2O]{h\nu} \text{Fe(II) } (C_2O_4)_2 + 2CO_2 + H_2O$$

The quantum yields of Fe(II) formation are near unity, and the product ferrous ion and its oxalate complex do not absorb the incident radiation measurably during photolysis. Following exposure, however, it is made to be highly absorbing by formation of the red-colored 1,10-phenanthrolene-Fe(II) complex, which is analyzed spectrophotometrically.

Selection of Emitting Wavelength

In addition to their use in spectrophotometric work, light sources are used in photochemical work for both the study of reaction mechanisms and for the conduction of preparative scale photoreactions. The choice of a poly- or monochromatic light source will depend on both the chemical nature of the reactants and products and whether a mechanistic or synthetic goal is desired.

For the study of reaction mechanisms a highly monochromatic source of radiation is desirable, if not essential. Absorption coefficients, quantum yields, and products may all depend on wavelength, so that monochromatic radiation is required to avoid the introduction of unknown variables.

In synthetic work polychromatic radiation of high intensity is often employed. It is often profitable, from the standpoint of over-all yield, rather than rate, to have a preliminary knowledge of the absorption spectrum of the reactants and the products, since the latter may themselves undergo photochemical change if they absorb the light emitted by the source. If possible, light absorbed by the products should be filtered out to avoid this complication, since this precaution will increase the net product yield, all other factors being equal.

In order to appreciate the relationship of available intensities to rate of conversion of molecules on a preparative scale, consider a source which delivers 10^{17} quanta sec^{-1} of monochromatic light at a certain wavelength into the reaction vessel. If the reaction under consideration possesses a quantum yield of unity, it would take 6×10^6 seconds or 1,700 hours to obtain one mole of product.

The breakdown of the energy involved may be seen in the following example. At 4,000 Å, 10^{17} quanta per second corresponds to 0.05 watt and at 2,000 Å, to 0.10 watt (see Table 10-1). Suppose a 1,000 watt

Table 10-1   *Relationship between joules, quanta, and wavelength*
(1 watt = J sec^{-1})

	Joules	Quanta ($\times 10^{18}$)
2,000 Å	1	1.0
3,000 Å	1	1.5
4,000 Å	1	2.0
5,000 Å	1	2.5
6,000 Å	1	3.0
7,000 Å	1	3.5

bulb emits 5% in a range of wavelengths of interest, say a 10 Å band. This radiation goes in all directions so that absorption of 1 to 10% of the useable radiation by the system may occur. Thus we achieve $1,000 \times 0.05 \times 0.01 = 0.5$ watts which should supply us with about 10^{17} to 10^{18} photons, depending on the wavelength but at 0.005% efficiency.

Since most of the energy input goes into heating the water which cools the source, and the output from any small band of wavelengths is quite small, for preparative work, it is desirable to surround the light source with a depth of material sufficient to absorb all of the incident radiation.

10-2. LASERS

Equation 3-6 indicates that the intensity of a beam of light diminishes as it passes through an absorbing material. This equation *assumes* that the number of molecules N_2 in the upper state is so small that stimulated emission may be neglected. Under certain conditions, however, stimulated emission can *dominate*, and the light beam may *amplify* as it passes through the material!

Theory of Laser Action [6, 7]

Suppose, for example, we rewrite Eq. 3-6 as

$$I = I_0 \exp (N_2 - N_1)\sigma l \qquad (10\text{-}1)$$

where N_2 is the number of molecules in the *upper* state, N_1 is the number of molecules in the lower state, σ is the absorption coefficient (which here reflects the absorbing molecular cross section), and l is the distance the light beam traverses. If $N_1 >>> N_2$, the emerging light intensity I is smaller than the incident intensity, I_0. Suppose, however, that a method is available to make $N_2 > N_1$—i.e., population inversion occurs. The

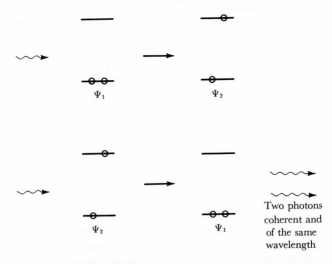

Fig. 10-6   *Stimulated emission of photons. "Stimulated" absorption of a photon (wavy arrow) produces an excited state* Ψ_2, *which may be stimulated to emit a photon, so that in addition to the stimulating photon a second photon of the same wavelength and in phase with the first is produced.*

exponent in Eq. 10-1 is now positive, and the light beam *grows exponentially as it passes through the sample!* The laser is capable of achieving such a condition and thereby releasing a sensational avalanche of photons!

Let us consider the basis of laser action in some detail. We have discussed the fact that an electronically excited state Ψ_2 is unstable and may emit a photon $h\nu$ by *spontaneous emission* and thereby return to the ground state. If an emitted photon of energy $h\nu$ happens to fall on a molecule of the same system which is still in the excited state Ψ_2, the excited molecule may be *stimulated* to emit a photon of energy $h\nu$, which is additional to the one which triggered its emission (see Fig. 10-6). The photon produced by *stimulated emission* has the important property of being completely in phase with the photon which stimulated it. The latter property is called *coherence*, the condition in which a precise correlation exists between the phases of monochromatic light at two points in a given light wave—i.e., the phase of the light wave is predictable with time.

Normally we expect that the greater the intensity of light absorbed by a system to, say, S_1, the greater the number of molecules promoted to an excited state. This process is in fact limited by two factors:

1. S_1 will spontaneously emit to the ground state after a short period of time;
2. S_1 will be stimulated to emit to S_0 by interaction with incident photons.

As a result, no matter how great the intensity populating S_1, no more than 50% of the molecules can be forced into S_1, because incident photons are just as likely to stimulate S_1 to S_0 as they are to be absorbed and cause excitation of S_0 to S_1. *Population inversion* cannot occur unless another state (say T_1) exists to which S_1 may convert radiationlessly. Since the lifetime of T_1 is many powers of ten longer than S_1 in general, consider what will happen when intense flux of photons of energy $h\nu_1$, is absorbed by the molecule: A large portion of molecules will be excited to S_1 and many will then convert to T_1, but since photons of energy $h\nu_1$, are not capable of stimulating emission from T_1 the population of the latter state may be greater than 50%—i.e., *population inversion may occur in* T_1. Now if photons of energy $h\nu_2$ are incident on the system where the population T_1 is inverted with respect to S_0, stimulated emission will occur, and the number of photons of energy $h\nu_2$ leaving the system will exceed the number entering it.

We see that the critical requirements of laser action for this system are (1) provision of a photon flux of energy $h\nu_2$ and (2) methods of amplification to build up the emitted flux to high values. The first condition may be provided by the molecule itself if it emits a photon of energy $h\nu_2$,

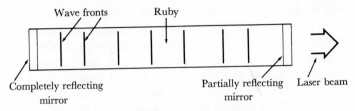

Wave fronts   Ruby

Completely reflecting   Partially reflecting   Laser beam
mirror   mirror

Fig. 10-7   *Schematic of an optical cavity for ruby laser.*

and the second condition is met by fashioning the medium containing the lasing material out of a cell capable of reflecting photons back and forth efficiently—i.e., an optical cavity (see Fig. 10-7).

In practice, only certain atoms have been found to lase efficiently. The first material to exhibit laser action was ruby, a crystal of aluminum oxide containing less than one percent of chromium oxide.

The energy level for ruby is given in Fig. 10-8. The absorption spectrum for excitation of the S_1 state for ruby is quite broad in the region of 5,500 Å, and allows for efficient "pumping" by an intense source. The radiative lifetime of this state is very short, less than 10^{-6} sec, while the lower-lying (doublet) state has a radiative lifetime of about 10^{-3} sec, and laser emission from this state occurs at 6,943 Å.

Photochemical Applications of Lasers

To date the laser's position in photochemistry resembles that of a solution for which there is no problem. A broad spectrum of laser emissions are now known, although the intensities of these sources are relatively feeble at wavelengths shorter than 6,000 Å. The most remarkable property of lasers—coherence and extreme monochromaticity—has not yet been exploited by photochemists, who seem more intrigued by the

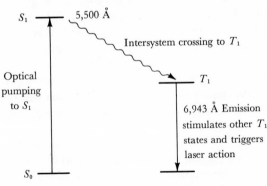

S_1 ———— 5,500 Å

Intersystem crossing to T_1

Optical
pumping
to S_1 T_1

6,943 Å Emission
stimulates other T_1
states and triggers
laser action

S_0 ————

Fig. 10-8   *Energy-level diagram of ruby.*

potential of lasers as high intensity sources. Presumably, a series of intense lasers spanning the region of photochemical interest will be developed, and a powerful tool would be added to the armament of the photochemist.

For example, triplet states might be excited *directly* by taking advantage of the sharp, intense laser beam. Problems of competitive absorption might be solved if one compound possesses a narrow "window" in its absorption spectrum, while a second (to be irradiated selectively) absorbs the laser beam at this frequency. *Infra-red* photochemistry may become possible if an absorption to $j = 3, 4, 5$, etc. of the *ground state* can be saturated by a laser beam. The laser will probably become an important member of the sources used to initiate photochemical reactions.

An especially intriguing laser is that produced by semiconductors. There lasers operate by the (electrical) excitation of an electron into the conduction band of the semiconductor. The electron then recombines with a positive "hole" and emits its excitation as light. In practice, a junction is made of semiconducting material, on one side of which electrons are produced and on the other side of which positive holes are produced. An applied voltage draws the electrons and holes into the junction region where they meet and are stimulated to emit recombination radiation. The exciting feature of the semiconductor laser is its economy (nearly 100% efficiency for the conversion of electricity into light!) and the possibility of varying the wavelengths of laser emission by changing temperature and other experimental conditions.

A very interesting spectroscopic phenomenon [7] has been observed by employing a ruby laser (6,943 Å) to excite naphthalene *at wavelengths where the hydrocarbon does not absorb!* The excitation is a two-photon (simultaneous) absorption producing the naphthalene singlet state at 2,900 Å! The two-photon absorption process is a result of the very intense monochromatic nature of the laser beam. A related potential of lasers is the formation of sufficient steady-state concentrations of excited triplets so that triplet-triplet or triplet-singlet reactions may be possible. It will be interesting to watch the promises of the laser fructify and amplify.

The Ruby Laser

As an example of the specifications of a laser, let us consider the ruby laser. Suppose the ruby laser is "pumped" into the condition of population inversion by an intense source of light of total input energy of about 5×10^3 J. A laser "spike" of 2 J of 6,943 Å light will be emitted in about 5×10^{-3} sec. This spike because of its coherence may be concentrated on an area of 0.1 mm^2. If the mean power of this beam is about 0.4 kW (2 J/5 $\times 10^{-3}$ sec), then the *intensity* of the beam is 0.4 kW/0.1 mm^2 = 4×10^3 kW/cm$^2 \cong 1.5 \times 10^{22}$ photons/sec/cm^2.

The total number of photons is small, of course, because the spike only lasts about 10^{-3} sec. This process may be repeated over and over again, however, to offset this disadvantage.

PROBLEMS

1. Does benzene absorb light more efficiently through pyrex or quartz?

2. If you wanted to photosensitize the dimerization of butadiene (λ_{max} for $S_1 \sim 2,200$ Å) with benzophenone would you use a pyrex or quartz vessel? Would a filter be necessary?

3. A 450 watt medium-pressure Hanovia immersion lamp emits 25.6 watts at 3,660 Å. Assuming a sample absorbs *all* of this light, how long will it take to photolyze one mole of the compound, if the quantum yield for the reaction is 0.1?

4. Show that (for low conversions) the benzophenone-benzhydrol system may be used as an actinometer for which intensity is given by

$$I = \frac{[1 - (P/B)] MNV}{\Phi_B t}$$

where t is the time of irradiation $[1 - (P/B)]$ is the fraction of benzophenone molecules which are reduced (measured spectrophotometrically so that P is the absorbance of the photolyzed solution and B is the absorbance of the blank), M is the benzophenone molarity of the blank solution, N is Avogadro's number, V is the volume in liters of the sample and Φ_B is the quantum yield for photoreduction given by

$$\frac{1}{\Phi_B} = 1 - \frac{k_d}{k_r[BH_2]} = 1 - \frac{0.033}{[BH_2]}$$

5. Choose an appropriate filter from Fig. 10-5 for the sensitization of naphthalene phosphorescence by benzophenone. Assume the lamp, whose emission specifications are given in Figure 10-4, is available for excitation.

6. Would a ruby laser be suitable for excitation of 1. benzophenone (see Fig. 4-2); 2. anthracene (see Fig. 4-1); 3. azulene (see Fig. 4-8); 4. 9,10-dibromoanthracene.

REFERENCES

1. An exhaustive review of this subject can be found in J. Calvert and J. N. Pitts, Jr., *Photochemistry* (New York: Wiley, 1966); see also L. R. Koller, *Ultraviolet Irradiation* (New York: Wiley, 1965).

2. W. A. Noyes, Jr. and P. A. Leighton, *Photochemistry of Gases* (New York: Reinhold, 1941).

3. C. R. Masson, V. Boekelheide, and W. A. Noyes, Jr., in *Technique of Organic Chemistry*, ed. A. Weissberger (Vol. II, New York: Interscience, 1956), p. 257.

4. R. B. Withrow and A. P. Withrow, in *Radiation Biology*, ed. A. Hollander (Vol. III, New York: McGraw-Hill, 1956).

5. C. G. Hatchard and C. A. Parker, *Proc. Royal Soc.*, **A235,** 518 (1956).
6. A. K. Levine, *Am. Sci.*, **51,** 14 (1963); G. Lengyel, *Lasers* (New York: Wiley, 1962).
7. For the possible role of triplets in lasers made of organic molecules see E. V. Shopleskii, *Soviet Phys.*, *Uspekhi*, **5,** 612 (1963); D. J. Morantz, B. G. White, and A. J. C. Wright, *Phys. Rev. Letters*, **8,** 23 (1962); *Proc. Chem. Soc.*, 26 (1962); *J. Chem. Phys.*, **37,** 2041 (1962).

Miscellaneous Topics

Answers

1. This experiment implies that the efficiency of the $S_1 \rightsquigarrow T_1$ process for benzene does not require collisional perturbation in order to occur, or the $S_1 \rightsquigarrow T_1$ process is faster than the time between collisions. (See G. Kistiakowski and C. Parmenter, *Abs. Am. Chem. Soc.* Meeting, 1964, p. 19V.)

    2. 1. See Fig. 3-4.

    2. Absorption occurs from the minimum $(j = 0)$ level of the S_0 potential curve to the steeply rising side of the S_1 curve, in general. Emission occurs from the minimum $(j = 0)$ level of S_1 to the vibration levels of S_0. If Franck-Condon absorption occurs from S_0 to a very steeply rising section of the S_1 potential curve, a large number of vibrational states will be intersected (all of which are allowed by the Franck-Condon principle because only a small change in r_{xy} is involved) and the absorption band will be structureless. On the other hand, Franck-Condon emission from S_1 to S_0 involves a set of rather widely spaced vibrational levels of the latter state (Fig. 3-11) and, if this is so, vibrational structures appear in the emission spectrum.

    3. The *n*-electrons of ketones are solvated in polar solvents. Franck-Condon excitation suddenly tends to reverse or diminish the polarity of the molecule *before* solvent can orient itself. As a result, the energy difference between S_0 and the n,π^* state is greater than it would be in nonpolar solvents where neither stabilization of S_0 or the n,π^* state is important. [See G. J. Brealey and M. Kasha, *J. Am. Chem. Soc.*, **77**, 4462 (1955), A. L. McClellan and G. C. Pimental, *The Hydrogen bond*, W. H. Freeman and Co., N.Y. (1960) p. 158.]

    4. The starting point of absorption and emission are the $j = 0$ levels of S_0 and the excited state, respectively. Therefore, O–O absorption and emission are the exact reverse of one another except for differences in solvation that may occur in each state.

    5. The crossing (isoenergetic) points of potential energy curves are optimum for intramolecular energy transfer from one state to another because no Franck-

Condon restrictions are violated by crossover at these points (see Fig. 4-10 and 4-11).

3. 1. Iodine possesses greater spin-orbital coupling because of its greater nuclear charge (see Eq. 3-26 and the following discussion).

2. Benzophenone should possess greater spin-orbital coupling because of its smaller singlet-triplet energy splitting,' and because its transitions involve a heteroatom.

3. Quinoline should possess stronger spin-orbital coupling because of interaction of the heteroatom with the π system.

4. The large $S_0 - T_1$ energy difference makes "mixing" of these states unlikely (see Eq. 3-26).

CHAPTER FOUR

1. Let

$$
\begin{array}{lll}
 & & \text{rate} \\
S_2 \longrightarrow S_0 + h\nu & & k_f{}^0[S_2] \\
S_2 \rightsquigarrow S_1 + \Delta & & k_{ic}[S_2]
\end{array}
$$

where

$$\Phi_f = \frac{k_f{}^0[S_2]}{I} = \frac{\text{rate of fluorescence}}{\text{rate of absorption to } S_2}$$

For the steady state,

$$\frac{k_{ic}}{k_f{}^0} > 10^4$$

since 0.01 % emission from S_2 could be detected. Upper excited singlets usually have higher inherent fluorescent rates than S_1 so that

$$k_f{}^0 \geq 10^8 \text{ sec}^{-1}$$

or

$$k_{ic} > 10^{12} \text{ sec}^{-1}$$

2. The transition probability for singlet-singlet transition is relatively constant with substitution of fluorine and iodine atoms, but singlet-triplet probability increases 10^4 times for the same substitution.

3. Conventional flash spectrometers are capable of detecting species with half-lives of the order of 10^{-5} sec. Since no benzene absorption is observed, the lifetime of benzene triplets must be less than 10^{-5} sec in fluid solution (unless benzene $T - T$ absorption is very weak or masked by singlet-singlet absorption—both unlikely circumstances).

4. Spin-orbital coupling is greatest for transitions for which the heavy atom involved interacts most strongly with the MO's of the π-electron system. The 9,10-positions of anthracene possess a node in the π orbital (zero interaction of the heavy atom with the π system to a first approximation), while the 2 and 6

positions do not possess nodes in either the π or π^* MO's (finite interaction of the heavy atom with the π system to a first approximation). [See D. S. McClure, *J. Chem. Phys.*, **17**, 905 (1949).]

5. The long wavelength low extinction bands are due to a $n - \pi^*$ transition. The shorter wavelength band is due to $\pi - \pi^*$ excitation. Nonluminescence implies very rapid radiationless processes which degrade $S_1(\tau_f \sim 10^{-6}$ sec) and T_1 so fast that they cannot emit.

6. A typical photolysis flash lasts 10^{-5} sec. Since the $S_2 \rightsquigarrow S_1$ and $S_3 \rightsquigarrow S_1$ processes take about 10^{-12} sec, all upper excited singlet states relax to S_1 long before the spectrometric flash is terminated. Furthermore, all S_1 states pass to T_1 or fluoresce in less than 10^{-6} sec.

7. One possible explanation of these phenomena is that chlorophyll has a lowest $\pi,\pi^*(S_1)$ state in hydroxylic solvents, but that $n,\pi^*(S_1)$ becomes lowest in hydrocarbon solvents. Since molecules with lowest n,π^* states undergo intersystem crossing more efficiently than molecules with lowest π,π^* states, the quenching of fluorescence would result from an enhanced intersystem crossing rate in hydrocarbon solvent. The formation of different molecular aggregates in the two solvents can also explain these results.

8.

	ϕ_p/ϕ_f	Reason
(a)	$\gg 1$	ketone (lowest S_1 is n,π^*)
(b)	<1	unsaturated hydrocarbon
(c)	>1	heteroatom in π system
(d)	>1	heavy atom (not large because atom is not in π system)
(e)	>1	heteroatom in π system
(f)	>1	heavy atom
(g)	~ 1	like benzene
(h)	>1	heavy atom
(i)	<1	simple hydrocarbon

9. From Eq. 4-2 and the values $\epsilon_{max} = 8 \times 10^3$, $\nu = 2.6 \times 10^4$ cm^{-1} $\Delta\nu_{1/2} \cong 1000$ cm^{-1} we have

$$\tau_f = \frac{3.5 \times 10^8}{\nu^2(\epsilon_m)\Delta\nu_{1/2}} = \frac{3.5 \times 10^8}{(2.67 \times 10^4)^2(8 \times 10^3)(10^3)}$$

$$\tau_f = 6.2 \times 10^{-8} \text{ sec}$$

10.

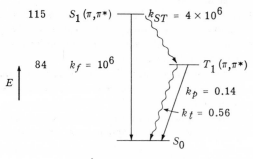

benzene

CHAPTER FIVE

1. In benzene $k_{\mathrm{dif}} = 10^{10}$ liter mole^{-1} sec^{-1}. Let the concentration of triplet biacetyl be $[B^*]$ and the concentration of quencher be $[Q]$. Then

$$- \frac{d[B^*]}{dt} = k_p[B^*] + k_q[B^*][Q]$$

We want to know for what value of $[Q]$ is energy transfer 100 times faster than phosphorescence, i.e.,

$$k_q[Q] = 10^2 k_p \qquad \text{(from Eq. 5-12)}$$

or

$$[Q] = \frac{10^2}{k_q} k_p$$

since $k_q = 10^{10}$ liter mole^{-1} sec^{-1} and $k_p = 10^3$ sec^{-1} we have

$$[Q] = 10^{-8} \times 10^3 = 10^{-5} \text{ mole liter}$$

2. 1. Benzene ($E_T = 85$, $E_S = 115$) will sensitize both phosphorescence and fluorescence of biacetyl ($E_T = 56$, $E_S = 62$).

2. Quinoline ($E_T = 91$, $E_S = 62$) will sensitize both emissions, also.

3. 9,10-Dibromoanthracene ($E_T = 42$ (?), $E_S = 74$) will sensitize fluorescence but not phosphorescence.

4. Fluorenone ($E_T = 53$, $E_S \sim 70$) will sensitize only fluorescence.

3. See the answer to Problem 7, Chapter 4.

4. 1. R = CH$_5$ should be similar to biacetyl, i.e., n,π^*.

2. $R = C_6H_5$ benzene ($E_T = 85$) cannot quench biacetyl-like triplet at 56 kcal mole^{-1}, therefore, n,π^* as in biacetyl.

3. $R = C_{10}H_8$ n,π^* same reason as (2), i.e., naphthalene has $E_T = 60$.

4. $R = C_{14}H_9$ π,π^* because anthracene triplet ($E_T = 42$) lies lower than biacetyl triplet.

5. $E_T \sim 60$ (like naphthalene).

6. $E_T \sim 65$ (like biphenyl).

7. $E_T \sim 42$ (like anthracene).

5. 1. Use a ketone or molecule with heavy atoms (no fluorescence) that has attached to it a nonphosphorescent group (e.g., azulene). Any ketone which possesses a group with $E_T < 42$ will probably be nonluminescent because of the rapid $T_1 \rightsquigarrow S_0$ process (see Reference 4-60).

2. Pick a molecule that has a large $S_1 - T_1$ energy separation, which does not possess heavy atoms or carbonyl groups and which has an intense absorption to S_1 (short τ_f), e.g., anthracene.

3. Any carbonyl compound with $E_T > 55$, an unsaturated hydrocarbon which possesses heavy atoms in the π system, e.g., benzophenone or 1-iodonaphthalene.

4. Aromatic hydrocarbon such as benzene.

6.
$$k_q[Q]_{1/2}[D_T] = h_1[D_T]$$

$$\therefore k_q = \frac{h_1}{[Q]_{1/2}} = \frac{2 \times 10^4}{2 \times 10^{-5}}$$

$$k_q = 1 \times 10^9 \text{ liters mole}^{-1} \text{ sec}^{-1}$$

7. Benzophenone has $E_T = 69$. Thus, butadiene ($E_T = 60$), anthracene ($E_T = 42$) and 2-acetonaphthone ($E_T = 59$) will quench benzophenone triplets at the diffusion controlled rate. Benzene ($E_T = 85$) and acetophenone ($E_T = 75$) will not.

8. Both will be equally efficient.

9. Benzil ($\Phi_{ST} = 1$) will be better than naphthalene ($\Phi_{ST} = 0.40$), although triplets of both molecules will transfer energy to biacetyl at the same rate.

CHAPTER SIX

1. 1. 2-Methylbenzophenone will have an energy level diagram similar to that of benzophenone given in Fig. 4-15. However, a new route for decay of T_1 is possible (see Section 6.3, p. 147).

2. Michler's ketone [4,4'-bis(dimethylamino)benzophenone] possesses a lowest $S_1(\pi,\pi^*)$ state ($\mu_{max} \cong 3800\text{Å}$, $6_{max} \cong 10^4$), and T_1 must be (π,π^*) also because of the long τ_p and low E_T.

3. 2,4-Dihydroxylbenzophenone possesses a lowest $S_1(\pi,\pi^*)$ state ($E_{S_1} \sim$ 95 kcal mole^{-1}) so that T_1 must be π,π^* (see Section 5.5). The lack of detectable emission from this compound may be attributed to the intramolecular hydrogen bond (see Section 6.3, p. 149).

4. 1-Naphthaldehyde possesses a lowest $S_1(\pi,\pi^*)$ state ($E_{S_1} \sim 89$ kcal mole^{-1}) and T_1 is also π,π^* since τ_p and E_T are similar to naphthalene.

2. From Equations 6-1 through 6-5 we have

$$aI = k_r[B^*][BH_2] + k_d[B^*]$$

or

$$[B^*] = \frac{aI}{k_r[BH_2] + k_d}$$

Since

$$\Phi_B \cdot \equiv \cdot \frac{k_r[B^*][BH_2]}{I}$$

we have

$$\Phi_B = \frac{ak_r[BH_2]}{k_r[BH_2] + k_d}$$

or

$$\frac{1}{\Phi_B} = \frac{1}{a} + \frac{k_d}{ak_r[BH_2]}$$

3. 1. One Possibility is

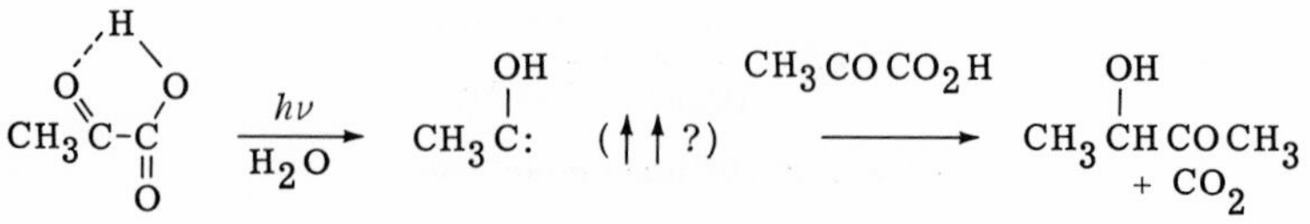

$$CH_3C-C \xrightarrow[H_2O]{h\nu} CH_3 \overset{OH}{\underset{|}{C}} : \quad (\uparrow\uparrow ?) \xrightarrow{CH_3 CO CO_2 H} CH_3 \overset{OH}{\underset{|}{CH}} COCH_3 + CO_2$$

2. A plausible mechanism is

$$CH_3 - C \xrightarrow{h\nu} CH_3 - C \longrightarrow 2 CH_3 CHO + CO$$

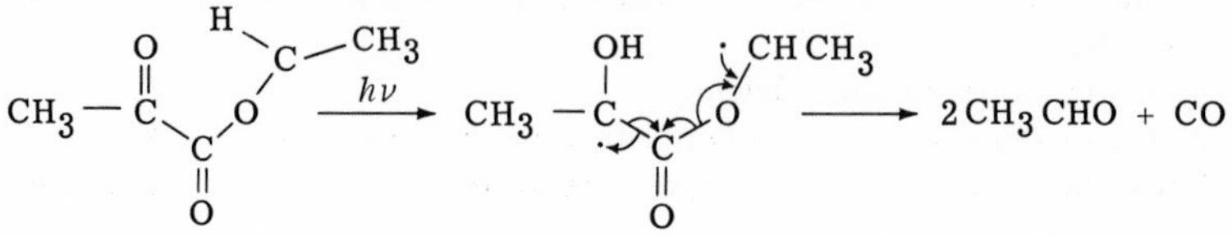

3. "Type II" process may be concerted or two step.

4. See Section 6-4.

4. 1. No "Type II" reaction because no γ-hydrogen is available.

2. "Type II" must compete with enolization.

3. "Type II" may be "quenched" because T_1 state is probably (π,π^*).

4. "Type II" should proceed in good yield.   Effect of chlorine is small on photoreduction.

5. "Type II" "quenched" because T_1 is π,π^*.

6. "Type II" cannot go because no γ-hydrogen is available.

5. No, because the molecule carries a built-in quencher around with it.   Each benzophenone triplet formed will be quenched at a rate much faster than hydrogen abstraction from solvent.

CHAPTER SEVEN

1. A plausible mechanism is

$$\xrightarrow[h\nu]{n,\pi^*} \quad \xrightarrow{?} \quad \xrightarrow{\pi^* \to n} $$

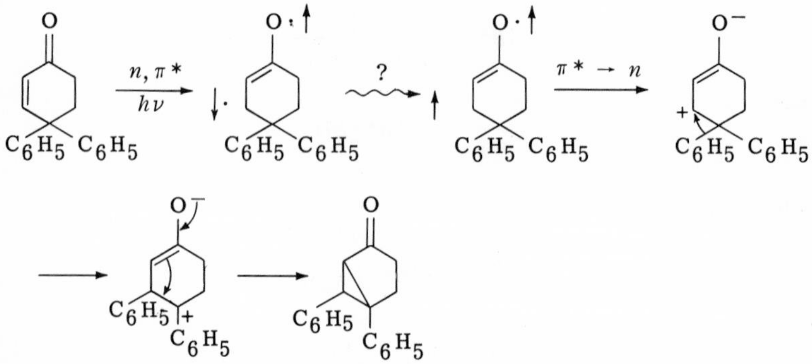

[See *J. Am. Chem. Soc.*, **86**, 4036 (1964).]   See Section 7.1 for description of how one tests for the intermediacy of S_1, T_1 or S_0^*.

2. A plausible mechanism is

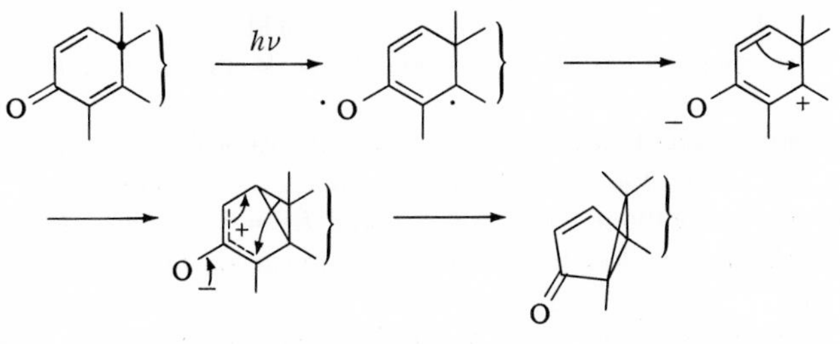

3. 1.

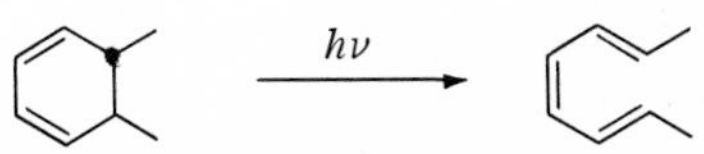

See R. B. Woodward, and R. Hoffman, *J. Am. Chem. Soc.*, **87**, 395 (1965) for a discussion of the stereochemistry of such reactions.

2.

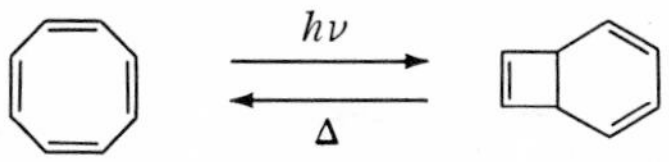

3.

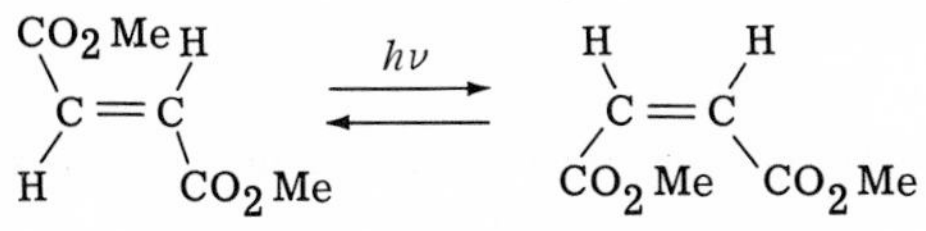

4. It is extremely difficult to define S_0^* as the site of reaction.   If the given reactions occurred thermally, this result would *not be inconsistent* with S_0^* as the site of reaction.   The argument is not compelling, however.   Quenching and sensitization experiments will usually be informative.

5. From Fig. 7-3, $E_T > 61$ kcal mole^{-1}

6. 1. 55% *trans.*
   2. 55% *trans.*
   3. 55% *trans.*
   4. ~80% *trans.*
   5. Not clear what this one would be because the energy transfer process is so endothermic.

CHAPTER EIGHT

1. 1. Benzene has $\Phi_{ST} = 0.24$ and $E_T = 85$, thus, it should sensitize the dimerization of cyclohexadiene with a quantum yield ≤ 0.24.

2. Acetophenone has $\Phi_{ST} = 1.0$ and $E_T = 74$, thus it should have $\Phi_{dim} \sim 1.0$.

3. 1-Bromonaphthalene has $\Phi_{ST} > 0.63$ (the value for 1-fluoronaphthalene) and $E_T = 60$. Thus, $\Phi_{dim} \geq 0.63$, probably much closer to one.

4. 2-Acetonaphthone has $\Phi_{ST} = 1.0$ and $E_T = 59$. Thus, $\Phi_{dim} \sim 1.0$.

5. Quinoline has $\Phi_{ST} = 0.32$ (in dry hydrocarbons) and $E_T = 62$. Thus, $\Phi_{dim} \leq 0.32$.

6. Anthracene has $E_T = 42$, so that irrespective of the value of Φ_{ST} it will not efficiently dimerize cyclohexadiene ($E_T = 53$).

7. Phenanthrene: $\Phi_{dim} \leq 0.76$.

8. Pyrene: low efficiency, $E_T = 49$.

9. Triphenylamine: $\Phi_{dim} \leq 0.88$.

2. See Section 5-6.

3. Benzophenone ($E_T = 69$) should add to tetramethylethylene ($E_T > 74$) and cyclohexene ($E_T > 74$), but should transfer energy to cyclohexadiene-1,3 ($E_T = 54$). However, hydrogen abstraction may compete with cycloaddition.

4. $E_T > 60$ kcal.

5.

The ratio of dimers will not vary because stereoisometric triplets are not possible.

6. 1.

2.

3.

CHAPTER NINE

1. 1.

$+$ CO

2.

? $\longrightarrow$ actually isolated

3.

? $\longrightarrow$ not known

4.

? $\longrightarrow$? not known

2. This reaction is analogous to stilbene-phenathrene interconversion. See text.

3. The same reaction occurs thermally so a "hot" ground state is a possibility as a site for reaction. Quenching and sensitization experiments are in order to determine the reaction site.

4. The meta compound should solvolyze faster. See text.

5. One possible mechanism is shown below.

$$(C_6H_5)_2C = O \xrightarrow{h\nu} (C_6H_5)_2C = O*$$

$$(C_6H_5)_2C = O* \ + \ H - \underset{\underset{CH_3}{|}}{\overset{\overset{CH_3}{|}}{C}}OH \longrightarrow (C_6H_5)_2\overset{\cdot}{C} - OH \ + \ (CH_3)_2\overset{\cdot}{C}OH$$

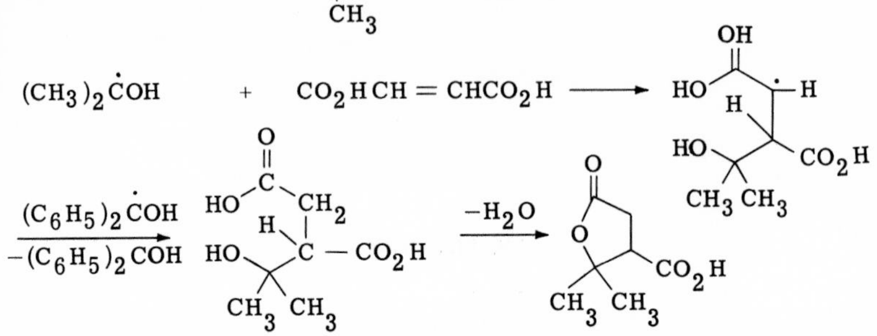

$(CH_3)_2\overset{\cdot}{C}OH \quad + \quad CO_2HCH = CHCO_2H \longrightarrow$ (diol intermediate structure)

$\xrightarrow[-(C_6H_5)_2\overset{\cdot}{C}OH]{(C_6H_5)_2\overset{\cdot}{C}OH}$ (lactol structure) $\xrightarrow{-H_2O}$ (lactone structure)

6. The dione in question should possess $E_T \sim 55$ kcal (similar to biacetyl). Since quenchers with $E_T > 55$ kcal quench biacetyl triplets at a rate which orders of magnitude is slower than quenchers whose $E_T < 55$ kcal (see Table 5-9). While one is tempted to believe a triplet is involved, it is not clear what the data given means; i.e., if naphthalene and anthracene were simply behaving as internal filters the same effects would be observed. The concentrations of quenchers and knowledge of their extinction coefficients as well as that of the dione is required for a quantitative explanation.

CHAPTER TEN

1. Benzene will absorb very little light through a pyrex filter (cut off $\sim$ 3000Å).

2. If a pyrex vessel and external source were used no other filter would be required as the benzophenone would absorb all of the light.

3. Since (Table 10-1) 25.6 watts = 25.6 joules/sec

$$= 25.6 \times 1.8 \times 10^{18} \text{ quant/sec}$$
$$= 4.6 \times 10^{19} \text{ quanta/sec}$$
$$= 7.6 \times 10^{-5} \text{ mole of quanta/sec}$$

Since

$$\Phi = \frac{\text{moles of compound phobolyzed}}{\text{moles of quanta absorbed}} = 0.1$$

we need to absorb 6×10^{24} quanta (10 moles) to produce one mole of product, thus

$$t = \frac{10 \text{ moles}}{7.6 \times 10^{-5} \text{ moles/sec}} = 1.3 \times 10^5 \text{ sec} \cong 3.6 \text{ hours}$$

4. See Question 5-2 for a similar problem. Since the intensity is given in Einsteins/liter sec for a unit volume (I = photon/sec cm³), if we know *both* the number of molecules of benzophenane destroyed and Φ_B for benzophenone destruction (from independent measurements), then

$$\frac{(1 - P/B)}{\Phi_B} = \frac{\text{molecules destroyed} \times \text{photons absorbed}}{\text{molecules destroyed}} = \text{photons absorbed}$$

Dividing by the time of photolysis, t, we arrive at an expression for I.

5. Filter 7-37 would work best.

6. Ruby lasers emit strongly at about 7000 Å (14,000 cm⁻¹) where (*a*) benzophenone and (*b*) benzene (Fig. 4-7) have zero absorption, (*c*) azulene (Fig. 4-8) absorbs strongly, and (*d*) 9,10-dibroanthracene has mainly $S_0 \rightarrow T$ absorption (Fig. 4-4).

Addendum

The supplementary references and problems given here are grouped by chapter. The references are related to the references in the text by their prefixed number. The problems are numbered consecutively with those in each chapter.

CHAPTER FOUR

REFERENCES

9A. P. Pringsheim, *Fluorescence and Phosphorescence* (New York: Interscience, 1949).

14A. W. H. Melhuish, *J. Am. Opt. Soc.*, **54**, 183 (1964).

17A. S. R. LaPaglia, *Spectrochimia Acta*, **18**, 1295 (1962).

18A. A. Grabowska, *ibid.*, **19**, 307 (1963).

19A. H. Tsubomuma and R. S. Mulliken, *J. Am. Chem. Soc.*, **82**, 5966 (1960).

21A. D. S. McClure, N. W. Blake, and P. L. Hanst, *J. Chem. Phys.*, **22**, 255 (1954).

29A. E. C. Lim and J. D. Laposa, *J. Chem. Phys.*, **41**, 3257 (1954); J. D. Laposa, E. C. Lim, and R. E. Kellogg, *J. Chem. Phys.*, **42**, 3025 (1965).

30A. G. Weber and F. W. J. Teale, *Trans. Faraday Soc.*, **53**, 646 (1957); *ibid.*, **54**, 640 (1958).

31A. R. M. Hochstrasser, *Spectrochimia Acta*, **16**, 497 (1960); *Canad. J. Chem.*, **38**, 233, (1960); *ibid.*, **37**, 1367 (1959).

38A. C. A. Hutchingson, *J. Chem. Phys.*, **40**, 3713 (1964).

40A. S. P. McGlynn, J. Daigre, and F. J. Smith, *J. Chem. Phys.*, **39**, 675 (1963).

49A. A. A. Lamola, W. G. Herkstroeter, J. C. Dalton, and G. S. Hammond, *J. Chem. Phys.*, **42**, 1715 (1965).

51A. For a review of radiationless transitions see: P. Seybold and M. Gouterman, *Chem. Rev.*, **65**, 413 (1965).

53A. J. C. D. Brand and D. G. Williamson, in *Advances in Physical Organic Chemistry*, ed. V. Gold (Vol. I, New York: Academic Press, 1963), p. 365.

55A. G. N. Lewis and M. Calvin, *Chem. Rev.*, **25**, 273 (1939).

58A. G. R. Hunt, E. F. McRoy, and I. G. Ross, *Aus. J. Chem.*, **15**, 591 (1962).

67A. Very weak, but measurable, phosphorescences of several compounds in fluid
    solutions at 25° C have been reported: C. A. Parker and C. G. Hatchard,
    Analyst, **87**, 664 (1962); C. A. Parker, *J. Chem. Phys.*, **66**, 2506 (1962).
68A. W. R. Ware, *J. Phys. Chem.*, **66**, 455 (1962); C. G. Jackson and R. Living-
    ston, *J. Chem. Phys.*, **35**, 2182 (1961).
76A. For a review see A. Weller, in *Progress in Reaction Kinetics*, ed. G. Porter
    (Vol. I, New York: Pergamon Press, 1961), p. 187.

CHAPTER FIVE

REFERENCES

1A. R. Livingston, *Quart. Rev.*, **14**, 174 (1960).
3A. For discussions of diffusion-controlled reactions see: E. F. Caldin, *Fast
    Reactions in Solution* (Oxford: Blackwell, 1964); R. M. Noyes, in *Progress in
    Reaction Kinetics*, ed. G. Porter (Vol. I, New York: Pergamon Press, 1961),
    p. 131.
4A. M. Kasha, *Radiation Research*, **20**, 55 (1963).
5A. K. B. Eisenthal and S. Siegel, *J. Chem. Phys.*, **41**, 652 (1964); A. S. Davydov,
    Theory of Molecular Excitons (New York: McGraw-Hill, 1962).
9A. W. Ware, *J. Am. Chem. Soc.*, **83**, 4374 (1961).
10A. For a system involving a relatively fixed separation between donor and
    acceptor see: S. A. Lott, H. T. Cheung, and E. R. Blout, *J. Am. Chem. Soc.*,
    87, 995 (1965).
14A. E. C. Lim and J. D. Laposa, *J. Chem. Phys.*, **41**, 3257 (1964).
16A. For a general review of energy transfer see: F. Wilkinson, in *Advances in
    Photochemistry*, ed. W. A. Noyes, Jr., G. S. Hammond, and J. N. Pitts, Jr.,
    (Vol. III, New York: Interscience, 1964), p. 241: see also, M. W. Windsor, in
    Physics and Chemistry of the Organic Solid State, ed. D. Fox, *et al.* (Vol. II, New
    York: Interscience, 1965), p. 343.
18A. S. Siegel and H. Judeikis, *J. Chem. Phys.*, **41**, 648 (1964).
33A. R. M. Noyes, *J. Am. Chem. Soc.*, **86**, 4529 (1964).
38A. K. Sandros, *Acta Chem. Scand.*, **18**, 2355 (1964); B. Stevens and M. S. Walker,
    Proc. Chem. Soc., **26**, 109 (1964).
41A. For examples of weak phosphorescence of molecules in fluid solution see:
    C. A. Parker and C. G. Hatchard, *Analyst*, **87**, 664 (1963).
42A. G. Porter and M. W. Windsor, *Discussions Faraday Soc.*, **27**, 18 (1959).
43A. C. A. Parker, *Spectrochimia Acta*, **19**, 989 (1963).
48A. J. Franck and H. Sponer, *J. Chem. Phys.*, **25**, 172 (1956).
55A. P. Yuster and S. I. Weissman, *J. Chem. Phys.*, **17**, 1182 (1949); M. L.
    Bhaumik and M. A. El-Sayed, *J. Chem. Phys.*, **42**, 787 (1965); *J. Phys. Chem.*,
    68, 275 (1965); J. L. Kropp and M. W. Windsor, *J. Chem. Phys.*, **42**, 1599
    (1965); P. K. Gallagher, A. Heller, and E. Wasserman, *ibid.*, **41**, 3921 (1964).
61A. G. N. Lewis and M. Clavin, *Chem. Rev.*, **25**, 273 (1939).
62A. R. V. Nauman, Ph.D. Thesis (Berkeley: University of California, 1947).
63A. W. G. Herkstroeter, Ph. D. Thesis (Pasadena: Caltech, 1966).

CHAPTER SIX

REFERENCES

2A. R. B. Woodward and R. Hoffmann, *J. Am. Chem. Soc.*, **87**, 397, 2046, 2511, (1965); H. C. Longuet-Higgins and E. W. Abrahamson, *ibid.*, **87**, 2045 (1965); D. Peters, *Trans. Faraday Soc.*, **59**, 1121 (1963); see also References 4-4, 4-30, 4-33, 4-63, and 5-54 (the first number indicates the chapter in which the reference appears).

5A. C. Weizmann, *et al.*, *J. Am. Chem. Soc.*, **60**, 1530 (1938).

6A. Formation of the "homo" pinacol is usually favored over the mixed pinacol— V. Franzen, *Ann.*, **633**, 1 (1960)—but exceptions are known: H. W. Johnson, Jr., J. N. Pitts, Jr., and W. Burleigh, *Chem. and Ind.*, 1493 (1964).

8A. G. S. Hammond and R. P. Foss, *J. Phys. Chem.*, **68**, 3739 (1964).

12A. For studies of the limiting quantum yield for photoreduction of benzophenone in isopropyl alcohol see: W. M. Moore and M. D. Ketchum, *J. Phys. Chem.*, **68**, 214 (1964); A. C. Testa, *J. Phys. Chem.*, **67**, 1341 (1963).

18A. A. Schönberg and A. Mustafa, *Chem. Rev.*, **40**, 181 (1947); see also References 1-5, 1-10, 1-11 and 1-14.

19A. F. Wilkinson, *J. Phys. Chem.*, **66**, 2569 (1962).

22A. G. Porter and P. Suppan, *Trans. Faraday Soc.*, **61**, 1664 (1965).

23A. C. Walling and M. Gibian, *J. Am. Chem. Soc.*, **87**, 3361 (1965).

25A. R. G. Norrish, *Trans. Faraday Soc.*, **33**, 1521 (1937); C. H. Bamford and R. G. Norrish, *J. Chem. Soc.*, 1544 (1938).

32A. For a number of related reactions see: N. C. Yang and M. J. Jorgenson, *Tetrahedron Letters*, 1203 (1964); *J. Am. Chem. Soc.*, **85**, 1698 (1963); M. J. Jorgenson, *Chem. Comm.*, 137 (1965).

36A. W. Discherl, *Z. für Physiol. Chem.*, **219**, 177 (1933); *ibid.*, **188**, 225 (1930).

41A. N. C. Yang and A. Morduchowitz, *J. Org. Chem.*, **29**, 1654 (1964).

PROBLEMS

6. Benzophenone sensitizes the following reaction (H. L. J. Backstrom, *The Svedberg Memorial Volume* (Upsala: Almquist and Wiksells Boktrycheri, 1944), p. 45; G. O. Schenck and H.-D. Becker, *Angew Chem.*, **70**, 504 (1958)):

$$(CH_3)_2CHOH + O_2 \xrightarrow[(C_6H_5)_2 CO]{h\nu} (CH_3)_2CO + H_2O_2$$

Propose a mechanism for this reaction.

7. Propose a mechanism for the following fact: aromatic mercaptans (potentially good hydrogen donors) and aromatic disulfides quench the photoreduction of benzophenone by benzhydrol (energy transfer to the aromatic mercaptan is unlikely for phenyl mercaptan or phenyl disulfide, $E_T = 74$). See S. G. Cohen and W. V. Sherman *J. Am. Chem. Soc.*, **85**, 1642 (1963).

8. Calculate the quantum yield for photoreduction by biacetyl singlets and triplets in isopropyl alcohol (assume the solvent to be 10 M) from the data in

Tables 4-13 and 5-8. Assume that the rate constant for hydrogen atom abstraction is 10^5 liter mole^{-1} sec^{-1} for both states.

9. Assuming that the measured lifetime for decay of 2-benzylbenzophenone triplets in cyclohexane at 25° is 2×10^3 sec^{-1}, calculate the maximum rate constant for photoreduction in isopropyl alcohol (Φ_B is less than 0.01 in this solvent). Assume that k_t is the same in both solvents.

10. It is known that 2-hydroxybenzophenone is completely nonluminescent at 77° K, whereas 2-alkylbenzophenones generally phosphoresce strongly under these conditions. From these facts, what conclusions can you make concerning the mechanism of suppression of photoreduction for both of these compounds?

CHAPTER SEVEN

REFERENCES

1A. H. E. Zimmerman and D. I. Schuster, *J. Am. Chem. Soc.*, **84,** 4527 (1962).

2A. See References 4-39 and 6-2.

3A. G. S. Hammond, N. J. Turro, and P. A. Leermakers, *J. Am. Chem. Soc.*, **83,** 2395 (1961).

8A. For reviews of dienone photochemistry see References 1-6, 1-13 and 1-14.

9A. P. J. Kropp and W. F. Erman, *J. Am. Chem. Soc.*, **85,** 2456 (1963); *Tetrahedron Letters*, 2049 (1963).

10A. H. E. Zimmerman and J. W. Wilson, *J. Am. Chem. Soc.*, **86,** 4036 (1964).

11A. See also Reference 9-39 for a related reaction.

13A. E. F. Ullman, *J. Am. Chem. Soc.*, **86,** 5357 (1964).

15A. W. G. Dauben and R. L. Cargill, *Tetrahedron*, **15,** 197 (1961).

17A. G. J. Fonken, *Tetrahedron Letters*, 549 (1962).

21A. For other examples of photoisomerizations of a butadiene to a bicyclobutane see W. G. Dauben and F. G. Wiley, *Tetrahedron Letters*, 893 (1962) and I. Haller and R. Srinivasan, *J. Chem. Phys.* **40,** 1992 (1964).

22A. For other examples of cyclobutene formation see K. J. Crowley, *Tetrahedron*, **21,** 1001 (1965) and references therein.

26A. R. Srinivasan, *J. Phys. Chem.*, **67,** 1367 (1963).

28A. O. L. Chapman, D. J. Pasto, and J. Griswald, Jr., *J. Am. Chem. Soc.*, **84,** 1220 (1962).

32A. P. P. Birnbaum and D. W. G. Style, *Trans. Faraday Soc.*, **50,** 1192 (1954).

34A. See also Reference 1-14; R. S. H. Liu, Ph. D. Dissertation, (Pasadena: California Institute of Technology, 1965).

35A. S. Malkin and E. Fischer, *J. Phys. Chem.*, **68,** 1153 (1964); E. Lippert and W. Luder, *J. Phys. Chem.*, **66,** 2430 (1962); H. Dyck and D. S. McClure, *J. Chem. Phys.*, **36,** 2326 (1962); D. Schulte-Frohlinde and H. Gunten, *Z. für Physik. Chem.*, **29,** 281 (1961).

37A. R. B. Cundall and T. F. Palmer, *Trans. Faraday Soc.*, **56,** 1211 (1960); *J. Am. Chem. Soc.*, **83,** 3902 (1961); *J. Chem. Phys.*, **39,** 3536 (1963).

39A. For examples of intramolecular "photosensitized" isomerizations see: H. Morrison, *J. Am. Chem. Soc.*, **87,** 932 (1965); *Tetrahedron Letters*, 3652 (1964).

274 MOLECULAR PHOTOCHEMISTRY

45A. See also G. O. Schenck, *Angew. Chem.*, **69**, 579 (1957); *Z. für Electrochem.*, **64**, 170 (1960); *ibid.*, **64**, 997 (1960); Fifth Intern. Symp. Free Radicals, Uppsala, 1961; *Stralentherapie*, **115**, 497 (1961); *ibid.*, **114**, 321 (1961); R. Hochstraser and G. Porter, *Quart. Rev.*, **14**, 146 (1960); W. Bergman and M. J. McLean, *Chem. Rev.*, **28**, 367 (1941); Reference 1-8; L. Bateman, *Quart. Rev.*, **8**, 147 (1954).

46A. For a cleaver experiment which indicated long ago that the chemically active species in photosensitized oxidation is a mobile species see: H. Kautsky, *Trans. Faraday Soc.*, **35**, 216 (1939). Singlet oxygen is also believed to be implicated in many chemluminescence reactions: A. U. Kahn and M. Kasha, *J. Chem. Phys.*, **39**, 2105 (1963); S. J. Arnold, *et al.*, *ibid.*, **40**, 1769 (1964); H. H. Seliger, *Anal. Biochem.*, **1**, 60 (1960); R. J. Browne and E. A. Ogryzlo, *Proc. Chem. Soc.*, 117 (1964).

PROBLEMS

7. Predict the stereochemical course of the following photoreaction (*Tetrahedron Letters*, 377 (1965)):

8. Predict the major product of the following reaction:

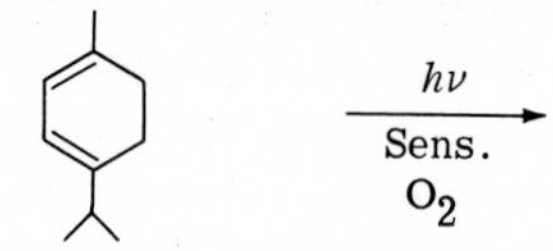

9. Predict the major product of the following reactions (Ref. 28 and *Chem. and Ind.* 1575 (1961)):

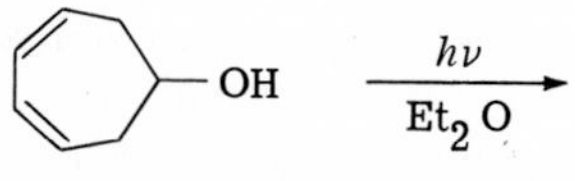

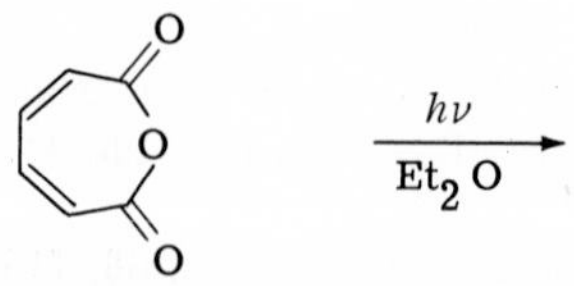

10. Write a detailed mechanism for the following reaction (*J. Am. Chem. Soc.*, **81**, 236 (1959)):

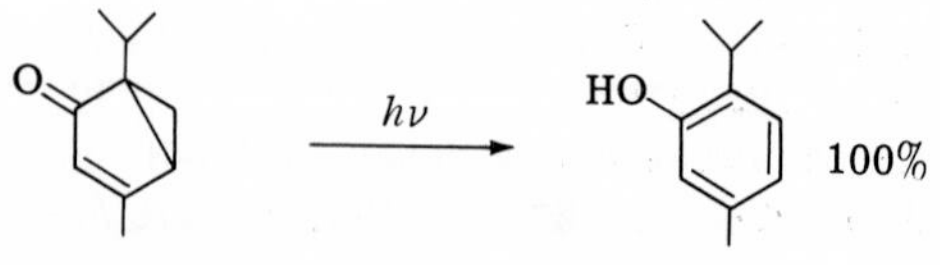

11. Write a detailed mechanism for the following reaction (*Angew. Chem.*, **76,** 600 (1964)):

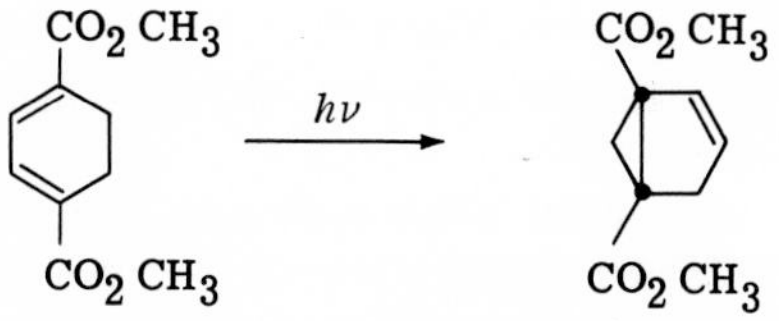

12. Propose a mechanism which is consistent with the following results (*J. Am. Chem. Soc.* **86,** 4053 (1964)):

(a)

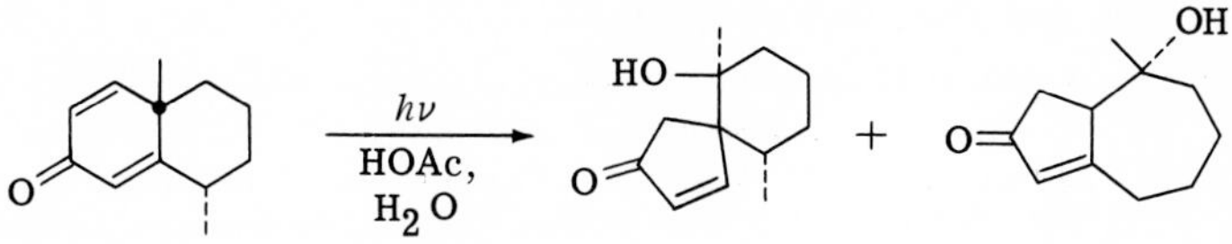

(b)

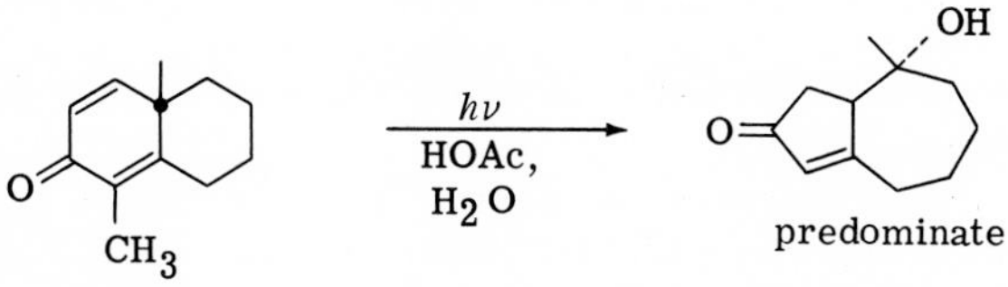

predominate product

(c)

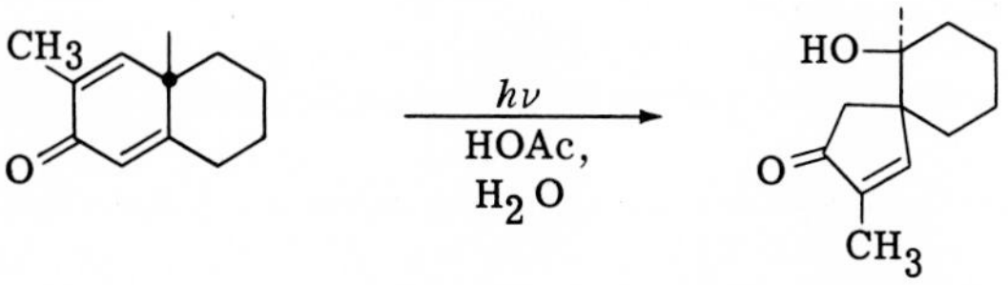

predominate product

CHAPTER EIGHT

REFERENCES

2A. R. Huisgen, R. Grashey, and J. Sauer, in *The Chemistry of Alkenes*, ed. S. Patai (New York: Wiley, 1964), p. 739.

21A. R. Robson, P. W. Brubb, and J. A. Barltrop, *J. Chem. Soc.*, 2153 (1964).

23A. H. D. Scharg and F. Korte, *Ber.*, **98,** 764 (1965).

29A. M. D. Cohen and G. M. J. Schmidt, *Tetrahedron Letters*, 2000, 2021 (1964).

30A. G. W. Griffin, A. F. Vellturo, and K. Furukawa, *J. Am. Chem. Soc.*, **84,** 1012 (1962).

33A. N. J. Turro and G. S. Hammond, *J. Am. Chem. Soc.*, **84,** 2841 (1962).

38A. For related papers see R. W. Yip, *Proc. Chem. Soc.*, 84 (1964), and F. Greene, *Bull. Soc. Chim. France*, 1356 (1960).

45A. R. S. H. Liu, Ph.D. Dissertation (Pasadena: California Institute of Technology, 1965).

46A. For a number of related reactions see G. O. Schenck, *et al.*, *Tetrahedron Letters*, 347, 353 (1965).

47A. For the related photoisomerization to *trans*-cycloheptenone see: E. J. Corey M. Tada, R. LaMahieu, and L. Libit, *J. Am. Chem. Soc.*, **87,** 2053 (1965); P. Eaton and K. Lin, *ibid.*, **87,** 937, 2053 (1965); see also E. J. Corey, *et al.*, *ibid.*, **87,** 937 (1965).

49A. N. C. Yang, *Pure Appl. Chem.*, **9,** 591 (1964); for other examples of wavelength-dependent anthracene photoreactions see O. L. Chapman, *et al.*, *Pure Appl. Chem.*, **9,** 585 (1964).

51A. For a review of the photochemistry of compounds containing heteroatoms see: A. Mustafa, in *Advances in Photochemistry*, ed. W. A. Noyes, Jr., G. S. Hammond, and J. N. Pitts, Jr., (Vol. II, New York: Interscience, 1964), p. 63.

53A. R. S. H. Liu, N. J. Turro, and G. S. Hammond, *J. Am. Chem. Soc.*, **87,** 3406 (1965). D. J. Trecker, R. L. Brandon, and J. P. Henry, *Chem. and Ind.*, 652 (1963).

60A. J. D. Roberts and C. M. Sharts, in *Organic Reactions* (Vol. XII, New York: Wiley, 1962), p. 1.

64A. At 36° acetone undergoes an unusual photoaddition to norbornene: W. Reusch, *J. Org. Chem.*, **27,** 1882 (1962); D. Scharf and F. Korte, *Tetrahedron Letters*, 821 (1963); D. Elad., *J. Chem. Soc.*, 800 (1965).

66A. See, for example, R. T. LaLonde and R. I. Akentijevich, *Tetrahedron Letters*, 23 (1965).

PROBLEMS

8. Predict the major products of the following reaction (*J. Am. Chem. Soc.*, **76,** 4327 (1954)):

$$C_6H_5\overset{\displaystyle O}{\overset{\displaystyle \|}{C}}CH_3 \ + \ C_4H_9C \equiv CC_4H_9 \quad \xrightarrow{\;h\nu\;}$$

9. Predict the course of the following reactions:

(a)  $\bigcirc$ $\xrightarrow[\;C_6H_6\;]{h\nu \ > \ 2200\,\overset{\circ}{A}}$

(b)  $\triangle$ $\xrightarrow[\;C_6H_6\;]{h\nu \ > \ 2200\,\overset{\circ}{A}}$

(c)  $\bigcirc$ $\xrightarrow[\;C_6H_6\;]{h\nu \ > \ 3000\,\overset{\circ}{A}}$

10. Predict the major product of the following reactions:

(a) 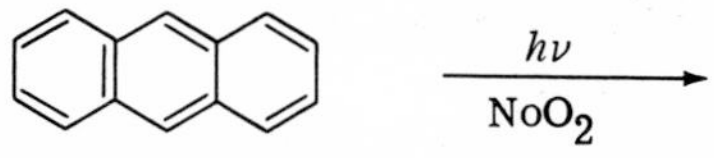 $\dfrac{h\nu}{NoO_2}$

(b) 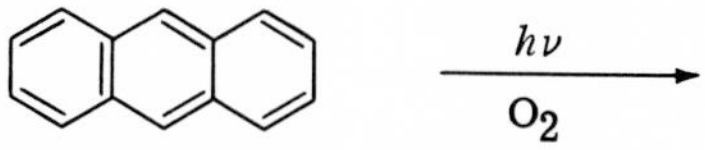 $\dfrac{h\nu}{O_2}$

CHAPTER NINE

REFERENCES

3A. W. Davis, *Chem. Rev.*, **40**, 201 (1974); W. A. Noyes, Jr., G. B. Porter, and J. E. Jolley, *ibid.*, **56,** 49 (1956).

5A. R. G. W. Norrish, *Trans. Faraday Soc.*, **33**, 1521 (1937).

8A. I. Haller and R. Srinivasan, *ibid.*, **87**, 1144 (1965); N. J. Turro, *et al.*, *ibid.*, **87**, 2613, 2774, (1965).

9A. For recent reviews of carbene chemistry see J. A. Bell, in *Progress in Physical Organic Chemistry*, ed. S. G. Cohen, *et al.*, (Vol. II, New York. Interscience, 1964), p. 1; W. B. DeMore and S. W. Benson, in *Advances in Photochemistry*, ed. W. A. Noyes, Jr., G. S. Hammond, and J. N. Pitts, Jr. (Vol. II, New York: Interscience, 1964) p. 219; P. Gaspar and G. S. Hammond in W. Kirmse, *Carbene Chemistry* (New York: Academic Press, 1964), p. 325.

26A. G. O. Schenck and R. Steinmetz, *Ber.*, **96**, 520 (1963).

31A. F. B. Mallory, *et al.*, *J. Org. Chem.*, **29**, 3373 (1964); *J. Am. Chem. Soc.*, **84,** 4361 (1962); *ibid.*, **85,** 828 (1963).

32A. S. M. Kupchan and C. Wormser, *Tetrahedron Letters*, 359 (1965).

34A. H. Linschitz and K. H. Grellman, *J. Am. Chem. Soc.*, **85**, 1881 (1963).

40A. R. C. Cookson, *Pure Appl. Chem.*, **9,** 575 (1964); G. W. Griffin *et al.*, *J. Am. Chem. Soc.*, **87**, 1410 (1965).

46A. C. Luner and M. Szwarc, *J. Chem. Phys.*, **23,** 1978 (1955).

47A. C. Walling and M. J. Gibian, *J. Am. Chem. Soc.*, **87**, 3413 (1965).

PROBLEMS

7. Predict the expected products of the following reaction (*J. Am. Chem. Soc.*, **85,** 2529 (1963)):

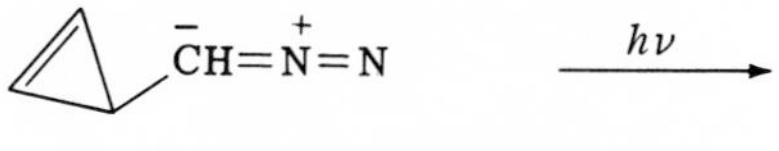

$\bar{C}H=\overset{+}{N}=N$ $\xrightarrow{h\nu}$

8. Predict the expected products of the following reactions:

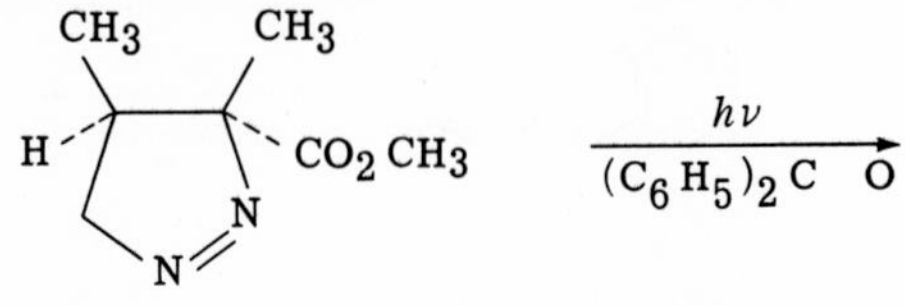

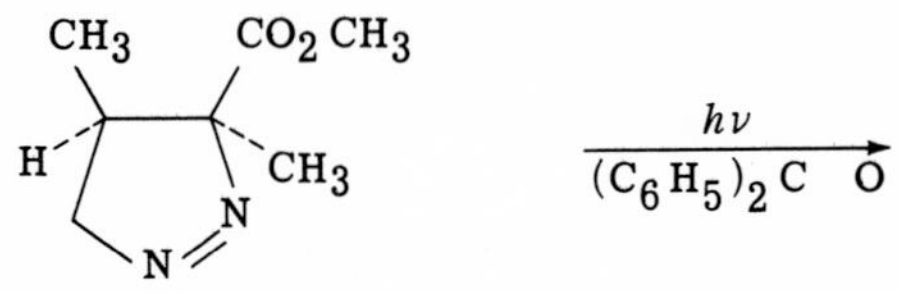

9. On the basis of theoretical predictions (Section 7-2), do you expect the hydrogens of the dihydrophenanthrene intermediate to be *cis* or *trans*?

Index